Glencoe Science
Features and Benefits

		Pages
Dynamic Instructional Strategies	... present clear and comprehensive coverage of middle school science.	
	■ Each engaging chapter opener includes a *Launch Lab* and *Foldables*™.	7, 39
	■ *National Geographic Visualizing* features illustrate important concepts in middle school science.	20, 48
A Strong Reading Strand	... encourages active reading and learning for students of all reading levels. In the *Student Edition:*	
	■ **as you read** gives students a preview of learning objectives and vocabulary for each section;	8, 40
	■ *Reading Checks* help students check their reading comprehension; and	10, 41
	■ *Caption questions* ask students to interpret visuals.	9, 40
	■ *Reading Essentials, An Interactive Student Textbook* is designed to help struggling readers comprehend core content. It is written at a reading level of about two to three grades below the *Student Edition.*	
Meeting the Needs of All Students	... facilitates understanding of science concepts for students of all learning levels. In the *Teacher Wraparound Edition:*	
	■ *Differentiated Instruction* strategies help meet the needs of students with learning disabilities and physical challenges, or create opportunities to enrich and extend students' learning;	9, 41
	■ *Daily Intervention* provides intervention strategies for struggling students; and	17, 44
	■ *Identifying Misconceptions* helps uncover and address common science misconceptions.	38F
	■ The *English/Spanish Glossary,* also in the *Student Edition,* helps English-language learners comprehend science terms.	165–169
Extensive Standardized Test Practice	... gives students the opportunity to practice for state and national exams.	
	■ Each chapter ends with a variety of standardized test practice questions, including *Multiple Choice, Short Response/Grid In,* and *Open Ended.*	94–95
A Variety of Labs	... gets students excited about being involved in science. The *Student Edition* provides:	
	■ *MiniLABs,* traditional labs, and *Design Your Own, Model and Invent,* and *Use the Internet* labs; and	15, 50
	■ *Extra Try at Home Labs* provide opportunities for students to practice their science skills at home with adult supervision using materials from the kitchen, junk drawer, or backyard.	140–141
	■ *Virtual Labs* CD-ROM contains an interactive virtual lab for each chapter.	47, 82
	■ *Video Labs* (VHS) reinforce lab techniques and safety skills, offer troubleshooting tips, and give expected outcomes.	62
	■ The *Science Lab Manual, Probeware Lab Manual,* and *Science Inquiry Lab Manual* provide additional opportunities to practice laboratory techniques.	
Multi-Level Review	... presents multiple opportunities for all students to review and master content.	
	■ Each section ends with a review that contains a *Summary* of the section's major concepts and a *Self Check* that has questions to assess student learning and practice math or science skills.	17, 44
	■ The *Study Guide* at the end of each chapter can preview, review, summarize, and visualize the chapter's main ideas.	33, 65
	■ *Study Guide* and *Reinforcement* help students grasp core content.	
Teacher Resources	... provide innovative strategies to help new and experienced teachers.	
	■ *Chapter Resources Fast File* ™ contains important reproducible masters.	38B
	■ Section Focus, Assessment, and Teaching transparencies accompany each chapter.	70C
	■ *Performance Assessment in the Science Classroom* has assessment guidelines, strategies, sample rubrics, and more.	
Online Resources	... enrich the learning experience with the click of a mouse.	
	■ For prescreened Web links, standardized test practice, self-check quizzes, chapter tests, *Vocabulary PuzzleMaker,* extra math practice, science career information, current science news, and *WebQuest* interactive projects, visit **bookk.msscience.com.**	
	■ The complete interactive *Student Edition* is available at The McGraw-Hill Learning Network Web site, **mhln.com.**	
Technology	... provides timesaving products to help teachers creatively engage their students.	
	■ *MindJogger Videoquizzes* (VHS & DVD) provide a game-show style interactive quiz for each chapter.	
	■ Easy to edit *Interactive Chalkboard* Microsoft® PowerPoint® presentations include step-by-step lessons, an image bank, chapter and section review questions, standardized test practice, and transparencies.	
	■ *ExamView® Pro Testmaker* CD-ROM in English or Spanish allows you to customize assessments.	
	■ *TeacherWorks* CD-ROM is your all-in-one resource center that helps you plan and organize lessons.	
	■ *StudentWorks* CD-ROM solves the heavy backpack problem.	

SAFETY SYMBOLS

SAFETY SYMBOLS	HAZARD	EXAMPLES	PRECAUTION	REMEDY
DISPOSAL	Special disposal procedures need to be followed.	certain chemicals, living organisms	Do not dispose of these materials in the sink or trash can.	Dispose of wastes as directed by your teacher.
BIOLOGICAL	Organisms or other biological materials that might be harmful to humans	bacteria, fungi, blood, unpreserved tissues, plant materials	Avoid skin contact with these materials. Wear mask or gloves.	Notify your teacher if you suspect contact with material. Wash hands thoroughly.
EXTREME TEMPERATURE	Objects that can burn skin by being too cold or too hot	boiling liquids, hot plates, dry ice, liquid nitrogen	Use proper protection when handling.	Go to your teacher for first aid.
SHARP OBJECT	Use of tools or glassware that can easily puncture or slice skin	razor blades, pins, scalpels, pointed tools, dissecting probes, broken glass	Practice common-sense behavior and follow guidelines for use of the tool.	Go to your teacher for first aid.
FUME	Possible danger to respiratory tract from fumes	ammonia, acetone, nail polish remover, heated sulfur, moth balls	Make sure there is good ventilation. Never smell fumes directly. Wear a mask.	Leave foul area and notify your teacher immediately.
ELECTRICAL	Possible danger from electrical shock or burn	improper grounding, liquid spills, short circuits, exposed wires	Double-check setup with teacher. Check condition of wires and apparatus.	Do not attempt to fix electrical problems. Notify your teacher immediately.
IRRITANT	Substances that can irritate the skin or mucous membranes of the respiratory tract	pollen, moth balls, steel wool, fiberglass, potassium permanganate	Wear dust mask and gloves. Practice extra care when handling these materials.	Go to your teacher for first aid.
CHEMICAL	Chemicals can react with and destroy tissue and other materials	bleaches such as hydrogen peroxide; acids such as sulfuric acid, hydrochloric acid; bases such as ammonia, sodium hydroxide	Wear goggles, gloves, and an apron.	Immediately flush the affected area with water and notify your teacher.
TOXIC	Substance may be poisonous if touched, inhaled, or swallowed.	mercury, many metal compounds, iodine, poinsettia plant parts	Follow your teacher's instructions.	Always wash hands thoroughly after use. Go to your teacher for first aid.
FLAMMABLE	Flammable chemicals may be ignited by open flame, spark, or exposed heat.	alcohol, kerosene, potassium permanganate	Avoid open flames and heat when using flammable chemicals.	Notify your teacher immediately. Use fire safety equipment if applicable.
OPEN FLAME	Open flame in use, may cause fire.	hair, clothing, paper, synthetic materials	Tie back hair and loose clothing. Follow teacher's instruction on lighting and extinguishing flames.	Notify your teacher immediately. Use fire safety equipment if applicable.

 Eye Safety Proper eye protection should be worn at all times by anyone performing or observing science activities.

 Clothing Protection This symbol appears when substances could stain or burn clothing.

 Animal Safety This symbol appears when safety of animals and students must be ensured.

 Handwashing After the lab, wash hands with soap and water before removing goggles.

Teacher Wraparound Edition

Glencoe Science

The Nature of Matter

NATIONAL GEOGRAPHIC

bookk.msscience.com

Glencoe

New York, New York   Columbus, Ohio   Chicago, Illinois   Peoria, Illinois   Woodland Hills, California

Glencoe Science

The Nature of Matter

This pancake ice has formed on a river in Sweden. Pancake ice forms when surface slush, arising from snow falling on water that is already at the freezing temperature, freezes. The surface slush collects into rounded floating pads that collide and separate.

Teacher Wraparound Edition

Glencoe Science

The Nature of Matter

NATIONAL GEOGRAPHIC

bookk.msscience.com

Glencoe

The McGraw-Hill Companies

Send all inquiries to:
Glencoe/McGraw-Hill
8787 Orion Place
Columbus, OH 43240-4027

ISBN 0-07-861765-0 (Student Edition)
ISBN 0-07-861764-2 (Teacher Wraparound Edition)

Printed in the United States of America.

1 2 3 4 5 6 7 8 9 10 027/111 09 08 07 06 05 04

Authors

NATIONAL GEOGRAPHIC
Education Division
Washington, D.C.

Patricia Horton
Mathematics and Science Teacher
Summit Intermediate School
Etiwanda, CA

Thomas McCarthy, PhD
Science Department Chair
St. Edward's School
Vero Beach, FL

Eric Werwa, PhD
Department of Physics and Astronomy
Otterbein College
Westerville, OH

Dinah Zike
Educational Consultant
Dinah-Might Activities, Inc.
San Antonio, TX

Series Consultants

CONSULTANTS

Jack Cooper
Ennis High School
Ennis, TX

Linda McGaw
Science Program Coordinator
Advanced Placement Strategies, Inc.
Dallas, TX

MATH

Michael Hopper, DEng
Manager of Aircraft Certification
L-3 Communications
Greenville, TX

READING

Barry Barto
Special Education Teacher
John F. Kennedy Elementary
Manistee, MI

SAFETY

Aileen Duc, PhD
Science 8 Teacher
Hendrick Middle School, Plano ISD
Plano, TX

Sandra West, PhD
Department of Biology
Texas State University-San Marcos
San Marcos, TX

ACTIVITY TESTERS

Nerma Coats Henderson
Pickerington Lakeview Jr. High
School
Pickerington, OH

Mary Helen Mariscal-Cholka
William D. Slider Middle School
El Paso, TX

**Science Kit and Boreal
Laboratories**
Tonawanda, NY

Series Reviewers

Sharla Adams
IPC Teacher
Allen High School
Allen, TX

Anthony J. DiSipio, Jr.
8th Grade Science
Octorana Middle School
Atglen, PA

Sandra Everhart
Dauphin/Enterprise Jr. High Schools
Enterprise, AL

George Gabb
Great Bridge Middle School
Chesapeake Public Schools
Chesapeake, VA

Michelle Mazeika
Whiting Middle School
Whiting, IN

Glencoe Science 15-Book Series

Teach science your way!

With the 15 Life, Earth, and Physical Science titles in our modular series, you can select the science topics you want to cover and customize your science curriculum in any way you choose.

K **The Nature of Matter**
1. Atoms, Elements, Compounds, and Mixtures
2. States of Matter
3. Properties and Changes of Matter
4. The Periodic Table

L **Chemistry**
1. Atomic Structure and Chemical Bonds
2. Chemical Reactions
3. Substances, Mixtures, and Solubility
4. Carbon Chemistry

M **Motion, Forces, and Energy**
1. Motion and Momentum
2. Force and Newton's Laws
3. Forces and Fluids
4. Work and Simple Machines
5. Energy and Energy Resources
6. Thermal Energy

N **Electricity and Magnetism**
1. Electricity
2. Magnetism
3. Electronics and Computers

O **Waves, Sound, and Light**
1. Waves
2. Sound
3. Electromagnetic Waves
4. Light, Mirrors, and Lenses

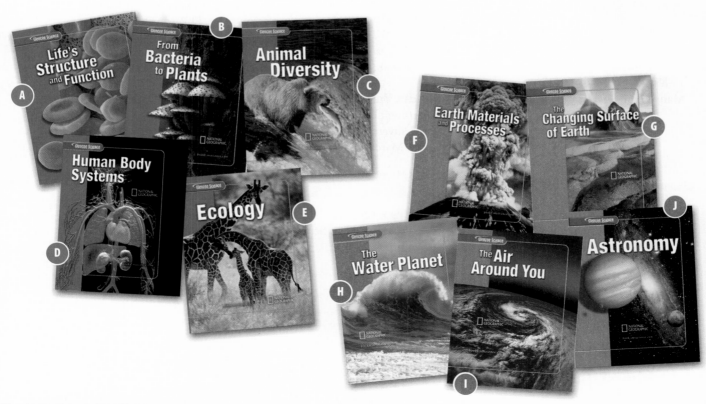

Multi-Level Review and Assessment

Each chapter provides five pages of review and testing to help you evaluate students' knowledge and ability to apply science concepts.

Section Review
- Summary pinpoints important concepts in the section.
- Skill-based questions promote critical thinking skills.

Study Guide
- Main idea summary of each section
- Concept mapping activity to help students visualize the main ideas

Chapter Review
- Using Vocabulary
- Checking Concepts
- Thinking Critically
- Performance Activities
- Applying Math

Standardized Test Practice
- Multiple Choice
- Short Response/ Grid In
- Open-Ended Questions

Dynamic Instruction

The consistent instructional strategies in each chapter strengthen students' learning—from the beginning of each chapter where students see "Chapter Preview," to the end where they have a chance to test the knowledge they have acquired and prepare for the next lesson.

Chapter Opener
- *Chapter Preview* introduces the main concepts.
- *Science Journal* promotes critical-thinking skills
- *Dinah Zike's Foldables*™ let students create interactive study guides.
- *Launch Labs* give students an opportunity to explore new ideas.

Section Opener
- *What You'll Learn* introduces main concepts.
- *Why It's Important* provides an answer to "Why do we have to learn this?"
- *Review Vocabulary* reviews a term that helps students better understand section content.
- *New Vocabulary* highlights new terms students will learn in the section.

Labs
- *Labs* allow students to design their own experiments or follow well-tested procedures, enabling them to learn and practice science processes.
- *MiniLABS* offer students quick and easy-to-do ways to clarify concepts and reinforce skills.

Assessment

Glencoe Science offers the Glencoe Assessment Advantage, a system designed to give you all the tools you need to prepare your students for success in any testing situation.

In the *Student Edition*

Section Review and **Applying Math** questions appear in every chapter.

Chapter Review questions help you evaluate students' knowledge and ability to apply science concepts.

Standardized Test Practice questions at the end of each chapter provide students with additional opportunities to practice their test-taking skills.

In the *Teacher Wraparound Edition*

Assessments located throughout the *Teacher Wraparound Edition* provide methods for assessing students' comprehension with Performance, Process, and Content exercises.

Teacher Classroom Resources

Performance Assessment in the Science Classroom
- Guidelines for assessing the performance of a task
- Reproducible activities for evaluating students
- Sample rubrics and checklists

***Fast File* Chapter Resources** provides six pages of assessement for every chapter including *Testing Concepts, Applying Concepts,* and *Writing Skills.*

Technology Support

MindJogger Videoquizzes are interactive video quizzes set in game show format. Each is designed for the full range of student learning styles.

Exam*View*® Pro Testmaker CD-ROM for Windows® and Macintosh® provides an easy way to create, edit, and customize your tests. Select your own test items by objective from two different levels of difficulty, or write and edit your own. Translate tests from English to Spanish and vice versa.

Rubrics

The following rubrics are sample scoring devices for short response and open-ended questions.

Short Response

Points	Description
2	The student demonstrates a thorough understanding of the science of the task. The response may contain minor flaws that do not detract from the demonstration of a thorough understanding.
1	The student has provided a response that is only partially correct.
0	The student has provided a completely incorrect solution or no response at all.

Open Ended

Points	Description
4	The student demonstrates a thorough understanding of the science of the task. The response may contain minor flaws that do not detract from the demonstration of a thorough understanding.
3	The student demonstrates an understanding of the science of the task. The response is essentially correct and demonstrates an essential but less than thorough understanding of the science.
2	The student demonstrates only a partial understanding of the science of the task. Although the student may have used the correct approach to a solution or may have provided a correct solution, the work lacks an essential understanding of the underlying science concepts.
1	The student demonstrates a very limited understanding of the science of the task. The response is incomplete and exhibits many flaws.
0	The student provides a completely incorrect solution or no response at all.

Time-Saving Teacher Resources

Glencoe Science provides an extensive array of support materials and resources designed to help you create and customize your science course quickly and easily.

FAST FILE Chapter Resources

For each chapter, Chapter Resources contain key reproducible masters along with additional teaching strategies, teacher support, and answer keys.

Teacher Wraparound Edition

The *Teacher Wraparound Edition* is your key to the teaching resources available. In addition to teaching strategies and suggestions, the *Teacher Wraparound Edition* provides a guide for all print and software materials available for each lesson.

Transparencies

Color Transparencies provides three types of transparencies for use while teaching each chapter. The *Section Focus Transparencies* are designed to generate interest and focus students' attention on the topic being presented in the section. The *Teaching Transparency* for each chapter addresses a major concept that will benefit from an extra visual learning aid. The *Assessment Transparency* for each chapter is set up to resemble standardized tests.

Exam*View*® Pro Testmaker CD-ROM

This CD-ROM will help you create, edit, and customize tests. In addition, it will help you create multiple versions of tests, translate tests from English to Spanish and vice versa, and build tests aligned with state standards.

Video Labs

These VHS cassettes contain step-by-step procedures for selected *Student Edition* labs. They also contain lab safety skills, teacher support, and troubleshooting advice.

Teacher Works™

This CD-ROM is your all-in-one teacher resource center. Personalize a lesson plan, access resources

from the *Teacher Wraparound Edition*, connect to the Internet, or make a to-do list. These are only a few of the many features that can assist you in the planning and organizing of your lessons.

Student Works™

This CD-ROM is a valuable resource for students to access content online and use online resources to continue learning chapter concepts.

INTERACTIVE CHALKBOARD with Image Bank — PowerPoint® Presentations

This CD-ROM brings Microsoft® PowerPoint® presentations right to your door. With the large number of graphics provided, students can use a visual approach to learning chapter content.

Virtual Labs CD-ROM Program

The Virtual Labs CD-ROM contains a collection of labs that allow students to complete labs that are too expensive, take too long to complete, or might be too dangerous in a classroom laboratory.

Science Online

This website is a portal to hundreds of pre-screened Internet sites (Web links) that correlate to content in the text. Visit this link to find interactive activities that review chapter concepts and to access the *Student Edition* online.

McGraw Hill **Learning Network** mhln.com

mhln.com is an online teaching and learning space for teachers, students, and parents.

Differentiated Instruction

Teaching Strategies

Following each suggested assessment and activity, ability levels are supplied to accommodate all students. For a key to the Teaching Strategies designations, see the C page before each chapter.

Identifying Misconceptions

These short, diagnostic, and perscriptive lessons target common science misconceptions.

Multiple Learning Styles

Look for these italicized designations under various activities to help you target your lessons to each student's preferred learning style.

- *Kinesthetic* learners learn through touch, movement, and manipulating objects.
- *Visual-Spatial* learners think in terms of images, illustrations, and models.
- *Interpersonal* learners understand and work well with other people.
- *Intrapersonal* learners can analyze their own strengths and weaknesses and may prefer to work on their own.
- *Linguistic* learners write clearly and easily understand the written word.
- *Logical-Mathematical* learners understand numbers easily and have highly-developed reasoning skills.

Daily Interventions

Found at the end of each chapter section, this feature is designed to intercept students who are struggling and prescribe a system to help them get back on track. *Reteach* provides reinforcement of the section's concepts through visual activities.

Differentiated Instruction

These activities present various teaching strategies designed to help you meet the special needs of students with learning disabilities, physical challenges, visual impairment, and hearing impairment. *Challenge* activities provide opportunities for students who excel to engage in activities and research projects that extend the chapter's concepts. English-language learners in the classroom will also find exercises that bridge the gap between language barriers and the chapter content.

Cultural Diversity

These readings provide insights into the unique ways in which people of different ethnicities and cultural heritage have approached science. The intent of these features is to build awareness and appreciation for the global community in which we live.

Inquiry-Based Science

The call for more inquiry-based science by the *National Science Education Standards* has been met by Glencoe Science.

Glencoe Science recognizes the importance of conducting inquiry-based science activities in the classroom. The process of doing inquiry models actual science practice, encouraging problem-solving strategies and developing critical thinking skills. Inquiry gets students actively involved in the learning process by allowing them to determine materials, procedures, or the topics and questions they want to investigate.

Inquiry can range from a very structured activity for those students who need more guidance to a more open-ended approach where students lead the investigations. Glencoe Science recognizes that the inquiry activities suggested will not look the same in every classroom. We encourage teachers to modify the suggested activities in a manner that best supports your students.

Glencoe also provides teachers with *Alternative Inquiry Labs,* teaching strategies or suggestions for making existing labs more inquiry-based.

Research-Based Learning Strategies

Glencoe Science incorporates the most current and applicable educational research on science learning and follows recommendations from the American Association for the Advancement of Science and the National Science Teachers Association. The following research-based strategies can be found throughout the text.

Learning Strategies

The following research-based strategies can be found throughout the text:

- **Using Prior Knowledge** Glencoe Science encourages students to use their prior knowledge to learn information because this adds relevance to the material. Students are referred back to other parts of the text or to their own real-life experiences.

- **Practicing Important Tasks** By offering students an opportunity to practice important tasks using a variety of labs and activities in the *Student Edition, Teacher Wraparound Edition,* ancillaries and technology, Glencoe Science makes learning fun and relevant for students.

- **Using Visuals to Communicate, Organize, and Reinforce Learning** High-quality art and photos throughout the text communicate concepts more efficiently and reinforce learning, while allowing students to organize information.

- **Motivating Students to Achieve** Active strategies and real-world experiences motivate students to achieve. Throughout Glencoe's programs, students are encouraged to apply their knowledge in ways that will motivate them to learn.

- **Developing Decoding and Reading Comprehension Strategies** Throughout the text, students are supplied with caption questions, reading checks, and other strategies to aid in comprehension.

- **Using Study Strategies** Through the use of highlighting, outlining, note-taking, summarizing, and other such strategies, students can monitor their own progress and organize information more effectively, thereby increasing their scientific literacy. These strategies are found throughout the text and ancillaries.

The use of these strategies within Glencoe Science will help teachers to achieve the goals set forth by the *National Science Education Standards.*

White Paper

The Glencoe Science White Paper outlines the educational strategies on which this program was based. This document provides specific examples from the *Student Edition, Teacher Wraparound Edition,* ancillary program, and technology resources, highlighting extensive use of educationally sound strategies that help students learn science.

Glencoe Science
15-Book Series for
Life, Earth, and
Physical Science

Field Research and Testing

Feedback from students, teachers, curriculum supervisors, department chairpersons, parents, learning specialists, and science content experts was invaluable in the development of this program. The following pre-publication and post-publication research was conducted.

Prior to Publication

- Detailed classroom teacher and curriculum supervisor **surveys** were conducted by independently contracted researchers.
- A **nationwide panel** of science teachers, curriculum supervisors, and department chairpersons provided countless hours of feedback and assistance throughout program development.
- A wide range of **educator and content reviewers** provided in-depth reviews of and suggestions for manuscripts and pre-publication versions of the program.
- **Face-to-face interviews** with science teachers provided insight into teachers' day-to-day challenges.

After Publication

- Field tests were conducted in which students and teachers used a pre-publication manuscript in the classroom.
- Follow-up interviews, observations, and surveys of Glencoe Science users provide ongoing opportunities for program development and verification of program success.

Field-Test Results

- Field-test research indicates that test scores increased among students using Glencoe Science programs.
- Nine out of ten students earned higher scores after using Glencoe programs.
- Scores improved among both male and female students.
- Scores improved among both minority and non-minority students.
- Overall, the gap between the average pre-test score and a perfect score closed by 33 percent. Stated differently, on average, **scores increased 77 percent after students used the Glencoe program.**

KS Studios

National Education Standards

Correlation of *Glencoe Science* to the National Science Education Standards.

Content Standard	Chapter and Section
(UCP) Unifying Concepts and Processes	
1. Systems, order, and organization	K1-1, K1-2, K1-3, K2-1, K2-2, K2-3, K3-1, K3-2, K4-1, K4-2, K4-3, L1-1, L1-2, L2-1, L2-2, L3-1, L3-2, L3-3, L4-1, L4-2, L4-3, M2-1, M2-2, M2-3, M5-1, M5-2, M5-3, M6-1, M6-2, M6-3, N1-1, N1-2, N1-3, N2-1, N2-2, N3-1, N3-2, O1-1, O1-2, O1-3, O2-1, O2-2, O3-1, O3-2, O3-3
2. Evidence, models, and explanation	K1-1, K1-2, K1-3, K2-1, K2-2, K2-3, K3-1, K3-2, K4-1, K4-2, K4-3, L1-1, L1-2, L2-1, L2-2, L3-1, L3-2, L3-3, L4-1, L4-2, L4-3, M1-1, M1-2, M1-3, M2-1, M2-2, M2-3, M3-1, M3-2, M3-3, M4-1, M4-2, M4-3, M5-1, M5-2, M5-3, M6-1, M6-2, M6-3, N1-1, N1-2, N1-3, N2-1, N2-2, N3-1, N3-2, O1-1, O1-2, O1-3, O2-1, O2-2, O3-1, O3-2, O3-3, O4-1, O4-2, O4-3, O4-4
3. Change, constancy, and measurement	K1-1, K1-2, K1-3, K2-1, K2-2, K2-3, K3-1, K3-2, K4-1, K4-2, K4-3, L1-1, L1-2, L2-1, L2-2, L3-1, L3-2, L3-3, L4-1, L4-2, L4-3, M1-1, M1-2, M1-3, M2-1, M2-2, M2-3, M3-1, M3-2, M3-3, M4-1, M4-2, M4-3, M5-1, M5-2, M5-3, M6-1, M6-2, M6-3, N1-1, N1-2, N1-3, N2-1, N2-2, N3-1, N3-2, O1-1, O1-2, O1-3, O2-1, O2-2, O3-1, O3-2, O3-3, O4-1, O4-2, O4-3, O4-4
4. Evolution and equilibrium	L3-1, L3-2, L3-3, M4-1, M4-2, M4-3
5. Form and function	K1-1, K1-2, K1-3, K2-1, K2-2, K2-3, K3-1, K3-2, K4-1, K4-2, K4-3, L1-1, L1-2, L2-1, L2-2, L3-1, L3-2, L3-3, L4-1, L4-2, L4-3, M1-1, M1-2, M1-3, M2-1, M2-2, M2-3, M3-1, M3-2, M3-3, M5-1, M5-2, M5-3, M6-1, M6-2, M6-3, N1-1, N1-2, N1-3, N2-1, N2-2, N3-1, N3-2, O1-1, O1-2, O1-3, O2-1, O2-2, O3-1, O3-2, O3-3, O4-1, O4-2, O4-3, O4-4
(A) Science as Inquiry	
1. Abilities necessary to do scientific inquiry	K1-1, K1-2, K1-3, K2-1, K2-2, K2-3, K3-1, K3-2, K4-1, K4-2, K4-3, L1-1, L1-2, L2-1, L2-2, L3-1, L3-2, L3-3, L4-1, L4-2, L4-3, M1-1, M1-2, M1-3, M2-1, M2-2, M2-3, M3-1, M3-2, M3-3, M4-1, M4-2, M4-3, M5-1, M5-2, M5-3, M6-1, M6-2, M6-3, N1-1, N1-2, N1-3, N2-1, N2-2, N3-1, N3-2, O1-1, O1-2, O1-3, O2-1, O2-2, O3-1, O3-2, O3-3, O4-1, O4-2, O4-3, O4-4
2. Understandings about scientific theory	K1-1, K1-2, K1-3, K2-1, K2-2, K2-3, K3-1, K3-2, K4-1, K4-2, K4-3, L1-1, L1-2, L2-1, L2-2, L3-1, L3-2, L3-3, L4-1, L4-2, L4-3, M1-1, M1-2, M1-3, M2-1, M2-2, M3-1, M3-2, M3-3, M4-1, M4-2, M4-3, M5-1, M5-2, M5-3, M6-1, M6-2, M6-3, N1-1, N1-2, N1-3, N2-1, N2-2, N3-1, N3-2, O1-1, O1-2, O1-3, O2-1, O2-2, O3-1, O3-2, O3-3, O4-1, O4-2, O4-3, O4-4
(B) Physical Science	
1. Properties and changes of properties in matter	K1-1, K1-2, K1-3, K2-1, K2-2, K2-3, K3-1, K3-2, K4-1, K4-2, K4-3, L1-1, L1-2, L2-1, L2-2, L3-1, L3-2, L3-3, L4-1, L4-2, L4-3, M1-1, M1-2, M1-3, M2-1, M2-2, M2-3, M3-1, M3-2, M3-3, M5-1, M5-2, M6-1, M6-2, N1-1, N1-2, N1-3, N2-1, N2-2, O2-1, O2-2, O3-1, O3-2, O3-3, O4-1
2. Motions and forces	K1-1, K2-1, K2-2, K2-1, L1-1, L1-2, L2-2, L3-2, M1-1, M1-2, M1-3, M2-2, M2-3, M3-1, M3-2, M3-3, M4-1, M4-2, M4-3, M5-1, M5-2, M6-2, M6-3, N1-1, N1-2, N1-3, N2-1, N2-2, O1-2, O1-3, O2-1, O2-2, O3-1, O3-2, O3-3, O4-1, O4-2, O4-3, O4-4
3. Transfer of energy	K2-1, K2-2, K3-2, K4-2, K4-3, L2-1, L2-2, L3-2, M2-2, M2-3, M4-1, M4-2, M4-3, M5-1, M5-2, M5-3, M6-1, M6-2, M6-3, N1-1, N1-2, N1-3, O1-2, O1-3, O2-1, O2-2, O3-1, O3-2, O3-3
(C) Life Science	
1. Structure and function in living systems	L4-1, L4-2, L4-3
(D) Earth and Space Science	
1. Structure of the Earth system	M3-1, O1-1, O1-2, O1-3
2. Earth's history	N2-1, N2-2
3. Earth and the solar system	O2-1, O3-2
(E) Science and Technology	
1. Abilities of technological design	K2-3
2. Understandings about science and technology	K2-3, N3-1, N3-2
(F) Science in Personal and Social Perspectives	
1. Personal health	K4-3
2. Populations, resources, and environments	M5-3, O2-2
3. Natural hazards	K3-2, M3-3, N1-3
4. Risks and benefits	M5-3
5. Science and technology in society	M2-3, N3-1, N3-2

Content Standard	Chapter and Section
(G) History and Nature of Science	
1. Science as a human endeavor	K1-1, K1-2, K1-3, K4-1, K4-3
2. Nature of science	M2-1, M3-2, M5-1
3. History of science	K1-1, K1-3, K2-3, K3-2, K4-1, M2-1, M5-1, N1-3, N3-2, O2-2, O4-4

How Glencoe Science Aligns with the National Science Education Standards

The correlations at the left and above show the close alignment between Glencoe Science and the grade-appropriate standards. Glencoe Science allows students to discover concepts within each of the content standards and gives students opportunities to make connections among the science disciplines. Hands-on activities and inquiry-based lessons reinforce the science processes emphasized in the standards.

How Glencoe Science Aligns with the NCTM Standards for Grades 6–8

Throughout Glencoe Science, each Applying Math activity provides students with the opportunity to practice and apply some of the mathematical concepts and applications described in the NCTM Standards. These activities serve to reinforce mathematical skills in real-life situations, thus preparing students to meet their needs in an ever-changing world.

Correlation of *Glencoe Science* to NCTM Standards

Math Standard	Page
1. Number and Operations	K-59, K-84, K-93, K-123, L-31, L-42, L-59, L-91, L-121, M-16, M-20, M-31, M-45, M-61, M-67, M-93, M-100, M-101, M-105, M-107, M-121, M-142, M-153, M-179, N-21, N-24, N-33, N-61, N-89, O-31, O-61, O-83, O-91, O-123
2. Algebra	K-84, K-93, K-123, L-42, L-59, L-121, M-16, M-20, M-31, M-45, M-61, M-67, M-93, M-100, M-101, M-105, M-107, M-121, M-142, M-153, M-160, M-179, N-21, N-24, N-33, N-89, O-31, O-83, O-91
3. Geometry	K-93, M-93
4. Measurement	K-84, K-93, L-91, M-160, M-179
5. Data Analysis and Probability	K-35, K-67, K-93, K-123, L-31, L-59, L-91, L-121, M-31, M-93, M-121, M-142, N-33, N-61, O-123
6. Problem Solving	K-59, L-31, M-142, O-123
7. Reasoning and Proof	K-59
8. Communication	M-142
9. Connections	K-84, K-93, K-123, L-31, L-42, L-59, L-91, L-121, M-16, M-20, M-31, M-45, M-61, M-67, M-93, M-100, M-101, M-105, M-107, M-121, M-142, M-153, M-160, M-179, N-21, N-24, N-33, N-89, O-31, O-61, O-83, O-91, O-123
10. Representation	K-67, L-42, L-59, M-142

Foldables™

Foldables™ are easy-to-make, three-dimensional, interactive graphic organizers that students create out of simple sheets of paper. These unique hands-on tools for studying and reviewing were created exclusively for Glencoe by education specialist Dinah Zike.

Research Behind Foldables™

According to research (Bransford, 1979; Corno, 1994), study strategies help students understand, organize, remember and apply new information presented in science textbooks. Some study strategies include concept mapping, highlighting, outlining, note taking, summarizing, and underlining (Peverly, Brobst, Graham & Shaw, 2003). Glencoe Science offers Dinah Zike's Foldables™ Study Organizers as an organizational tool and study guide for students.

Foldables™

- Build prereading skills
- Encourage active reading and writing
- Summarize content for review

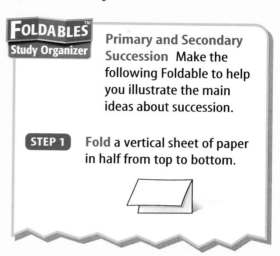

FOLDABLES™ Study Organizer

Primary and Secondary Succession Make the following Foldable to help you illustrate the main ideas about succession.

STEP 1 Fold a vertical sheet of paper in half from top to bottom.

For more ideas on how to incorporate Foldables™ into your lessons consult **Dinah Zike's *Teaching Science with Foldables*™**

Educational Partnerships

NATIONAL GEOGRAPHIC

Some topics in the chapter either require or benefit from a larger, more detailed visual explanation. The National Geographic Society has created *Visualizing* features that call out an important concept from the chapter and illustrate it in a way that will inform, excite, and motivate your students.

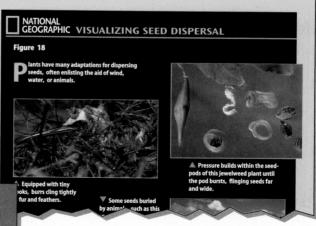

NATIONAL GEOGRAPHIC VISUALIZING SEED DISPERSAL

Figure 18

Plants have many adaptations for dispersing seeds, often enlisting the aid of wind, water, or animals.

▲ Pressure builds within the seed-pods of this jewelweed plant until the pod bursts, flinging seeds far and wide.

▲ Equipped with tiny hooks, burrs cling tightly fur and feathers.

▼ Some seeds buried by animals, such as this

TIME SCIENCE AND HISTORY SCIENCE CAN CHANGE THE COURSE OF HISTORY!

Overcoming the Odds

TIME

TIME magazine brings science topics and history together to further explain the chapter's main ideas and show how science relates to real life.

Safety in the Laboratory

All activities are designed to minimize dangers in the laboratory. Careful laboratory planning and management by both the instructor and the student are essential to a safe laboratory experience. **Local, state, and federal laboratory safety laws and regulations must be strictly followed.** The information provided here is one of the many resources to which you can refer for information about laboratory safety.

Classroom and Laboratory Preparation

1. Store equipment properly and securely and other thing.
   a. Clean and dry all equipment before storing.
   b. Protect electronic equipment and microscopes from dust, humidity, and extreme temperatures.
   c. Number, catalog, and organize equipment.
2. Ensure adequate work space for each student.
3. Ensure adequate classroom and storeroom ventilation.
4. Explain and post safety and evacuation guidelines along with expectations of conduct.
5. Ensure that all safety equipment is functioning properly and is clearly visible.
6. Provide hot plates as a heat source whenever possible. If gas burners are used, know where the central gas supply shutoff valve is located.
7. Ensure that each workstation has a GFCI-protected electrical source.
8. Provide safety goggles consistent with ANSI Standard Z87.1 for each student, including students who wear corrective lenses.

Before Each MiniLAB or Lab

1. Arrange the lab in such a way that equipment and supplies are clearly labeled and easily accessible.
2. Have available only equipment and supplies needed to complete the assigned investigation.
3. Review the procedure with students, emphasizing any caution statements or safety symbols that appear.
4. Be sure all students know the proper procedures to follow if an accident should occur.

After the MiniLAB or Lab

1. Be certain that students have returned all equipment and disposed of broken glassware and chemicals properly.
2. Be sure that all hot plates and electrical connections are off.

Storage of Chemicals

Be sure to store all chemicals properly. The following are guidelines commonly used. Your school, city, county, or state may have additional requirements for handling chemicals. It is the responsibility of each teacher to become informed of the rules or guidelines in effect in his or her area.

1. Separate chemicals by reaction type. Strong acids should be stored together. Likewise, strong bases should be stored together and should be separated from acids. Oxidants should be stored away from easily oxidized materials, and so on.
2. Be sure all chemicals are stored in labeled containers indicating contents, concentration, source, date purchased (or prepared), any precautions for handling and storage, and expiration date.
3. Hazardous chemicals require special storage containers and conditions. Be sure to know which chemicals those are and the accepted practices for your area. Some substances must be stored outside the building.

Disposal of Chemicals

Local, state, and federal laws regulate the proper disposal of chemicals. These laws should be consulted before chemical disposal is attempted. Although many substances encountered in the science classroom can be flushed down the drain with plenty of water, it is not safe to assume that this is always true.

DISCLAIMER

Glencoe Publishing Company makes no claims to the completeness of this discussion of laboratory safety and chemical storage. The material presented is not all-inclusive, nor does it address all of the hazards associated with handling, storing, and disposing of chemicals, or with laboratory management.

Preparation of Solutions

It is important to use safe laboratory techniques when handling all chemicals. Always check the MSDS (Material Safety Data Sheet) for each chemical before using it in the classroom. Many substances might appear harmless, but might be toxic, corrosive, or very reactive. Chemicals should never be ingested. Use proper techniques to smell any chemical, wear safety goggles and an apron in the laboratory, and observe the following precautions.

1. **Dilution of Acids and Bases** When diluting acids with water, always add the acids to the water. Never add water to acids. When sulfuric acid and sodium hydroxide are added to water, a large amount of thermal energy is released. Use extra care when handling these substances.

2. **Poisonous and Corrosive Liquids or Vapors** Use a fume hood if possible. Examples include hydrochloric acid, acetic acid, nitric acid, and ammonium hydroxide.

3. **Poisonous and Corrosive to Eyes, Lungs, and Skin** Examples include acids, bases, silver nitrate, iodine, and potassium permanganate.

Bromthymol blue: Add 0.5 g bromthymol blue powder to 500 mL distilled water to make a BTB stock solution. Dilute 40 mL BTB stock solution to 2 L with distilled water. Solution should be bright blue. If not, add one drop of NaOH at a time, swirling to mix. Check color.

Hydrochloric acid (HCL) solution: To make a 5% solution, add 13.6 mL concentrated HCl to 73 mL water while stirring. To make a $0.1M$ solution, add 1 mL concentrated hydrochloric acid to 100 mL water while stirring.

Iodine solution/Iodine stain: Dilute 1 part Lugol's solution with 15 parts water.

Lugol's solution: Dissolve 10 g potassium iodide in 100 mL distilled water. Then add and dissolve 5 g iodine. Store in dark bottle. Keeps indefinitely.

Phenolphthalein indicator: From a drug store, buy a package of any laxative that contains phenolphthalein. To make 1% solution, mash 4 tablets and pour the powder into 10 mL of rubbing alcohol. Let mixture soak for 15 minutes. Pour liquid into and store in a dropper bottle.

Potassium permanganate: For a $0.01M$ solution of potassium permanganate, dissolve 0.15 g $KMnO_4$ in 100 mL water.

Red cabbage concentrate: Put 5 leaves of red cabbage in a pot. Add 1 L of water, bring to a boil, and simmer until water turns a deep purple. Pour liquid through a strainer or piece of cheesecloth into a storage bottle. Keep refrigerated.

Salt solution: For a 3.5% salt (NaCl) solution that simulates the concentration of ocean water, dissolve 35 g of salt (NaCl) in 965 mL of water. For a 1% solution (weak), dissolve 1 g of salt (NaCl) in 99 mL of water. For a 6% solution, dissolve 6 g of salt (NaCl) in 94 mL of water.

Silver nitrate solution: To make a 10% solution, put 5 g of silver nitrate in 50 mL of distilled water.

Sugar solution: Add 1 tablespoon of sugar to 1 cup of warm water in a deep jar or flask. Stir to dissolve.

Sodium hydroxide (dilute): To make a 1% solution, dissolve 1 g NaOH in 99 mL of water.

Equipment and Materials List

Refer to the Chapter Organizer in front of each chapter for a list of equipment and materials used for each laboratory activity in the chapter.

Consumables			
Material	**Launch Lab (Chapter)**	**MiniLAB (Chapter-Section)**	**Lab (Chapter-Section)**
alcohol, rubbing		1-3, 2-2	
apple			3-1
apple juice			3-2
baking soda			1-3
bread, sliced			3-1
cereal, dry			3-1
clay	1		
cornstarch			1-3
egg			3-1, 3-2
feather			3-1
index card		2-3	1-2
iodine solution			1-3
lemon juice, concentrated			3-2
metal pieces	1		
plant or flower			3-1
plate, paper		3-2	
salad oil		1-3	
sand			3-1
soil			3-1
steel wool, fine		3-2	
sugar, granulated		1-3	
sugar, powdered			1-3
thumbtacks			1-2
toothpaste			3-2
toothpick(s)	1		
vegetable			3-1
vinegar, white			1-3
Nonconsumables			
balance			2-3
beaker		1-3	1-3, 2-2
block of wood			3-1
bulletin board, large			1-2
carpet			3-1
dropper		2-2	
dropper bottles			1-3
encyclopedia			1-2
graduated cylinder		2-1	2-3
hot plate			1-3, 2-2
magnet			3-1
marbles			2-3
Merck Index			1-2
metal bar or metal ruler			3-1
obsidian	3		
paint brush			3-2
pie pan, small			1-3
plastic bin			3-1
pumice	3		
rock			3-1
rubber ball			3-1
scoops, small			1-3
spring scale(s)			3-1
stirring rod			2-2

Glencoe Science

The Nature of Matter

NATIONAL GEOGRAPHIC

bookk.msscience.com

McGraw Hill Glencoe

New York, New York   Columbus, Ohio   Chicago, Illinois   Peoria, Illinois   Woodland Hills, California

HOW TO...
Use Your Science Book

Why do I need my science book?

Have you ever been in class and not understood all of what was presented? Or, you understood everything in class, but at home, got stuck on how to answer a question? Maybe you just wondered when you were ever going to use this stuff?

These next few pages are designed to help you understand everything your science book can be used for . . . besides a paperweight!

Before You Read

- **Chapter Opener** Science is occurring all around you, and the opening photo of each chapter will preview the science you will be learning about. The **Chapter Preview** will give you an idea of what you will be learning about, and you can try the **Launch Lab** to help get your brain headed in the right direction. The **Foldables** exercise is a fun way to keep you organized.

- **Section Opener** Chapters are divided into two to four sections. The **As You Read** in the margin of the first page of each section will let you know what is most important in the section. It is divided into four parts. **What You'll Learn** will tell you the major topics you will be covering. **Why It's Important** will remind you why you are studying this in the first place! The **Review Vocabulary** word is a word you already know, either from your science studies or your prior knowledge. The **New Vocabulary** words are words that you need to learn to understand this section. These words will be in **boldfaced** print and highlighted in the section. Make a note to yourself to recognize these words as you are reading the section.

The Nature of Matter

As You Read

- **Headings** Each section has a title in large red letters, and is further divided into blue titles and small red titles at the beginnings of some paragraphs. To help you study, make an outline of the headings and subheadings.

- **Margins** In the margins of your text, you will find many helpful resources. The **Science Online** exercises and **Integrate** activities help you explore the topics you are studying. **MiniLabs** reinforce the science concepts you have learned.

- **Building Skills** You also will find an **Applying Math** or **Applying Science** activity in each chapter. This gives you extra practice using your new knowledge, and helps prepare you for standardized tests.

- **Student Resources** At the end of the book you will find **Student Resources** to help you throughout your studies. These include **Science, Technology,** and **Math Skill Handbooks,** an **English/Spanish Glossary,** and an **Index.** Also, use your **Foldables** as a resource. It will help you organize information, and review before a test.

- **In Class** Remember, you can always ask your teacher to explain anything you don't understand.

FOLDABLES™
Study Organizer

Science Vocabulary Make the following Foldable to help you understand the vocabulary terms in this chapter.

STEP 1 Fold a vertical sheet of notebook paper from side to side.

STEP 2 Cut along every third line of only the top layer to form tabs.
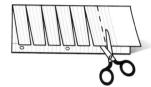

STEP 3 Label each tab with a vocabulary word from the chapter.
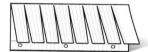

Build Vocabulary As you read the chapter, list the vocabulary words on the tabs. As you learn the definitions, write them under the tab for each vocabulary word.

Look For...

FOLDABLES™

At the beginning of every section.

In Lab

Working in the laboratory is one of the best ways to understand the concepts you are studying. Your book will be your guide through your laboratory experiences, and help you begin to think like a scientist. In it, you not only will find the steps necessary to follow the investigations, but you also will find helpful tips to make the most of your time.

- Each lab provides you with a **Real-World Question** to remind you that science is something you use every day, not just in class. This may lead to many more questions about how things happen in your world.

- Remember, experiments do not always produce the result you expect. Scientists have made many discoveries based on investigations with unexpected results. You can try the experiment again to make sure your results were accurate, or perhaps form a new hypothesis to test.

- Keeping a **Science Journal** is how scientists keep accurate records of observations and data. In your journal, you also can write any questions that may arise during your investigation. This is a great method of reminding yourself to find the answers later.

Look For...

- **Launch Labs** start every chapter.
- **MiniLabs** in the margin of each chapter.
- **Two Full-Period Labs** in every chapter.
- **EXTRA Try at Home Labs** at the end of your book.
- the **Web site** with **laboratory demonstrations.**

Before a Test

Admit it! You don't like to take tests! However, there *are* ways to review that make them less painful. Your book will help you be more successful taking tests if you use the resources provided to you.

- Review all of the **New Vocabulary** words and be sure you understand their definitions.

- Review the notes you've taken on your **Foldables,** in class, and in lab. Write down any question that you still need answered.

- Review the **Summaries** and **Self Check questions** at the end of each section.

- Study the concepts presented in the chapter by reading the **Study Guide** and answering the questions in the **Chapter Review.**

a or b?
?
T or F?

Look For...
- **Reading Checks** and **caption questions** throughout the text.
- the **Summaries** and **Self Check questions** at the end of each section.
- the **Study Guide** and **Review** at the end of each chapter.
- the **Standardized Test Practice** after each chapter.

Let's Get Started

To help you find the information you need quickly, use the Scavenger Hunt below to learn where things are located in Chapter 1.

1. What is the title of this chapter?

2. What will you learn in Section 1?

3. Sometimes you may ask, "Why am I learning this?" State a reason why the concepts from Section 2 are important.

4. What is the main topic presented in Section 2?

5. How many reading checks are in Section 1?

6. What is the Web address where you can find extra information?

7. What is the main heading above the sixth paragraph in Section 2?

8. There is an integration with another subject mentioned in one of the margins of the chapter. What subject is it?

9. List the new vocabulary words presented in Section 2.

10. List the safety symbols presented in the first Lab.

11. Where would you find a Self Check to be sure you understand the section?

12. Suppose you're doing the Self Check and you have a question about concept mapping. Where could you find help?

13. On what pages are the Chapter Study Guide and Chapter Review?

14. Look in the Table of Contents to find out on which page Section 2 of the chapter begins.

15. You complete the Chapter Review to study for your chapter test. Where could you find another quiz for more practice?

Teacher Advisory Board

The Teacher Advisory Board gave the authors, editorial staff, and design team feedback on the content and design of the Student Edition. They provided valuable input in the development of the 2005 edition of *Glencoe Science.*

John Gonzales
Challenger Middle School
Tucson, AZ

Rachel Shively
Aptakisic Jr. High School
Buffalo Grove, IL

Roger Pratt
Manistique High School
Manistique, MI

Kirtina Hile
Northmor Jr. High/High School
Galion, OH

Marie Renner
Diley Middle School
Pickerington, OH

Nelson Farrier
Hamlin Middle School
Springfield, OR

Jeff Remington
Palmyra Middle School
Palmyra, PA

Erin Peters
Williamsburg Middle School
Arlington, VA

Rubidel Peoples
Meacham Middle School
Fort Worth, TX

Kristi Ramsey
Navasota Jr. High School
Navasota, TX

Student Advisory Board

The Student Advisory Board gave the authors, editorial staff, and design team feedback on the design of the Student Edition. We thank these students for their hard work and creative suggestions in making the 2005 edition of *Glencoe Science* student friendly.

Jack Andrews
Reynoldsburg Jr. High School
Reynoldsburg, OH

Peter Arnold
Hastings Middle School
Upper Arlington, OH

Emily Barbe
Perry Middle School
Worthington, OH

Kirsty Bateman
Hilliard Heritage Middle School
Hilliard, OH

Andre Brown
Spanish Emersion Academy
Columbus, OH

Chris Dundon
Heritage Middle School
Westerville, OH

Ryan Manafee
Monroe Middle School
Columbus, OH

Addison Owen
Davis Middle School
Dublin, OH

Teriana Patrick
Eastmoor Middle School
Columbus, OH

Ashley Ruz
Karrer Middle School
Dublin, OH

The Glencoe middle school science Student Advisory Board taking a timeout at COSI, a science museum in Columbus, Ohio.

Contents

Nature of Science:
Pencils into Diamonds—2

chapter
1

Atoms, Elements, Compounds, and Mixtures—6

Section 1 **Models of the Atom** 8

Section 2 **The Simplest Matter** 18

Lab Elements and the Periodic Table 24

Section 3 **Compounds and Mixtures** 25

Lab: Design Your Own
Mystery Mixture 30

chapter
2

States of Matter—38

Section 1 **Matter** 40

Section 2 **Changes of State** 45

Lab The Water Cycle 53

Section 3 **Behavior of Fluids** 54

Lab: Design Your Own
Design Your Own Ship 62

In each chapter, look for these opportunities for review and assessment:
• Reading Checks
• Caption Questions
• Section Review
• Chapter Study Guide
• Chapter Review
• Standardized Test Practice
• Online practice at bookk.msscience.com

Contents

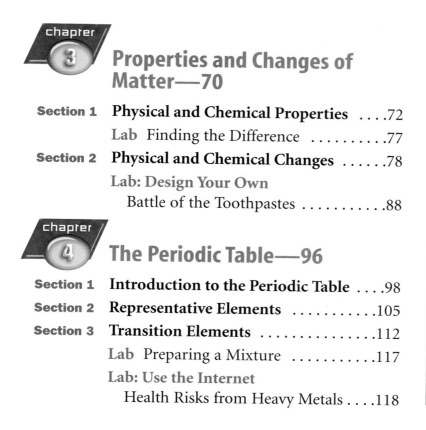

chapter 3

Properties and Changes of Matter—70

Section 1 **Physical and Chemical Properties** 72
Lab Finding the Difference 77
Section 2 **Physical and Chemical Changes** 78
Lab: Design Your Own
Battle of the Toothpastes 88

chapter 4

The Periodic Table—96

Section 1 **Introduction to the Periodic Table** 98
Section 2 **Representative Elements** 105
Section 3 **Transition Elements** 112
Lab Preparing a Mixture 117
Lab: Use the Internet
Health Risks from Heavy Metals 118

Student Resources

Science Skill Handbook—128
Scientific Methods 128
Safety Symbols 137
Safety in the Science
Laboratory 138

Extra Try at Home Labs—140

**Technology Skill
Handbook—142**
Computer Skills 142
Presentation Skills 145

Math Skill Handbook—146
Math Review 146
Science Applications 156

Reference Handbooks—161
Physical Science
Reference Tables 161
Periodic Table of
the Elements 162

**English/Spanish
Glossary—165**

Index—170

Credits—174

Cross-Curricular Readings/Labs

available as a video lab

NATIONAL GEOGRAPHIC VISUALIZING

1 The Periodic Table 20
2 States of Matter 48
3 Recycling. 86
4 Synthetic Elements. 115

TIME SCIENCE AND Society

1 Ancient Views of Matter 32

Oops! Accidents in SCIENCE

2 Incredible Stretching Goo 64

Science and Language Arts

15 "Anansi Tries to Steal All the
Wisdom in the World" 120

SCIENCE Stats

3 Strange Changes. 90

Launch LAB

1 Model the Unseen 7
2 Experiment with a
Freezing Liquid 39
3 The Changing Face
of a Volcano 71
4 Make a Model of a
Periodic Pattern 97

Mini LAB

1 Comparing Compounds 26
2 Observing Vaporization 50
3 Measuring Properties. 74
3 Identifying an
Unknown Substance 75
4 Designing a Periodic Table 99

Mini LAB Try at Home

1 Modeling the Nuclear Atom 15
2 Predicting a Waterfall 57
3 Comparing Changes 81

One-Page Labs

1 Elements and the
Periodic Table. 24
2 The Water Cycle 53
3 Finding the Difference. 77
4 Metals and Nonmetals. 117

Design Your Own Labs

1 Mystery Mixture 30–31
2 Design Your Own Ship 62–63
3 Battle of the Toothpastes. 88–89

Use the Internet Labs

4 Health Risks from
Heavy Metals 118–119

Applying Math

2 Calculating Density 59
3 Converting Temperatures 84

Applying Science

1 What's the best way to desalt
ocean water? 27
2 How can ice save oranges? 49
4 What does *periodic* mean
in the periodic table? 103

INTEGRATE

Astronomy: 83
Career: 108
Chemistry: 120
Earth Science: 29
Health: 116
History: 19, 42
Life Science: 28, 61, 81, 109
Physics: 16, 46, 114

28, 43, 49, 51, 61, 76, 81, 102, 116

Standardized Test Practice

36–37, 68–69, 94–95, 124–125

Content Details

Pencils into Diamonds

Introduction

This feature introduces students to the history of the manufacture synthetic of diamonds. It first describes the structure of natural diamonds and graphite and how the first synthetic diamonds were made from graphite. It then explains the subtle differences between natural and synthetic diamonds that can be used to tell them apart. Finally it discusses uses of synthetic diamonds and the places where research is carried on to find better ways to make synthetic diamonds and new uses for these synthetic gems.

1 Motivate

Use a glass cutter to score and cut a piece of glass. Then use a diamond-tipped engraving tool to write a series of numbers on a piece of metal or glass. Hold up both tools for the class to see. **Why is it possible to cut glass with this tool and to write on glass or metal with this tool?** Possible answers: Both tools have sharp edges; both tools have hard edges or points.

What do both of the tools have in common? Some students may know that both have diamond edges or points. Explain that diamond is the hardest substance known, which is why it is used in cutting tools.

Pencils into Diamonds

Figure 1 Uncut diamonds are ground and shaped into highly prized gems.

Diamond, the hardest mineral, is both beautiful and strong. Diamonds can cut steel, conduct heat, and withstand boiling acid. Unfortunately, to find a one carat gem-quality diamond, an average of 250 tons of rock must be mined!

But what if there were another way to get gems? In 1902, Auguste Verneuil, a French scientist, created the world's first synthetic ruby by carefully heating aluminum oxide powder. When other elements were added to this mixture, other colored gemstones were created.

Natural Diamonds

During World War II (1939–1945), there was a sudden need for hard gems used in the manufacturing of precision instruments. Around this time, scientists made the first diamond from carbon, or graphite—the same substance that is in #2 pencils. Graphite is made up of sheets of well-bonded carbon atoms. However, the sheets are only loosely bonded together. This gives graphite its flaky, slippery quality. Diamond, however, is made up of carbon atoms bonded strongly in three dimensions.

Figure 2 **A** Graphite has a layered structure of carbon atoms. Strong bonds exist within the layers and weak bonds exist between the layers. **B** All bonds between carbon atoms in diamond are strong.

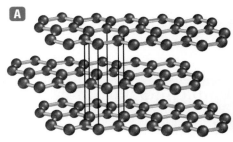
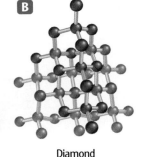

Graphite

Diamond

Differentiated Instruction

Visually Impaired Allow these students to feel the texture of graphite that is used as a lubricant. Ask them to describe how it feels and why its physical properties make it a good lubricant. Have students wash their hands when finished. Then, if possible, allow students to feel a diamond in a piece of jewelry and compare it to the graphite.

Making Synthetic Diamond

To change graphite to diamond, scientists expose it to extreme pressures and to temperatures as high as 3,000°C. The first experiments were unsuccessful. Scientists then reasoned that since diamond is a crystal, it might grow out of a super-concentrated solution as other crystals do. To dissolve carbon, they added melted troilite to their experiments. Troilite is a metal found surrounding tiny diamonds at meteorite impact sites. Finally, they succeeded. The first synthetic diamonds were yellowish, but they could be used in industry.

Diamond is a valuable material for industry. It is used to make machine-tool coatings, contact lenses, and electrodes. Computer engineers expect that diamond will soon be used to make high-speed computer chips.

Telling Them Apart

Of course, no one has forgotten the diamond's first use: decoration. The first synthetic diamonds were flawed by tiny pieces of metal from the diamond-making process and yellowed by the nitrogen in our atmosphere. Today, diamond makers have eliminated many of these problems. In just five days, labs now produce colorless, jewelry-grade synthetic diamonds that are much less expensive than natural diamonds. One natural diamond company now determines which stones are synthetic by using phosphorescence. Unlike natural diamonds, synthetic diamonds will glow in the dark for a few seconds after being exposed to ultraviolet light. Synthetic diamond makers are already working to eliminate this difference, too.

Some people are excited about affordable diamonds. Others are concerned that synthetic gem quality diamonds will be sold as natural diamonds. Some people also wonder if a diamond that was made in a laboratory in a few days has the same symbolic significance as a diamond formed naturally over millions of years.

Figure 4 A machine like this one can produce the temperature and pressure required to create a diamond.

Figure 3 Diamond is sought after for its beauty and for its useful properties.

2 Teach

Content Background

Fewer than 20% of the diamonds mined each year are suitable for use as gems. The rest go to industrial uses such as diamond-studded rotary bits used to drill oil wells or bore tunnels. Much low-grade diamond is crushed and used as abrasive powder. The powder is used in grinding wheels, glass cutters, and glass-etching pencils. Today synthetic diamonds are made throughout the world. In many industrial uses, synthetic diamonds are preferred over natural diamonds because they can be manufactured to the specific size and shape requirements of an application. The estimated world market for synthetic diamonds is about one billion dollars and could grow as new applications are developed.

Discussion

Explain that during the Middle Ages, alchemists unsuccessfully tried to find ways to turn common metals, such as lead, into gold, which is very valuable. Ask students to think about scientists' attempts to make synthetic diamonds. **How is the work of these scientists similar to that of the alchemists? How is it different?** Like the alchemists who tried to turn lead into gold, the scientists were trying to turn graphite, a common substance, into diamond, a valuable substance. Unlike the alchemists, the scientists succeeded in making diamonds from graphite.

Use Science Words

Word Origin Have students use a dictionary to find the origin of the word *diamond*. Ask them to explain why they think the substance was given that name. The word *diamond* comes from the Greek work *adamas* meaning "indestructible." Diamond is the hardest substance known, so it seems indestructible.

Activity

Have small groups of students research the characteristics of diamonds that are used to describe and judge gem-quality diamonds. Have students make a poster titled *The Five Cs of Diamonds* that illustrates what they learned. Students should find that diamonds are judged by carat, cost, clarity, color, and cut.

Teacher FYI

In 1999 a method was developed for making poor-quality, brownish diamonds into much whiter (E-color) stones that are indistinguishable from natural white stones. These stones are labeled, but the labels can be ground off with diamond-powder sanders.

Extension

Interested students can work together to research the technology used to tell the difference between natural and synthetic diamonds. Have them make an oral presentation on how the technology was developed and how it works. COOP LEARN

IS Interpersonal

The NATURE OF SCIENCE

Figure 5 The need for diamond-coated drill bits and cutting blades sparked research into the creation of gem-quality diamonds.

Science

The path to tomorrow's high-speed diamond computer chips will have begun with people trying to make jewelry! Such pathways are reminders of how science touches many aspects of human life. Like the pieces in a puzzle, each scientific breakthrough reveals more about how the world works.

Physical science includes the chemistry that produces synthetic diamonds. In this book, you'll learn how the elements on the periodic table combine to make up everything you see around you. You'll also learn how chemistry can change many aspects of the world around you.

Science Today

Scientists work to find solutions and to answer questions. As people's needs change, scientists who are developing new technologies change the direction of their work. For example, the need for diamonds during World War II triggered research into making synthetic diamonds.

Where Do Today's Scientists Work?

Scientists today work in a variety of places for a variety of reasons. Both scientists who study natural diamonds and people who make synthetic diamonds might work in controlled laboratory environments. They may also study diamonds where they are found in nature.

Public and Private Research

The United States government supports a great deal of scientific research. Publicly funded research usually deals with topics that affect the health and welfare of the country's citizens.

In the private sector, many companies, large and small, have their own laboratories. Their scientists research new technologies, use the technologies in the products that they sell, and test the new products. The world's first synthetic diamond was created by a private company that needed diamond for its products. Another private company, a diamond company, has created many of the world's synthetic diamonds in its laboratory! Why? The diamond company wants to understand how synthetic diamonds are made so that they can see the differences between their naturally formed diamonds and their competitors' manufactured diamonds. Research has helped them to develop a machine that identifies synthetic diamonds.

Curriculum Connection

Mathematics Explain to students that diamonds are measured in carats and that 5 carats equals 1 gram. Have students calculate the masses in grams of the following diamonds: 44.5-carat Hope Diamond 9.1 g, 127-carat Portuguese Diamond 25.4 g, 2.9-carat DeYoung Pink Diamond 0.58 g, 31-carat Eugenie Blue Diamond 6.2 g

Science Journal

Natural Versus Synthetic Ask students to describe in their Science Journals how large quantities of synthetic industrial and gem-quality diamonds might affect the value of natural diamonds. Ask if they would be willing to pay more for jewelry made with natural diamonds than they would pay for jewelry made with synthetic diamonds. **IS Linguistic**

Research at Universities

Major universities also have laboratories. Their work with the government or corporations allows academic and industrial scientists to learn from one another. Industry and the government also provide grants and funding for university laboratories.

Dr. Rajiv K. Singh is a professor at the University of Florida, Gainesville. He and his colleague James Adair created the world's largest synthetic diamond using a process called chemical vapor deposition (CVD). Dr. Singh researches many different materials for the University. His work with synthetic diamonds also involves research in flat-panel displays, thin film batteries, electronics, and superconductors.

Figure 6 Researchers at the University of Florida created the world's largest synthetic diamond.

You Do It

You probably have many devices at home that new discoveries in science have made possible. For example, DVD and MP3 players are technologies that didn't exist just a few years ago. Research the science behind your favorite "gadget" and explain to the class how it works.

Make a Model

Using **Figure 2** as a guide, have students use clay balls or gumdrops and toothpick halves to model the structure of carbon atoms in graphite and in diamonds. Then have them research the third form of carbon, the buckeyball or buckminsterfullerence, and make a model of that structure. **L̶S̶ Visual-Spatial and Kinesthetic**

Use An Analogy

Ask students if they have ever seen a movie or TV show in which Superman squeezes a lump of coal in his powerful fist, then opened his hand to reveal a diamond. Point out to students that, like Superman, scientists at the University of Florida make synthetic diamonds using extremely high pressures and temperatures.

3 Assess

Use the presentations in You Do It to assess understanding. Presentations should relate to the science behind each student's favorite "gadget" and be as specific as possible.

You Do It

Have each student name several of his or her favorite gadgets as you list them on the board. You may want to have students who share an interest in the same gadget work together on their research and presentation. Encourage students to use Internet as well as library resources to find out how the gadgets work. Students could make multimedia presentations, including an actual gadget, a labeled diagram explaining how it works, and an oral account of the research behind its development. COOP LEARN **L̶S̶ Linguistic and Interpersonal**

Section/Objectives	Standards		Labs/Features
	National	State/Local	
Chapter Opener	See pp. 9T–10T for a Key to Standards.		**Launch Lab:** Model the Unseen, p. 7 **Foldables,** p. 7
Section 1 Models of the Atom ⏱ 2 sessions ▭ 1 block 1. **Explain** how scientists discovered subatomic particles. 2. **Explain** how today's model of the atom developed. 3. **Describe** the structure of the nuclear atom.	National Content Standards: UCP.1, UCP.2, UCP.3, UCP.5, A.1, A.2, B.1, B.2, G.3		**MiniLAB:** Modeling the Nuclear Atom, p. 15 **Integrate Physics,** p. 16
Section 2 The Simplest Matter ⏱ 3 sessions ▭ 1.5 blocks 4. **Describe** the relationship between elements and the periodic table. 5. **Explain** the meaning of atomic mass and atomic number. 6. **Identify** what makes an isotope. 7. **Contrast** metals, metalloids, and nonmetals.	National Content Standards: UCP.1, UCP.2, UCP.3, UCP.5, A.1, A.2, B.1		**Integrate History,** p. 19 **Visualizing the Periodic Table,** p. 20 **Lab:** Elements and the Periodic Table, p. 24
Section 3 Compounds and Mixtures ⏱ 4 sessions ▭ 2 blocks 8. **Identify** the characteristics of a compound. 9. **Compare and contrast** different types of mixtures.	National Content Standards: UCP.1, UCP.2, UCP.3, UCP.5, A.1, A.2, B.1, G.3		**MiniLAB:** Comparing Compounds, p. 26 **Applying Science:** What's the best way to desalt ocean water?, p. 27 **Science Online,** p. 28 **Integrate Earth Science,** p. 29 **Lab:** Mystery Mixtures, pp. 30–31 **Science and History:** Ancient Views of Matter, p. 32

Lab Materials	Reproducible Resources	Section Assessment	Technology
Launch Lab: balls of clay, metal objects (paper clips, screws, nuts, washers), toothpicks	**Chapter FAST FILE Resources** Foldables Worksheet, p. 13 Directed Reading Overview, p. 15 Note-taking Worksheets, pp. 29–31	GLENCOE'S ASSESSMENT ADVANTAGE	TeacherWorks includes: • Interactive Teacher Edition • Lesson Planner with calendar • Access to all program blacklines • Correlations to standards • Web links
MiniLAB: sheet of paper, drawing compass, colored paper dots, glue	**Chapter FAST FILE Resources** Transparency Activity, p. 40 MiniLAB, p. 3 Lab Activity, pp. 9–10 Enrichment, p. 26 Reinforcement, p. 23 Directed Reading, p. 16 **Cultural Diversity,** pp. 55, 59	**Portfolio** Science Journal, p. 14 Use Science Words, p. 14 **Performance** MiniLAB, p. 15 Applying Math, p. 17 **Content** Section Review, p. 17	Section Focus Transparency Virtual Labs CD-ROM Guided Reading Audio Program Interactive Chalkboard CD-ROM
Lab: colored markers, large index cards, Merck index, encyclopedia, large bulletin board, 8 1/2 × 14-inch paper, thumbtacks *Need materials?* Contact Science Kit at 1-800-828-7777 or www.sciencekit.com on the Internet.	**Chapter FAST FILE Resources** Transparency Activity, p. 41 Enrichment, p. 27 Reinforcement, p. 24 Directed Reading, p. 17 Transparency Activity, pp. 43–44 Lab Worksheet, pp. 5–6 **Science Inquiry Labs,** pp. 43–44	**Portfolio** Differentiated Instruction, p. 22 **Performance** Applying Math, p. 23 **Content** Section Review, p. 23	Section Focus Transparency Teaching Transparency Virtual Labs CD-ROM Guided Reading Audio Program Interactive Chalkboard CD-ROM
MiniLAB: granular sugar, rubbing alcohol, salad oil, beakers (3), hot water, spoons (3) **Lab:** test tubes (4), cornstarch, powdered sugar, baking soda, small scoops (3), iodine solution and white vinegar in dropper bottles, hot plate, 250-mL beaker, test-tube holder, small pie pan, matches	**Chapter FAST FILE Resources** Transparency Activity, p. 42 MiniLAB, p. 4 Lab Activity, pp. 11–12 Enrichment, p. 28 Reinforcement, p. 25 Directed Reading, pp. 17, 18 Lab Worksheets, pp. 7–8 **Lab Management and Safety,** p. 49	**Portfolio** Curriculum Connection, p. 28 **Performance** MiniLAB, p. 26 Applying Science, p. 27 Applying Skills, p. 29 **Content** Section Review, p. 29	Section Focus Transparency Virtual Labs CD-ROM Guided Reading Audio Program Interactive Chalkboard CD-ROM Video Lab

End of Chapter Assessment

Blackline Masters	Technology	Professional Series
Chapter FAST FILE Resources Chapter Review, pp. 33–34 Chapter Tests, pp. 35–38 **Standardized Test Practice,** pp. 7–10	MindJogger Videoquiz Virtual Labs CD-ROM ExamView® Pro Testmaker TeacherWorks CD-ROM Interactive Chalkboard CD-ROM	**Performance Assessment in the Science Classroom (PASC)**

chapter 1 Atoms, Elements, Compounds, and Mixtures

Transparencies

Section Focus

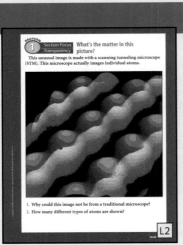

1 Section Focus Transparency **What's the matter in this picture?**

This unusual image is made with a scanning tunneling microscope (STM). This microscope actually images individual atoms.

1. Why could this image not be from a traditional microscope?
2. How many different types of atoms are shown?

L2

2 Section Focus Transparency **Some Call It Quicksilver**

This element is a liquid at room temperature. It is probably best known as the liquid in traditional thermometers; however, it is so toxic that people often choose digital or alcohol thermometers that do not contain this element.

1. Describe what you see in the picture. What characteristics does this element have?
2. Which element do you think this is? Do you know of any other uses for it?

L2

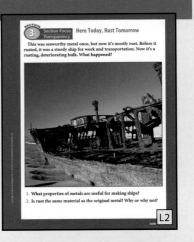

3 Section Focus Transparency **Here Today, Rust Tomorrow**

This was seaworthy metal once, but now it's mostly rust. Before it rusted, it was a sturdy ship for work and transportation. Now it's a rusting, deteriorating hulk. What happened?

1. What properties of metals are useful for making ships?
2. Is rust the same material as the original metal? Why or why not?

L2

This is a representation of key blackline masters available in the Teacher Classroom Resources. See Resource Manager boxes within the chapter for additional information.

Key to Teaching Strategies

The following designations will help you decide which activities are appropriate for your students.

L1 Level 1 activities should be appropriate for students with learning difficulties.

L2 Level 2 activities should be within the ability range of all students.

L3 Level 3 activities are designed for above-average students.

ELL ELL activities should be within the ability range of English Language Learners.

COOP LEARN Cooperative Learning activities are designed for small group work.

LS Multiple Learning Styles logos, as described on page 6T, are used throughout to indicate strategies that address different learning styles.

P These strategies represent student products that can be placed into a best-work portfolio.

PBL Problem-Based Learning activities apply real-world situations to learning.

Assessment

Assessment Transparency **Inside the Atom**

Directions: Carefully review the tables and answer the following questions.

Table A
Gold
Water
Salt
Sugar

Table B
Vegetable soup
Pancake batter
Blood
Air

1. The substances in Table A are different from the substances in Table B because only the substances in Table A are ____.
   A mixtures C compounds
   B metals D pure elements
2. Which of the following belongs with the matter in Table A above?
   F chocolate-chip ice cream H iron nail
   G chicken noodle soup J milk shake
3. Heterogeneous mixtures are mixtures that have different parts that are large enough to be visibly identified. According to this information, which of the substances in Table B is a heterogeneous mixture?
   A vegetable soup C blood
   B pancake batter D air

L2

Teaching

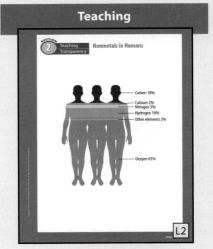

2 Teaching Transparency **Nonmetals in Humans**

Carbon 18%
Calcium 2%
Nitrogen 3%
Hydrogen 10%
Other elements 2%
Oxygen 65%

L2

Hands-on Activities

Student Text Lab Worksheet

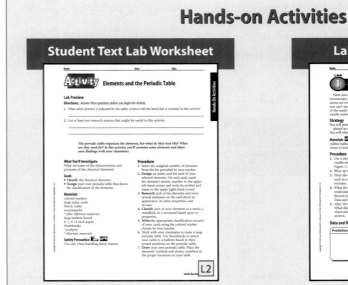

Activity Elements and the Periodic Table

Lab Preview
Directions: Answer these questions before you begin the Activity.
1. What safety practice is indicated by the safety symbol with the hand that is included in this activity?
2. List at least two research sources that might be useful in this activity.

The periodic table organizes the elements, but what do they look like? What are they used for? In this activity, you'll examine some elements and share your findings with your classmates.

What You'll Investigate
What are some of the characteristics and purposes of the chemical elements?

Goals
• Classify the chemical elements.
• Design your own periodic table that shows the classification of the elements.

Materials
colored markers
large index cards
Merck index
encyclopedia
other reference materials
large bulletin board
8 ½ × 14-inch paper
thumbtacks
pushpins
Alternate materials

Safety Precaution
Use care when handling sharp objects.

Procedure
1. Select the assigned number of elements from the list provided by your teacher.
2. Design an index card for each of your selected elements. On each card, mark the element's atomic number in the upper left-hand corner and write its symbol and name in the upper right-hand corner.
3. Research each of the elements and write several sentences on the card about its appearance, its other properties, and its uses.
4. Classify each of your elements as a metal, a metalloid, or a nonmetal based upon its properties.
5. Write the appropriate classification on each of your cards using the colored marker chosen by your teacher.
6. Work with your classmates to make a large periodic table. Use thumbtacks to attach your cards to a bulletin board in their proper positions on the periodic table. Place the elements' symbols and atomic numbers in the proper locations on your table.
7. Draw your own periodic table on the elements' symbols and atomic numbers in the proper locations on your table.

L2

Laboratory Activities

1 Laboratory Activity **Atoms—Smaller Than You Think!**

Have you ever seen an atom? Unless you've been lucky enough to look through a very powerful microscope, you haven't seen anything close in size to an atom. Matter is composed of atoms, and atoms are everywhere. You can't see atoms or even molecules. They are too small. But even though you can't see an atom with your own eyes, you can use other senses to detect the presence of some of the small molecules made from atoms. In this experiment, you will study the small size of vanilla molecules.

Strategy
You will predict what happens when drops of a liquid that is made up of small molecules are placed in a balloon.
You will observe some aspects of small molecules.

Materials
rubber balloon dropper
closet or locker vanilla extract (2 mL)

Procedure
1. Use a dropper to place 20 to 40 drops of vanilla extract into a rubber balloon. (See Figure 1.)
2. Blow up the balloon, and tie it tightly.
3. Place the balloon in a small, enclosed area such as a closet or locker for at least 30 minutes.
4. What do you think will happen to the molecules of vanilla while it is in the balloon? Record your predictions in the table in the Data and Observations section.
5. After 30 minutes, open the closet or locker. What did you observe? Record your observation in the Data and Observations section.

Figure 1

Data and Observations

Predictions	Observations

L2

Meeting Different Ability Levels

Content Outline
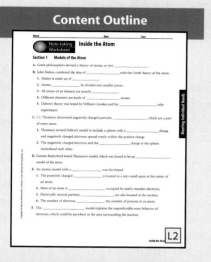
L2

Reinforcement
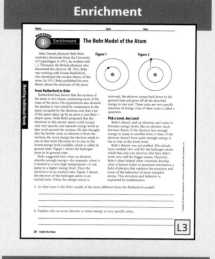
L2

Enrichment

L3

Directed Reading (English/Spanish)
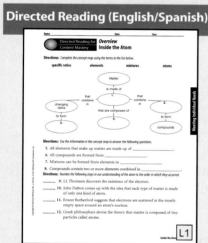
L1

Study Guide

Study Guide

Features
- Contains a study guide page for each section of the chapter
- Reviews key concepts
- Includes answer pages

L2

Reading Essentials

Reading Essentials for Glencoe Science
An Interactive Student Workbook

Features
- Condensed core content
- Actively involves students in reading
- Reinforces key vocabulary

L1

Assessment

Test Practice Workbook
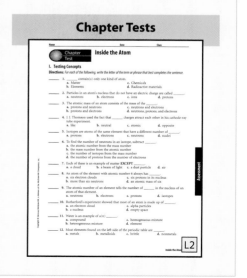
GO ON ▶ L2

Chapter Review

L2

Chapter Tests

L2

Science Content Background

section 1 Models of the Atom
Early Greek Philosophers
It is thought that the idea that matter can be divided into smaller particles called atoms was developed by the Greek philosopher Democritus around 430 B.C. Other early philosophers such as Aristotle, Titus Lucretius Carus, and Plato disagreed with Democritus's idea of atoms and proposed that matter was continuous and could not be divided. The idea of continuous matter, although incorrect, was widely accepted for the next 2,000 years.

Evidence to Support Atomic Theory
Antoine Lavoisier proposed the law of conservation of mass that states that although matter may undergo chemical reactions and change, it cannot be created or destroyed. Joseph Proust observed that specific substances always contain elements in the same ratio by mass. In the 1800s, John Dalton expanded upon the work of Lavoisier, Proust, and other chemists. Dalton proposed that matter is composed of atoms and now scientific evidence is available to support this theory. Since Dalton's time, the atomic model has undergone may changes as more scientific evidence became available.

section 2 The Simplest Matter
Triads and Octaves
Dmitri Mendeleev arranged the 63 known elements into his first published periodic table in 1869. This was not the first attempt to organize the elements, nor was it the final version of the periodic table. In 1817 J.W. Döbereiner, a German chemist, showed that the atomic weight of strontium fell halfway between calcium and barium. He called this a triad, and showed that other triads also existed. John Newlands, an English chemist, proposed another method of organizing the elements in 1865. Newlands found that if the elements were organized in the order of increasing atomic weight, similarities occurred in intervals of seven. (The noble gases were not discovered until 1894.) Newlands's method of organizing the elements is called the law of octaves.

Mendeleev's Table
Mendeleev's periodic table was similar to Newlands's because he arranged the elements in order of increasing atomic mass and according to similar chemical and physical properties. But unlike Newlands's table, where the elements are in groups of seven, the first two rows of Mendeleev's table had seven elements, and the next two rows had seventeen. On the modern periodic table, periods 2–5 have this arrangement. Recall that the noble gases were not discovered until later.

Moseley's Contribution
In 1911, the English scientist Henry Gwyn-Jeffreys Moseley discovered that the positive charge in the nucleus increased by one as you went sequentially higher in Mendeleev's periodic table. When the table was organized by increasing positive charge or atomic number, the inconsistencies in Mendeleev's table were corrected. Moseley's work led to the modern statement of periodic law that states the properties of the elements are a periodic function of their atomic numbers.

Teacher to Teacher
Petrolia Moss
North Heights Junior High
Texarkana, Arkansas

"I like to use multicolored clay as an inexpensive and reusable material for middle school students to use to visualize science concepts. The students use their creativity to make 'atoms' that have touchable protons, neutrons, and electrons."

Petrolia Moss

Fine-Tuning the Table

As new elements were discovered and synthesized, they were added to the periodic table in increasing order of atomic number. Additional research in atomic structure revealed that the electron configuration of the elements was responsible for their chemical properties. Because electron configuration and chemical properties of the elements are considered when placing elements on the periodic table, the center of the table grew to a cumbersome width. For this reason, the lanthanide and actinide series of elements are placed below the periodic table. This gives the table a more manageable size.

section 3 Compounds and Mixtures

Classifying Matter

Matter is organized and classified into groups based on its composition. The diagram below shows the hierarchy of matter classification. Notice that the broadest classification of matter is materials. Materials are then broken down into homogeneous and heterogeneous materials.

Homogeneous and Heterogeneous Materials

Homogeneous materials have the same composition throughout; heterogeneous materials do not. For example, sodium chloride is a compound composed of sodium and chlorine. It has the same composition throughout the substance. A beaker of sand and iron filings is a heterogeneous mixture because it has distinct areas that have different properties. Substances (elements and compounds) and solutions are homogeneous materials. Mixtures are heterogeneous materials.

chapter content resources

Internet Resources
For additional content background, visit
bookk.msscience.com to:
- access your book online
- find references to related articles in popular science magazines
- access Web links with related content background
- access current events with science journal topics

Print Resources
Chemistry, Steve S. Zumdahl, Susan A. Zumdahl, Houghton Mifflin Company, 2003
Chemistry, Raymond Chang, McGraw-Hill College, 2001
General Chemistry, Ralph Petrucci, William Harwood, Prentice Hall, 1997

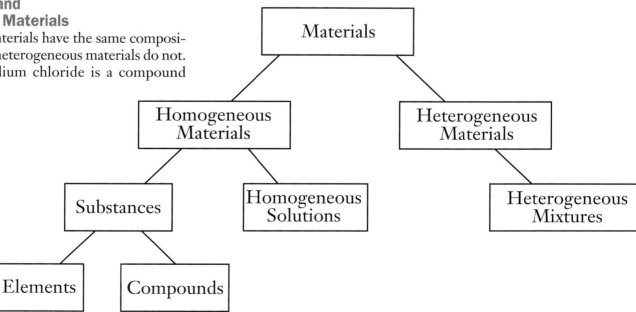

Chapter Vocabulary

element, p. 9
electron, p. 11
proton, p. 14
neutron, p. 15
electron cloud, p. 17
atomic number, p. 21
isotope, p. 21
mass number, p. 21
atomic mass, p. 22
metal, p. 22
nonmetal, p. 23
metalloid, p. 23
substance, p. 25
compound, p. 25
mixture, p. 27

Science Journal Answers will vary, but may include that atoms are the building blocks of matter, are extremely small, and are capable of releasing energy.

INTERACTIVE CHALKBOARD with Image Bank

PowerPoint® Presentations

This CD-ROM is an editable Microsoft® PowerPoint® presentation that includes:
• a pre-made presentation for every chapter
• interactive graphics
• animations
• audio clips
• image bank
• all new section and chapter questions
• Standardized Test Practice
• transparencies
• pre-lab questions for all labs
• Foldables directions
• links to bookk.msscience.com

Atoms, Elements, Compounds, and Mixtures

chapter preview

sections

1 Models of the Atom

2 The Simplest Matter
  Lab Elements and the Periodic Table

3 Compounds and Mixtures
  Lab Mystery Mixtures
  Virtual Lab Atoms, Elements, Compounds, and Mixtures

What an impressive sight!

Have you ever seen iron on an atomic level? This is an image of 48 iron atoms surrounding a single copper atom. In this chapter, you will learn about scientists and their discoveries about the nature of the atom.

Science Journal Based on your knowledge, describe what an atom is.

6 ◆ K

Theme Connection

Stability and Change The nucleus of an atom can undergo changes that can be useful but dangerous. These changes occur in a predictable pattern.

About the Photo

Scanning Microscope This image was produced by a scanning tunneling microscope, which uses the electrical interaction of a very small needle with the material under examination to develop images. Individual atoms can be arranged by the microscope's tip, and the wave properties of the electrons can be seen in the ripples in the circle of atoms.

Start-Up Activities

Model the Unseen

Have you ever had a wrapped birthday present that you couldn't wait to open? What did you do to try to figure out what was in it? The atom is like that wrapped present. You want to investigate it, but you cannot see it easily.

1. Your teacher will give you a piece of clay and some pieces of metal. Count the pieces of metal.

2. Bury these pieces in the modeling clay so they can't be seen.

3. Exchange clay balls with another group.

4. With a toothpick, probe the clay to find out how many pieces of metal are in the ball and what shape they are.

5. **Think Critically** In your Science Journal, sketch the shapes of the metal pieces as you identify them. How does the number of pieces you found compare with the number that were in the clay ball? How do their shapes compare?

FOLDABLES Study Organizer

Parts of the Atom Make the following Foldable to help you organize your thoughts and review parts of an atom.

STEP 1 Collect two sheets of paper and layer them about 1.25 cm apart vertically. Keep the edges level.

STEP 2 Fold up the bottom edges of the paper to form four equal tabs.

STEP 3 Fold the papers and crease well to hold the tabs in place. Staple along the fold. Label the flaps *Atom, Electron, Proton,* and *Neutron* as shown.

Read and Write As you read the chapter, describe how each part of the atom was discovered and record other facts under the flaps.

Science Online

Preview this chapter's content and activities at
bookk.msscience.com

Purpose Use this Launch Lab to help students discover how scientists find out about things they can't see. L1 ELL COOP LEARN LS **Kinesthetic**

Materials small metal objects such as washers, nuts, and bolts; modeling clay; toothpick; paper towels

Teaching Strategy Demonstrate Step 4 to show students how to use a probe to feel things that can't be seen.

Think Critically
Answers will vary. Some shapes will be easier to identify than others.

Assessment
Oral Have students work in groups to share their results. Ask them to compare their evidence and to discuss how they discovered what each hidden item was. Use **Performance Assessment in the Science Classroom,** p. 169. L1

FOLDABLES Study Organizer | **Dinah Zike Study Fold**

Student preparation materials for this Foldable are available in the **Chapter *FAST FILE* Resources.**

Models of the Atom

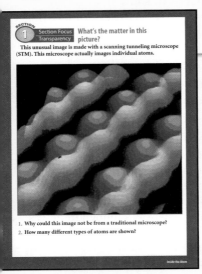
as you read

What You'll Learn

- **Explain** how scientists discovered subatomic particles.
- **Explain** how today's model of the atom developed.
- **Describe** the structure of the nuclear atom.

Why It's Important

All matter is made up of atoms. Atoms make up everything in your world.

Review Vocabulary

matter: anything that has mass and takes up space

New Vocabulary

- element
- electron
- proton
- neutron
- electron cloud

First Thoughts

Do you like mysteries? Are you curious? Humans are curious. Someone always wants to know something that is not easy to detect or to see what can't be seen. For example, people began wondering about matter more than 2,500 years ago. Some of the early philosophers thought that matter was composed of tiny particles. They reasoned that you could take a piece of matter, cut it in half, cut the half piece in half again, and continue to cut again and again. Eventually, you wouldn't be able to cut any more. You would have only one particle left. They named these particles *atoms*, a term that means "cannot be divided." Another way to imagine this is to picture a string of beads like the one shown in **Figure 1.** If you keep dividing the string into pieces, you eventually come to one single bead.

Describing the Unseen The early philosophers didn't try to prove their theories by doing experiments as scientists now do. Their theories were the result of reasoning, debating, and discussion—not of evidence or proof. Today, scientists will not accept a theory that is not supported by experimental evidence. But even if these philosophers had experimented, they could not have proven the existence of atoms. People had not yet discovered much about what is now called chemistry, the study of matter. The kind of equipment needed to study matter was a long way from being invented. Even as recently as 500 years ago, atoms were still a mystery.

Figure 1 You can divide this string of beads in half, and in half again until you have one, indivisible bead. Like this string of beads, all matter can be divided until you reach one basic particle, the atom.

8 ◆ **K CHAPTER 1** Atoms, Elements, Compounds, and Mixtures

Section 1 Resource Manager

Chapter *FAST FILE* Resources

Transparency Activity, p. 40

Directed Reading for Content Mastery, pp. 15, 16

Note-taking Worksheets, pp. 29–31

Enrichment, p. 26

MiniLAB, p. 3

Lab Activity, pp. 9–10

Reinforcement, p. 23

Cultural Diversity, pp. 55, 59

A Model of the Atom

A long period passed before the theories about the atom were developed further. Finally during the eighteenth century, scientists in laboratories, like the one on the left in **Figure 2,** began debating the existence of atoms once more. Chemists were learning about matter and how it changes. They were putting substances together to form new substances and taking substances apart to find out what they were made of. They found that certain substances couldn't be broken down into simpler substances. Scientists came to realize that all matter is made up of elements. An **element** is matter made of atoms of only one kind. For example, iron is an element made of iron atoms. Silver, another element, is made of silver atoms. Carbon, gold, and oxygen are other examples of elements.

Dalton's Concept   John Dalton, an English schoolteacher in the early nineteenth century, combined the idea of elements with the earlier theory of the atom. He proposed the following ideas about matter: (1) Matter is made up of atoms, (2) atoms cannot be divided into smaller pieces, (3) all the atoms of an element are exactly alike, and (4) different elements are made of different kinds of atoms. Dalton pictured an atom as a hard sphere that was the same throughout, something like a tiny marble. A model like this is shown in **Figure 3.**

Scientific Evidence   Dalton's theory of the atom was tested in the second half of the nineteenth century. In 1870, the English scientist William Crookes did experiments with a glass tube that had almost all the air removed from it. The glass tube had two pieces of metal called electrodes sealed inside. The electrodes were connected to a battery by wires.

Figure 2 Even though the laboratories of the time were simple compared to those of today, incredible discoveries were made during the eighteenth century.

Figure 3 Dalton pictured the atom as a hard sphere that was the same throughout.
Describe *Dalton's theory of the atom.*

Make a Model

Early Atom Have each student construct a three-dimensional model of the atom as it was first defined by Greek philosophers. Students can use materials such as clay, paper, aluminum foil, Velcro, toothpicks, and wire. As they progress through this section, have students modify their models to reflect each new scientific understanding of the structure of the atom. L2 ELL IS **Kinesthetic**

Use an Analogy

Newspaper Picture To help students understand the concept that matter is made from atoms, have them observe a picture in a newspaper. Then have them take a closer look using a hand lens or microscope. Point out that from a distance we see a picture, but when we get close we can see the dots that make the picture. Atoms in matter are like the ink dots in a newspaper picture. L1 ELL IS **Visual-Spatial**

Activity

Elements Have students locate the periodic table at the back of their book. Explain to students that the table includes all known elements. Have them read the names of the elements and discuss elements with which they are familiar. Explain that all things are made from these elements. L1 ELL IS **Linguistic**

Caption Answer

Figure 3 Dalton's atomic theory held that atoms were homogeneous, and could not be divided into further particles.

Differentiated Instruction

Learning Disabled Assist these students in completing the activity using a skill sequence—model one skill at a time and have students perform the skill immediately after it is observed. Copy the data table for students and distribute. Model Step 2, and then have students perform Step 2. Continue to model each step and write students' responses to questions on the board. L1

Teacher FYI

Ratios Dalton based his theory of the atom on experiments which showed that the weight ratio of elements in a given compound was always the same. Although his measurements were poor and the values he assigned elements were incorrect, most of his conclusions were correct.

Caption Answer
Figure 4 a stream of particles

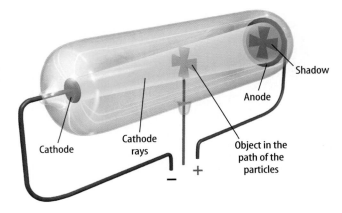

Shadow

Anode

Cathode rays

Object in the path of the particles

Cathode

Figure 4 Crookes used a glass tube containing only a small amount of gas. When the glass tube was connected to a battery, something flowed from the negative electrode (cathode) to the positive electrode (anode).
Explain *if this unknown thing was light or a stream of particles.*

A Strange Shadow An electrode is a piece of metal that can conduct electricity. One electrode, called the anode, has a positive charge. The other, called the cathode, has a negative charge. In the tube that Crookes used, the metal cathode was a disk at one end of the tube. In the center of the tube was an object shaped like a cross, as you can see in **Figure 4.** When the battery was connected, the glass tube suddenly lit up with a greenish-colored glow. A shadow of the object appeared at the opposite end of the tube—the anode. The shadow showed Crookes that something was traveling in a straight line from the cathode to the anode, similar to the beam of a flashlight. The cross-shaped object was getting in the way of the beam and blocking it, just like when a road crew uses a stencil to block paint from certain places on the road when they are marking lanes and arrows. You can see this in **Figure 5.**

Figure 5 Paint passing by a stencil is an example of what happened with Crookes' tube, the cathode ray, and the cross.

Cathode Rays Crookes hypothesized that the green glow in the tube was caused by rays, or streams of particles. These rays were called cathode rays because they were produced at the cathode. Crookes' tube is known as a cathode-ray tube, or CRT. **Figure 6** shows a CRT. They were used for TV and computer display screens for many years now.

What are cathode rays?

Discovering Charged Particles

The news of Crookes' experiments excited the scientific community of the time. But many scientists were not convinced that the cathode rays were streams of particles. Was the greenish glow light, or was it a stream of charged particles? In 1897, J.J. Thomson, an English physicist, tried to clear up the confusion. He placed a magnet beside the tube from Crookes' experiments. In **Figure 7,** you can see that the beam is bent in the direction of the magnet. Light cannot be bent by a magnet, so the beam couldn't be light. Therefore, Thomson concluded that the beam must be made up of charged particles of matter that came from the cathode.

The Electron Thomson then repeated the CRT experiment using different metals for the cathode and different gases in the tube. He found that the same charged particles were produced no matter what elements were used for the cathode or the gas in the tube. Thomson concluded that cathode rays are negatively charged particles of matter. How did Thomson know the particles were negatively charged? He knew that opposite charges attract each other. He observed that these particles were attracted to the positively charged anode, so he reasoned that the particles must be negatively charged.

These negatively charged particles are now called **electrons.** Thomson also inferred that electrons are a part of every kind of atom because they are produced by every kind of cathode material. Perhaps the biggest surprise that came from Thomson's experiments was the evidence that particles smaller than the atom do exist.

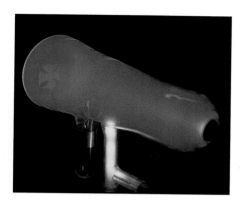

Figure 6 The cathode-ray tube got its name because the particles start at the cathode and travel to the anode. At one time, a CRT was in every TV and computer monitor.

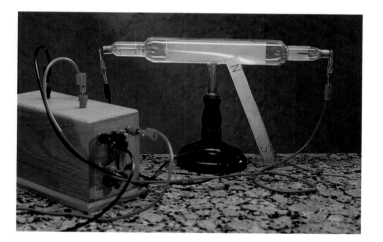

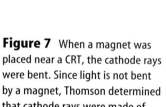

Figure 7 When a magnet was placed near a CRT, the cathode rays were bent. Since light is not bent by a magnet, Thomson determined that cathode rays were made of charged particles.

Visual Learning

Reading Check

Answer Thomson's model had electrons spread evenly among the positive charge.

Caption Answer

Figure 8 Thomson knew from his cathode-ray tube experiments that atoms contain negatively-charged electrons. As atoms are neutral in charge, he inferred the existence of a positively-charged particle to balance the overall atomic charge.

Teacher FYI

Alpha Particle Angles Rutherford began studying the scattering of alpha particles in 1906. He continued his experiments in 1907 and 1908 with the help of Hans Wilhelm Geiger. All of the experiments done during these three years looked for small scattering angles, and what they found confirmed Thomson's description of the atom. It wasn't until 1909 when a graduate student of Rutherford's detected alpha particles that had been deflected by large angles. This was the experiment that led to the new understanding of the atom.

Figure 8 Modeling clay with ball bearings mixed through is another way to picture the J.J. Thomson atom. The clay contains all the positive charge of the atom. The ball bearings, which represent the negatively charged electrons, are mixed evenly in the clay.
Explain *why Thomson included positive particles in his atomic model.*

Thomson's Atomic Model Some of the questions posed by scientists were answered in light of Thomson's experiments. However, the answers inspired new questions. If atoms contain one or more negatively charged particles, then all matter, which is made of atoms, should be negatively charged as well. But all matter isn't negatively charged. Could it be that atoms also contain some positive charge? The negatively charged electrons and the unknown positive charge would then neutralize each other in the atom. Thomson came to this conclusion and included positive charge in his model of the atom.

Using his new findings, Thomson revised Dalton's model of the atom. Instead of a solid ball that was the same throughout, Thomson pictured a sphere of positive charge. The negatively charged electrons were spread evenly among the positive charge. This is modeled by the ball of clay shown in **Figure 8.** The positive charge of the clay is equal to the negative charge of the electrons. Therefore, the atom is neutral. It was later discovered that not all atoms are neutral. The number of electrons within an element can vary. If there is more positive charge than negative electrons, the atom has an overall positive charge. If there are more negative electrons than positive charge, the atom has an overall negative charge.

Reading Check
What particle did Thomson's model have scattered through it?

Rutherford's Experiments

A model is not accepted in the scientific community until it has been tested and the tests support previous observations. In 1906, Ernest Rutherford and his coworkers began an experiment to find out if Thomson's model of the atom was correct. They wanted to see what would happen when they fired fast-moving, positively charged bits of matter, called alpha particles, at a thin film of a metal such as gold. Alpha particles, which come from unstable atoms, are positively charged, and so they are repelled by particles of matter which also have a positive charge.

Figure 9 shows how the experiment was set up. A source of alpha particles was aimed at a thin sheet of gold foil that was only 400 nm thick. The foil was surrounded by a fluorescent (floo REH sunt) screen that gave a flash of light each time it was hit by a charged particle.

Differentiated Instruction

Learning Disabled Students will find it easier to deal with this abstract material if you use physical models of atoms or drawings as often as possible while you are discussing the parts of the atom. To help students organize the facts in this chapter, make flash cards for each section and help them add facts to their cards. L1 IS **Linguistic**

Expected Results Rutherford was certain he knew what the results of this experiment would be. His prediction was that most of the speeding alpha particles would pass right through the foil and hit the screen on the other side, just like a bullet fired through a pane of glass. Rutherford reasoned that the thin, gold film did not contain enough matter to stop the speeding alpha particle or change its path. Also, there wasn't enough charge in any one place in Thomson's model to repel the alpha particle strongly. He thought that the positive charge in the gold atoms might cause a few minor changes in the path of the alpha particles. However, he assumed that this would only occur a few times.

That was a reasonable hypothesis because in Thomson's model, the positive charge is essentially neutralized by nearby electrons. Rutherford was so sure of what the results would be that he turned the work over to a graduate student.

The Model Fails Rutherford was shocked when his student rushed in to tell him that some alpha particles were veering off at large angles. You can see this in **Figure 9.** Rutherford expressed his amazement by saying, "It was about as believable as if you had fired a 15-inch shell at a piece of tissue paper, and it came back and hit you." How could such an event be explained? The positively charged alpha particles were moving with such high speed that it would take a large positive charge to cause them to bounce back. The uniform mix of mass and charges in Thomson's model of the atom did not allow for this kind of result.

Figure 9 In Rutherford's experiment, alpha particles bombarded the gold foil. Most particles passed right through the foil or veered slightly from a straight path, but some particles bounced right back. The path of a particle is shown by a flash of light when it hits the fluorescent screen.

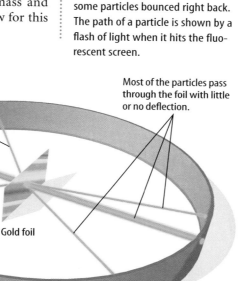

Source of positively charged particles

A few of the particles ricochet back toward the source.

Positively charged particle beam

Most of the particles pass through the foil with little or no deflection.

Gold foil

Detector screen

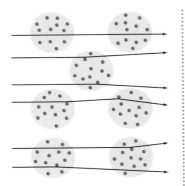

• Proton ⟶ Path of alpha particle

Figure 10 Rutherford thought that if the atom could be described by Thomson's model, as shown above, then only minor bends in the paths of the particles would have occurred.

Figure 11 The nuclear model was new and helped explain experimental results.

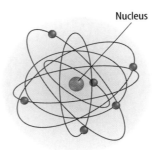

Nucleus

Rutherford's model included the dense center of positive charge known as the nucleus.

A Model with a Nucleus

Now Rutherford and his team had to come up with an explanation for these unexpected results. They might have drawn diagrams like those in **Figure 10,** which uses Thomson's model and shows what Rutherford expected. Now and then, an alpha particle might be affected slightly by a positive charge in the atom and turn a bit off course. However, large changes in direction were not expected.

The Proton The actual results did not fit this model, so Rutherford proposed a new one, shown in **Figure 11.** He hypothesized that almost all the mass of the atom and all of its positive charge are crammed into an incredibly small region of space at the center of the atom called the nucleus. Eventually, his prediction was proved true. In 1920 scientists identified the positive charges in the nucleus as protons. A **proton** is a positively charged particle present in the nucleus of all atoms. The rest of each atom is empty space occupied by the atom's almost-massless electrons.

✔ Reading Check *How did Rutherford describe his new model?*

Figure 12 shows how Rutherford's new model of the atom fits the experimental data. Most alpha particles could move through the foil with little or no interference because of the empty space that makes up most of the atom. However, if an alpha particle made a direct hit on the nucleus of a gold atom, which has 79 protons, the alpha particle would be strongly repelled and bounce back.

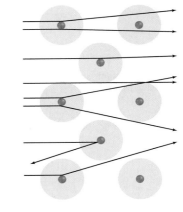

● Nucleus
⟶ Path of alpha particle

Figure 12 This nucleus that contained most of the mass of the atom caused the deflections that were observed in his experiment.

The Neutron Rutherford's nuclear model was applauded as other scientists reviewed the results of the experiments. However, some data didn't fit. Once again, more questions arose and the scientific process continued. For instance, an atom's electrons have almost no mass. According to Rutherford's model, the only other particle in the atom was the proton. That meant that the mass of an atom should have been approximately equal to the mass of its protons. However, it wasn't. The mass of most atoms is at least twice as great as the mass of its protons. That left scientists with a dilemma and raised a new question. Where does the extra mass come from if only protons and electrons make up the atom?

It was proposed that another particle must be in the nucleus to account for the extra mass. The particle, which was later called the **neutron** (NEW trahn), would have the same mass as a proton and be electrically neutral. Proving the existence of neutrons was difficult though, because a neutron has no charge. Therefore, the neutron doesn't respond to magnets or cause fluorescent screens to light up. It took another 20 years before scientists were able to show by more modern experiments that atoms contain neutrons.

✓ Reading Check *What particles are in the nucleus of the nuclear atom?*

The model of the atom was revised again to include the newly discovered neutrons in the nucleus. The nuclear atom, shown in **Figure 13,** has a tiny nucleus tightly packed with positively charged protons and neutral neutrons. Negatively charged electrons occupy the space surrounding the nucleus. The number of electrons in a neutral atom equals the number of protons in the atom.

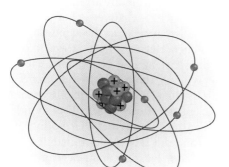

Figure 13 This atom of carbon, atomic number 6, has six protons and six neutrons in its nucleus.
Identify *how many electrons are in the "empty" space surrounding the nucleus.*

Mini LAB

Modeling the Nuclear Atom

Procedure
1. On a sheet of **paper,** draw a circle with a diameter equal to the width of the paper.
2. **Small dots of paper in two colors** will represent protons and neutrons. Using a dab of **glue** on each paper dot, make a model of the nucleus of the oxygen atom in the center of your circle. Oxygen has eight protons and eight neutrons.

Analysis
1. What particle is missing from your model of the oxygen atom?
2. How many of that missing particle should there be, and where should they be placed?

Try at Home

Mini LAB

Purpose Students will make a model of Rutherford's atom.
L2 IS **Visual-Spatial**

Materials unlined paper, dots of colored paper, glue

Teaching Strategy Demonstrate Step 2 with an element other than oxygen. Emphasize the idea that these models do *not* represent the relative sizes of the nucleus and the atoms. In reality, the nucleus and the electrons are much smaller than the atom. The diameter of the atom is 100,000 times larger than the diameter of the nucleus.

Analysis
1. the electron
2. Eight electrons; they should be placed in the circle surrounding the nucleus.

Assessment

Content Have each student make a model of a nucleus for a different element. Use the models to reinforce the concept of atomic number and its relationship to the number of protons and electrons in an atom. Use **Performance Assessment in the Science Classroom,** p. 123.

Try at Home

✓ Reading Check

Answer protons and neutrons

Caption Answer
Figure 13 six

Teacher FYI

Neutral Radiation In 1932, Iréne and Frédéric Joliot-Curie found that when they bombarded beryllium with alpha particles, neutral radiation was emitted. James Chadwick proposed that the radiation was a stream of neutrons, particles having the same mass as the proton but no charge.

✓ Active Reading

Reflective Journal Have students write reflective journals about this activity. Have them record their thoughts under headings such as *What I Did, What I Learned, Questions I Have, Surprises I Had,* and *Overall Response.* Ask volunteers to share their reflections with the class. L2

Physics In 1926, Austrian physicist Erwin Schrödinger developed the wave particle theory that treated the hydrogen atom's electron as a wave. In 1927, the German nuclear physicist Werner Heisenberg developed what is known as the Uncertainty Principle. The Uncertainty Principle states that it is impossible to locate a subatomic particle. The Schrödinger equation limits an electron's energy level to certain values.

Inquiry Lab

An Analogy for Isotopes

Purpose Students will gain a tactile understanding of isotopes.

Possible Materials two sizes of nuts, bolts, and/or small objects; scales, small containers

Estimated Time one class session

Teaching Strategies

• In each container, put a group of similar objects of two different sizes. For example, a group might consist of eighteen 1/2" nuts and two 5/8" nuts.

• Ask students to figure out what the isotopic mass of the element "nut" would be. If they need guidance, you can share the method below.

• Method: Have students weigh each of the two sizes of objects and record the mass. Then, multiply the mass of the smaller object by the number of smaller objects, add it to the mass of the larger object times the number of larger objects, and divide by the total number of objects.

• Have students develop their own analogy for isotopes. They may use the same model here, and bring in a group of objects to be similarly weighed and calculated, or they may come up with a model of their own.

For additional inquiry activities, see *Science Inquiry Labs*.

Figure 14 If this Ferris wheel in London, with a diameter of 132 m, were the outer edge of the atom, the nucleus would be about the size of a single letter *o* on this page.

**INTEGRATE
Physics**

Physicists In the 1920s, physicists began to think that electrons—like light—have a wave/particle nature. This is called quantum theory. Research which two scientists introduced this theory. In your Science Journal, infer how thoughts about atoms changed.

Size and Scale Drawings of the nuclear atom such as the one in **Figure 13** don't give an accurate representation of the extreme smallness of the nucleus compared to the rest of the atom. For example, if the nucleus were the size of a table-tennis ball, the atom would have a diameter of more than 2.4 km. Another way to compare the size of a nucleus with the size of the atom is shown in **Figure 14.** Perhaps now you can see better why in Rutherford's experiment, most of the alpha particles went directly through the gold foil without any interference from the gold atoms. Plenty of empty space allows the alpha particles an open pathway.

Further Developments

Even into the twentieth century, physicists were working on a theory to explain how electrons are arranged in an atom. It was natural to think that the negatively charged electrons are attracted to the positive nucleus in the same way the Moon is attracted to Earth. Then, electrons would travel in orbits around the nucleus. A physicist named Niels Bohr even calculated exactly what energy levels those orbits would represent for the hydrogen atom. His calculations explained experimental data found by other scientists. However, scientists soon learned that electrons are in constant, unpredictable motion and can't be described easily by an orbit. They determined that it was impossible to know the precise location of an electron at any particular moment. Their work inspired even more research and brainstorming among scientists around the world.

16 ◆ **K CHAPTER 1** Atoms, Elements, Compounds, and Mixtures

Differentiated Instruction

Challenge Physicists have identified particles called quarks that combine to form protons and neutrons. Have students find out about quarks and make oral reports of their findings to the class. It takes three quarks to make up a proton or a neutron. A proton is made up of two up quarks and one down quark. An up quark has a charge of $+2/3$, and a down quark has a charge of $-1/3$, so the total charge on a proton is $+2/3 + 2/3 - 1/3 = +1$. A neutron is made up of one up quark and two down quarks. Its charge is $+2/3 - 1/3 - 1/3 = 0$. [L3] [LS] **Logical-Mathematical**

Electrons as Waves Physicists began to wrestle with explaining the unpredictable nature of electrons. Surely the experimental results they were seeing and the behavior of electrons could somehow be explained with new theories and models. The unconventional solution was to understand electrons not as particles, but as waves. This led to further mathematical models and equations that brought much of the experimental data together.

The Electron Cloud Model The new model of the atom allows for the somewhat unpredictable wave nature of electrons by defining a region where the electron is most likely to be found. Electrons travel in a region surrounding the nucleus, which is called the **electron cloud.** The current model for the electron cloud is shown in **Figure 15.** The electrons are more likely to be close to the nucleus rather than farther away because they are attracted to the positive charges of the protons. Notice the fuzzy outline of the cloud. Because the electrons could be anywhere, the cloud has no firm boundary. Interestingly, within the electron cloud, the electron in a hydrogen atom probably is found in the region Bohr calculated.

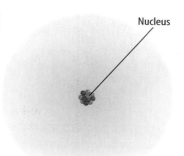
Nucleus

Figure 15 The electrons are more likely to be close to the nucleus rather than farther away, but they could be anywhere. **Explain** *why the electrons woud be closer to the nucleus.*

Check for Understanding
Visual-Spatial Have students draw diagrams of Thomson's and Rutherford's experiments. Have them label all parts and write brief descriptions of how the experiments worked. L2 IS

Reteach
Atom Diagrams On the board, make diagrams of Dalton's, Thomson's, and Rutherford's models of the atom. Ask students what evidence there was to support Dalton's model. What experiments led to the abandonment of Dalton's model and the adoption of Thomson's? Do the same for Thomson's and Rutherford's models. L2 IS **Visual-Spatial**

✓ Assessment

Content Have each student make a concept map using the terms *element, electron, proton, neutron,* and *electron cloud.* Use **Performance Assessment in the Science Classroom,** p. 161.

Caption Answer
Figure 15 Electrons have a negative charge and are therefore attracted to the positively-charged nucleus.

---

section 1 review

Summary

Models of the Atom

- Some early philosophers believed all matter was made of small particles.
- John Dalton proposed that all matter is made of atoms that were hard spheres.
- J. J. Thomson showed that the particles in a CRT were negatively charged particles, later called electrons. These were smaller than an atom. He proposed the atom as a sphere of positive charge with electrons spread evenly among the charge.
- In his experiments, Rutherford showed that positive charge existed in a small region of the atom which he called the nucleus. The positive charge was called a proton.
- In order to explain the mass of an atom, the neutron was proposed, an uncharged particle the same mass as a proton and in the nucleus.
- Electrons are now believed to move about the nucleus in an electron cloud.

Self Check

1. **Explain** how the nuclear atom differs from the uniform sphere model of the atom.
2. **Determine** how many electrons a neutral atom with 49 protons has.
3. **Describe** what cathode rays are and how they were discovered.
4. **Think Critically** In Rutherford's experiment, why wouldn't the electrons in the atoms of the gold foil affect the paths of the alpha particles.
5. **Concept Map** Design and complete a concept map using all the words in the vocabulary list for this section. Add any other terms or words that will help create a complete diagram of the section and the concepts in contains.

Applying Math

6. **Solve One-Step Equations** The mass of an electron is 9.11×10^{-28} g. The mass of a proton is 1,836 times more than that of the electron. Calculate the mass of the proton in grams and convert that mass into kilograms.

---

section 1 review

1. In the nuclear atom, all the positive charge and almost all the mass are in a tiny nucleus with the electrons occupying the space around it. In the uniform sphere, the atom was the same throughout.
2. 49 electrons

3. Cathode rays are streams of electrons, first discovered by running electricity through an anode and a cathode in a vacuum.
4. Electrons are too small to affect the path of a fast-moving alpha particle.

5. Answers should include all section vocabulary words and should specify how they relate to one another.
6. $(9.11 \times 10^{-28}$ g$) \times 1,836 = 1.67 \times 10^{-24}$ g $= 1.67 \times 10^{-27}$ kg

The Simplest Matter

as you read

What You'll Learn

- **Describe** the relationship between elements and the periodic table.
- **Explain** the meaning of atomic mass and atomic number.
- **Identify** what makes an isotope.
- **Contrast** metals, metalloids, and nonmetals.

Why It's Important

Everything on Earth is made of the elements that are listed on the periodic table.

Review Vocabulary
mass: a measure of the amount of matter

New Vocabulary
- atomic number
- isotope
- mass number
- atomic mass
- metals
- nonmetals
- metalloids

The Elements

Have you watched television today? TV sets are common, yet each one is a complex system. The outer case is made mostly of plastic, and the screen is made of glass. Many of the parts that conduct electricity are metals or combinations of metals. Other parts in the interior of the set contain materials that barely conduct electricity. All of the different materials have one thing in common. They are made up of even simpler materials. In fact, if you had the proper equipment, you could separate the plastics, glass, and metals into these simpler materials.

One Kind of Atom Eventually, though, you would separate the materials into groups of atoms. At that point, you would have a collection of elements. Recall that an element is matter made of only one kind of atom. At least 115 elements are known and about 90 of them occur naturally on Earth. These elements make up gases in the air, minerals in rocks, and liquids such as water. Examples of naturally occurring elements include the oxygen and nitrogen in the air you breathe and the metals gold, silver, aluminum, and iron. The other elements are known as synthetic elements. These elements have been made in nuclear reactions by scientists with machines called particle accelerators, like the one shown in **Figure 16.** Some synthetic elements have important uses in medical testing and are found in smoke detectors and heart pacemaker batteries.

Figure 16 The Tevatron has a circumference of 6.3 km—a distance that allows particles to accelerate to high speeds. These high-speed collisions can create synthetic elements.

18 ◆ K CHAPTER 1 Atoms, Elements, Compounds, and Mixtures

Figure 17 When you look for information in the library, a system of organization called the Dewey Decimal Classification System helps you find a book quickly and efficiently.

The Periodic Table

Suppose you go to a library, like the one shown in **Figure 17,** to look up information for a school assignment. How would you find the information? You could look randomly on shelves as you walk up and down rows of books, but the chances of finding your book would be slim. Not only that, you also would probably become frustrated in the process. To avoid such haphazard searching, some libraries use the Dewey Decimal Classification System to categorize and organize their volumes and to help you find books quickly and efficiently.

Charting the Elements When scientists need to look up information about an element or select one to use in the laboratory, they need to be quick and efficient, too. Chemists have created a chart called the periodic table of the elements to help them organize and display the elements. **Figure 18** shows how scientists changed their model of the periodic table over time.

On the inside back cover of this book, you will find a modern version of the periodic table. Each element is represented by a chemical symbol that contains one to three letters. The symbols are a form of chemical shorthand that chemists use to save time and space—on the periodic table as well as in written formulas. The symbols are an important part of an international system that is understood by scientists everywhere.

The elements are organized on the periodic table by their properties. There are rows and columns that represent relationships between the elements. The rows in the table are called periods. The elements in a row have the same number of energy levels. The columns are called groups. The elements in each group have similar properties related to their structure. They also tend to form similar bonds.

Dewey Decimal Classification System	
000	Computers, information, and general reference
100	Philosophy and psychology
200	Religion
300	Social sciences
400	Language
500	Science
600	Technology
700	Arts and recreation
800	Literature
900	Philosophy and psychology

INTEGRATE History

Dewey Decimal System Melvil Dewey is the man responsible for organizing our knowledge and libraries. His working in the Amherst College library led him to propose a method of classifying books. The Dewey Decimal System divides books into ten categories. Since 1876, this classification system has helped us locate information easily.

Teacher FYI

Ancient Elements Elements such as gold, silver, tin, copper, lead, and mercury have been known since ancient times. As more elements were discovered, people began to recognize patterns in their properties. Later, scientists used the patterns to classify the elements.

Differentiated Instruction

English-Language Learners Ask the students to pick 8–10 elements and share with the class both the English and their native pronunciation of each element. L2 **ELL**

---

2 Teach

IDENTIFYING Misconceptions

Learning About Elements Students may think that all aspects of the structure and building blocks of matter are completely known. Point out that much remains to be learned about atoms and elements.

INTEGRATE History

Dewey Decimal System Have students investigate how the number system works. Each of the classes have ten divisions. These divisions are divided again and again. The more divisions there are, the more specific the topic becomes.

Activity

Familiar Elements Have students skim the periodic table for symbols and names of familiar elements. Have them share with the class the things that these elements are found in. Example: Ca—calcium is found in milk and other food products. L2 **IS** **Interpersonal**

Use an Analogy

Calendar Point out to students the ways in which a month's calendar is like the periodic table. The days are arranged from left to right, as periods of elements are arranged from left to right. Days with the same name are arranged in columns, as groups of elements are arranged in the table.

Visualizing the Periodic Table

Have students examine the pictures and read the captions. Then ask the following questions.

Why do you think the periodic table is so useful to scientists? It helps them organize and understand the chemical properties of the elements.

One big difference between Mendeleev's table and the one used today is that his table lacks the column containing the elements helium through radon. Why do you think this is? None of the elements in that column had been discovered in Mendeleev's time. This is because they are not common and they don't readily undergo chemical reactions.

Activity

Element Groups Divide the class into eighteen groups. Assign each group a different group of elements from the periodic table. Have them research the similarities and differences among the elements in their respective groups and make posters illustrating the properties of these elements. L2
COOP LEARN ▮▮ **Interpersonal**

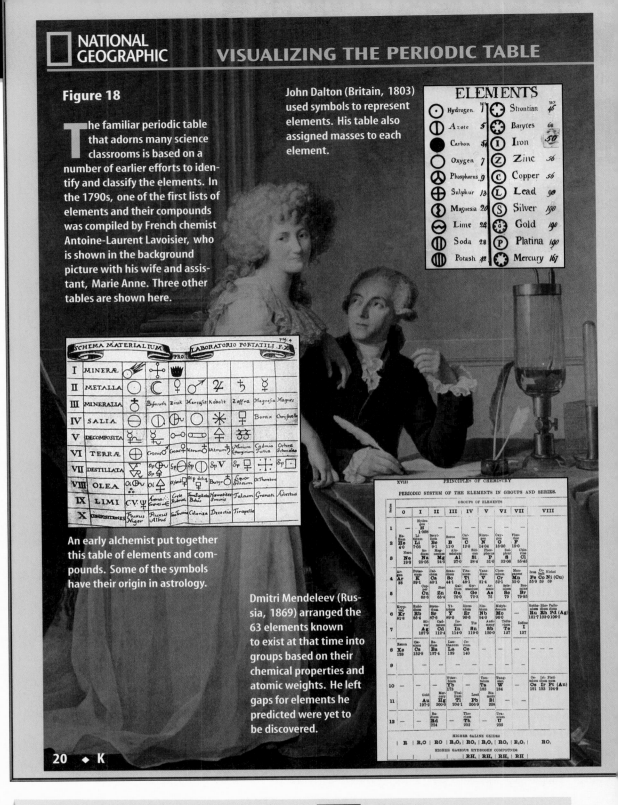

NATIONAL GEOGRAPHIC — VISUALIZING THE PERIODIC TABLE

Figure 18

The familiar periodic table that adorns many science classrooms is based on a number of earlier efforts to identify and classify the elements. In the 1790s, one of the first lists of elements and their compounds was compiled by French chemist Antoine-Laurent Lavoisier, who is shown in the background picture with his wife and assistant, Marie Anne. Three other tables are shown here.

John Dalton (Britain, 1803) used symbols to represent elements. His table also assigned masses to each element.

An early alchemist put together this table of elements and compounds. Some of the symbols have their origin in astrology.

Dmitri Mendeleev (Russia, 1869) arranged the 63 elements known to exist at that time into groups based on their chemical properties and atomic weights. He left gaps for elements he predicted were yet to be discovered.

20 ◆ K

Teacher FYI

Mendeleev's Periodic Table Dmitri Mendeleev's periodic table was based on the patterns in the properties and masses of elements. He made a card for each of the elements known at the time. Each card contained the element's symbol, atomic mass, and its chemical and physical properties. By arranging the cards in order of increasing atomic mass, and by grouping elements of similar properties, he created a "periodic table" that showed vertical, horizontal, and diagonal relationships. Mendeleev left gaps in his table for yet unknown elements, and was able to predict the properties of some of them in detail.

Identifying Characteristics

Each element is different and has unique properties. These differences can be described in part by looking at the relationships between the atomic particles in each element. The periodic table contains numbers that describe these relationships.

Number of Protons and Neutrons Look up the element chlorine on the periodic table found on the inside back cover of your book. Cl is the symbol for chlorine, as shown in **Figure 19,** but what are the two numbers? The top number is the element's **atomic number.** It tells you the number of protons in the nucleus of each atom of that element. Every atom of chlorine, for example, has 17 protons in its nucleus.

☑ Reading Check *What are the atomic numbers for Cs, Ne, Pb, and U?*

Isotopes Although the number of protons changes from element to element, every atom of the same element has the same number of protons. However, the number of neutrons can vary even for one element. For example, some chlorine atoms have 18 neutrons in their nucleus while others have 20. These two types of chlorine atoms are chlorine-35 and chlorine-37. They are called **isotopes** (I suh tohps), which are atoms of the same element that have different numbers of neutrons.

You can tell someone exactly which isotope you are referring to by using its mass number. An atom's **mass number** is the number of protons plus the number of neutrons it contains. The numbers 35 and 37, which were used to refer to chlorine, are mass numbers. Hydrogen has three isotopes with mass numbers of 1, 2, and 3. They are shown in **Figure 20.** Each hydrogen atom always has one proton, but in each isotope the number of neutrons is different.

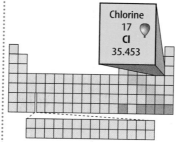

Figure 19 The periodic table block for chlorine shows its symbol, atomic number, and atomic mass.
Determine *if chlorine atoms are more or less massive than carbon atoms.*

Figure 20 Three isotopes of hydrogen are known to exist. They have zero, one, and two neutrons in addition to their one proton. Protium, with only the one proton, is the most abundant isotope.

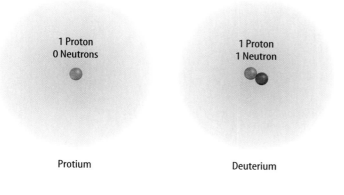

Protium

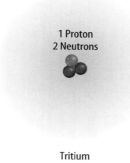

Deuterium

Tritium

⚙ LAB DEMONSTRATION

Purpose To demonstrate the structures of isotopes of nitrogen
Materials gumdrops or small foam balls in three different colors, toothpicks
Procedure Make a model of nitrogen-14 using 7 protons, 7 neutrons, and 7 electrons. Place the neutrons and protons

close together and the electrons away from the nucleus. Now make a model of nitrogen-15 using 7 protons, 8 neutrons, and 7 electrons.
Expected Outcome Students should observe differences in the models of the two nitrogen atoms.

Assessment

What is used to determine the mass of an element? the total number of neutrons and protons What is the mass number of the first nitrogen isotope? 14 What is the mass number of the second nitrogen isotope? 15

Circle Graph Showing Abundance of Chlorine Isotopes
Average atomic mass = 35.45 u

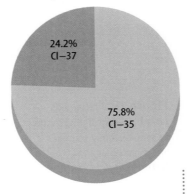

24.2% Cl−37

75.8% Cl−35

Figure 21 If you have 1,000 atoms of chlorine, about 758 will be chlorine-35 and have a mass of 34.97 u each. About 242 will be chlorine-37 and have a mass of 36.97 u each. The total mass of the 1,000 atoms is 35,454 u, so the average mass of one chlorine atom is about 35.45 u.

Atomic Mass The **atomic mass** is the weighted average mass of the isotopes of an element. The atomic mass is the number found below the element symbol in **Figure 19.** The unit that scientists use for atomic mass is called the atomic mass unit, which is given the symbol u. It is defined as 1/12 the mass of a carbon-12 atom.

The calculation of atomic mass takes into account the different isotopes of the element. Chlorine's atomic mass of 35.45 u could be confusing because there aren't any chlorine atoms that have that exact mass. About 76 percent of chlorine atoms are chlorine-35 and about 24 percent are chlorine-37, as shown in **Figure 21.** The weighted average mass of all chlorine atoms is 35.45 u.

Classification of Elements

Elements fall into three general categories—metals, metalloids (ME tuh loydz), and nonmetals. The elements in each category have similar properties.

Metals generally have a shiny or metallic luster and are good conductors of heat and electricity. All metals, except mercury, are solids at room temperature. Metals are malleable (MAL yuh bul), which means they can be bent and pounded into various shapes. The beautiful form of the shell-shaped basin in **Figure 22** is a result of this characteristic. Metals are also ductile, which means they can be drawn into wires without breaking. If you look at the periodic table, you can see that most of the elements are metals.

Figure 22 The artisan is chasing, or chiseling, the malleable metal into the desired form.

Other Elements **Nonmetals** are elements that are usually dull in appearance. Most are poor conductors of heat and electricity. Many are gases at room temperature, and bromine is a liquid. The solid nonmetals are generally brittle, meaning they cannot change shape easily without breaking. The nonmetals are essential to the chemicals of life. More than 97 percent of your body is made up of various nonmetals, as shown in **Figure 23.** You can see that, except for hydrogen, the nonmetals are found on the right side of the periodic table.

Metalloids are elements that have characteristics of metals and nonmetals. On the periodic table, metalloids are found between the metals and nonmetals. All metalloids are solids at room temperature. Some metalloids are shiny and many are conductors, but they are not as good at conducting heat and electricity as metals are. Some metalloids, such as silicon, are used to make the electronic circuits in computers, televisions, and other electronic devices.

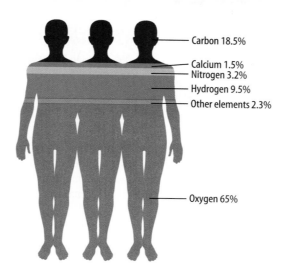

Carbon 18.5%
Calcium 1.5%
Nitrogen 3.2%
Hydrogen 9.5%
Other elements 2.3%
Oxygen 65%

Figure 23 You are made up of mostly nonmetals.

---

section **2** review

Summary

The Elements

- An element is matter made of only one type of atom.
- Some elements occur naturally on Earth. Synthetic elements are made in nuclear reactions in particle accelerators.

The Periodic Table

- The periodic table arranges and displays all known elements in an orderly way.
- Each element has been given a chemical symbol that is used on a periodic table.

Identifying Characteristics

- Each element has a unique number of protons, called the atomic mass number.
- Isotopes of elements are important when determining the atomic mass of an element.

Classification of Elements

- Elements are divided into three categories based on certain properties: metal, metalloids, and nonmetals.

Self Check

1. **Explain** some of the uses of metals based on their properties.
2. **Describe** the difference between atomic number and atomic mass.
3. **Define** the term *isotope*. Explain how two isotopes of an element are different.
4. **Think Critically** Describe how to find the atomic number for the element oxygen. Explain what this information tells you about oxygen.
5. **Interpret Data** Look up the atomic mass of the element boron in the periodic table inside the back cover of this book. The naturally occurring isotopes of boron are boron-10 and boron-11. Explain which of the two isotopes is more abundant?

Applying Math

6. **Solve One-Step Equations** An atom of niobium has a mass number of 93. How many neutrons are in the nucleus of this atom? An atom of phosphorus has 15 protons and 15 neutrons in the nucleus. What is the mass number of this isotope?

DAILY INTERVENTION

Check for Understanding

Linguistic Have small groups of students classify objects in the classroom as being made mostly of metals or nonmetals and record their answers on chart. Then have students write a statement that can be used to determine if their chart is correct.

Possible Answers:

Metal	Nonmetal
File cabinet	Carpet
Chair legs	Plastic seat

Metal items are shiny, solid at room temperature, conduct heat and electricity, and can be pounded into different shapes without breaking. Nonmetals do not have these properties. L2

Reteach

Periodic Table Write all the information found on the periodic table for one element on the board. Have students tell what each symbol or number represents. L2 IS **Visual-Spatial**

✓ Assessment

Oral Name elements on the periodic table at random. Ask students to tell whether each selected element is a metal, a metalloid, or a nonmetal. L2

---

section **2** review

1. good conductors of heat and electricity (electrical circuits and cookware), malleable (formed into tools), ductile (drawn into wires)
2. atomic number: the number of protons in the nucleus of each atom of an element; mass number: the sum of an atom's protons and neutrons

3. Isotopes are atoms of the same element that contain different numbers of neutrons.
4. Locate oxygen on the periodic table. Oxygen's atomic number (8) is the whole number in the element's box (above the element symbol) and means that every atom of oxygen

contains eight protons in its nucleus.
5. Boron-11; boron's atomic mass is 10.811, which is closer to 11 than 10.
6. $93 - 41 = 52$ n; 15 p $+ 15$ n $= 30$

Elements and the Periodic Table

The periodic table organizes the elements, but what do they look like? What are they used for? In this lab, you'll examine some elements and share your findings with your classmates.

▶ Real-World Questions

What are some of the characteristics and purposes of the chemical elements?

Goals
- **Classify** the chemical elements.
- **Organize** the elements into the groups and periods of the periodic table.

Materials
colored markers	large bulletin board
large index cards	8 1/2-in × 14-in paper
Merck Index	thumbtacks
encyclopedia	*pushpins*
other reference materials	*Alternate materials*

Safety Precautions
WARNING: *Use care when handling sharp objects.*

▶ Procedure

1. **Select** the assigned number of elements from the list provided by your teacher.
2. **Design** an index card for each of your selected elements. On each card, mark the element's atomic number in the upper left-hand corner and write its symbol and name in the upper right-hand corner.
3. **Research** each of the elements and write several sentences on the card about its appearance, its other properties, and its uses.
4. **Classify** each element as a metal, a metalloid, or a nonmetal based upon its properties.

5. **Write** the appropriate classification on each of your cards using the colored marker chosen by your teacher.
6. **Work** with your classmates to make a large periodic table. Use thumbtacks to attach your cards to a bulletin board in their proper positions on the periodic table.
7. **Draw** your own periodic table. Place the elements' symbols and atomic numbers in the proper locations on your table.

▶ Conclude and Apply

1. **Interpret** the class data and classify the elements into the categories metal, metalloid, and nonmetal. Highlight each category in a different color on your periodic table.
2. **Predict** the properties of a yet-undiscovered element located directly under francium on the periodic table.

𝒞ommunicating Your Data

Compare and contrast your table with that of a friend. Discuss the differences. **For more help, refer to the** Science Skill Handbook.

𝒞ommunicating Your Data

Have students use a database program to display their results. The printed database can be shared with a small group or with the class.

Compounds and Mixtures

Substances

Scientists classify matter in several ways that depend on what it is made of and how it behaves. For example, matter that has the same composition and properties throughout is called a **substance.** Elements, such as a bar of gold or a sheet of aluminum, are substances. When different elements combine, other substances are formed.

Compounds The elements hydrogen and oxygen exist as separate, colorless gases. However, these two elements can combine, as shown in **Figure 24,** to form the compound water, which is different from the elements that make it up. A **compound** is a substance whose smallest unit is made up of atoms of more than one element bonded together.

Compounds often have properties that are different from the elements that make them up. Water is distinctly different from the elements that make it up. It is also different from another compound made from the same elements. Have you ever used hydrogen peroxide (H_2O_2) to disinfect a cut? This compound is a different combination of hydrogen and oxygen and has different properties from those of water.

Water is a nonirritating liquid that is used for bathing, drinking, cooking, and much more. In contrast, hydrogen peroxide carries warnings on its labels such as *Keep Hydrogen Peroxide Out of the Eyes.* Although it is useful in solutions for cleaning contact lenses, it is not safe for your eyes as it comes from the bottle.

Figure 24 A space shuttle is powered by the reaction between liquid hydrogen and liquid oxygen. The reaction produces a large amount of energy and the compound water. **Explain** *why a car that burns hydrogen rather than gasoline would be friendly to the environment.*

SECTION 3 Compounds and Mixtures **K ◆ 25**

as you read

What **You'll Learn**

- **Identify** the characteristics of a compound.
- **Compare and contrast** different types of mixtures.

Why **It's Important**

The food you eat, the materials you use, and all matter can be classified by compounds or mixtures.

⊘ **Review Vocabulary**
formula: shows which elements and how many atoms of each make up a compound.

New Vocabulary
- substance
- compound
- mixture

1 Motivate

INTERACTIVE CHALKBOARD
PowerPoint® Presentations

Bellringer

Section Focus Transparencies also are available on the Interactive Chalkboard CD-ROM.
L2 ELL

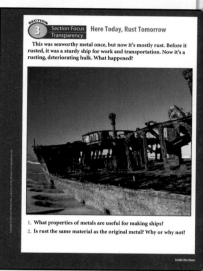

Tie to Prior Knowledge
Chemical Formulas Have students recall chemical formulas for substances such as water or salt. H_2O and $NaCl$ Show a periodic table and point out that these substances are combinations of elements from the periodic table.

Caption Answer
Figure 24 It would produce water rather than pollution.

Section 3 Resource Manager

Chapter *FAST FILE* Resources
  Transparency Activity, p. 42
  Directed Reading for Content Mastery, pp. 17, 18
  MiniLAB, p. 4
  Enrichment, p. 28

  Reinforcement, p. 25
  Lab Worksheet, pp. 7–8
Mathematics Skill Activities, p. 19
Cultural Diversity, p. 65

Visual Learning

Figure 25 Ask students to write the formula for hydrogen peroxide. H_2O_2 Point out how much easier it is to write the chemical formulas than it is to write out all of the words. L2

Mini LAB

Purpose Students observe and compare the properties of three compounds. L2 ELL LS
Visual-Spatial

Materials sugar, rubbing alcohol, salad oil, beakers (3), hot water, spoon

Teaching Strategy Warn students to use hot, not boiling, water.

Analysis

1. Rubbing alcohol is colorless; salad oil is golden, and sugar is white in color. Sugar is a solid; rubbing alcohol and the oil are liquids. Salad oil is more viscous than alcohol. Rubbing alcohol has a strong chemical smell; the other substances have little or no odor. Sugar and rubbing alcohol dissolve easily in water, but salad oil floats on the water.
2. The number of atoms of each element and their arrangement account for the different properties.

Assessment

Content Have students draw pictures showing how the substances mixed with water in the MiniLAB. Use **Performance Assessment in the Science Classroom,** p. 127.

✔ Reading Check

Answer C_3H_8

Figure 25 The elements hydrogen and oxygen can form two compounds—water and hydrogen peroxide. Note the differences in their structure.

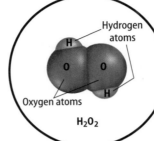

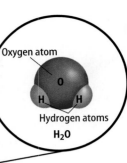

Oxygen atom

O

H   H

Hydrogen atoms

H_2O

Hydrogen atoms

O   O

H

Oxygen atoms

H_2O_2

Mini LAB

Comparing Compounds

Procedure

1. Collect the following substances—**granular sugar, rubbing alcohol, and salad oil.**
2. Observe the color, appearance, and state of each substance. Note the thickness or texture of each substance.
3. Stir a spoonful of each substance into separate **beakers of hot water** and observe.

Analysis

1. Compare the different properties of the substances.
2. The formulas of the three substances are made of only carbon, hydrogen, and oxygen. Infer how they can have different properties.

Compounds Have Formulas What's the difference between water and hydrogen peroxide? H_2O is the chemical formula for water, and H_2O_2 is the formula for hydrogen peroxide. The formula tells you which elements make up a compound as well as how many atoms of each element are present. Look at **Figure 25.** The subscript number written below and to the right of each element's symbol tells you how many atoms of that element exist in one unit of that compound. For example, hydrogen peroxide has two atoms of hydrogen and two atoms of oxygen. Water is made up of two atoms of hydrogen and one atom of oxygen.

Carbon dioxide, CO_2, is another common compound. Carbon dioxide is made up of one atom of carbon and two atoms of oxygen. Carbon and oxygen also can form the compound carbon monoxide, CO, which is a gas that is poisonous to all warm-blooded animals. As you can see, no subscript is used when only one atom of an element is present. A given compound always is made of the same elements in the same proportion. For example, water always has two hydrogen atoms for every oxygen atom, no matter what the source of the water is. No matter what quantity of the compound you have, the formula of the compound always remains the same. If you have 12 atoms of hydrogen and six atoms of oxygen, the compound is still written H_2O, but you have six molecules of H_2O ($6 H_2O$), not $H_{12}O_6$. The formula of a compound communicates its identity and makeup to any scientist in the world.

✔ Reading Check *Propane has three carbon and eight hydrogen atoms. What is its chemical formula?*

Cultural Diversity

Ocher Ocher is an iron oxide (Fe_2O_3) that occurs naturally. It is formed by the weathering of rocks. It was used historically to produce rock paintings and continues to be used for artwork today. It comes in a variety of colors, depending on the percentage of iron oxide present. Hematite ore is one source of ocher that can be ground to produce a bright red color. Ocher has also been found in burial plots of several different cultures. Have students find out the other colors produced by iron oxide ores. Other colors produced include black (magnetite), brown to dark yellow (limonite), and brown (siderite and pyrite). L2

Mixtures

When two or more substances (elements or compounds) come together but don't combine to make a new substance, a **mixture** results. Unlike compounds, the proportions of the substances in a mixture can be changed without changing the identity of the mixture. For example, if you put some sand into a bucket of water, you have a mixture of sand and water. If you add more sand or more water, it's still a mixture of sand and water. Its identity has not changed. Air is another mixture. Air is a mixture of nitrogen, oxygen, and other gases, which can vary at different times and places. Whatever the proportion of gases, it is still air. Even your blood is a mixture that can be separated, as shown in **Figure 26** by a machine called a centrifuge.

 **Reading Check** *How do the proportions of a mixture relate to its identity?*

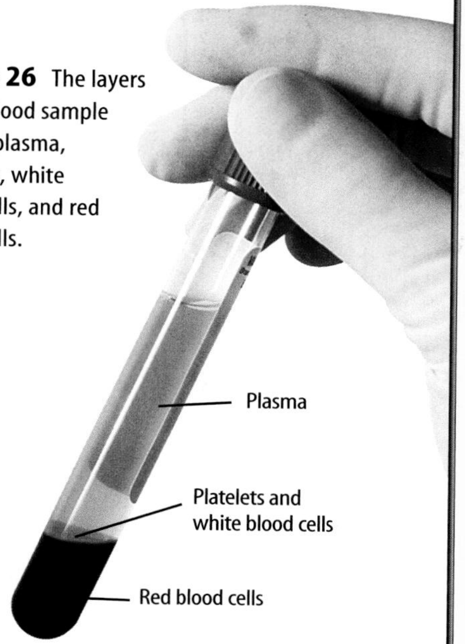

Figure 26 The layers in this blood sample include plasma, platelets, white blood cells, and red blood cells.

— Plasma

— Platelets and white blood cells

— Red blood cells

Applying Science

What's the best way to desalt ocean water?

You can't drink ocean water because it contains salt and other suspended materials. Or can you? In many areas of the world where drinking water is in short supply, methods for getting the salt out of salt water are being used to meet the demand for fresh water. Use your problem solving skills to find the best method to use in a particular area.

Methods for Desalting Ocean Water

Process	Amount of Water a Unit Can Desalt in a Day (m^3)	Special Needs	Number of People Needed to Operate
Distillation	1,000 to 200,000	lots of energy to boil the water	many
Electrodialysis	10 to 4,000	stable source of electricity	1 to 2 persons

Identifying the Problem

The table above compares desalting methods. In distillation, the ocean water is heated. Pure water boils off and is collected, and the salt is left behind. Electrodialysis uses electric current to pull salt particles out of water.

Solving the Problem

1. What method(s) might you use to desalt the water for a large population where energy is plentiful?
2. What method(s) would you choose to use in a single home?

Plasma Whole blood is often separated into plasma and packed cells. The plasma component contains substances that dissolve in water.

Career Have students investigate the medical field of phlebotomy, which is the science of therapeutic bloodletting. Ask them to report on the various careers which work with human blood and blood products.

Use Science Words

Word Usage Ask students to classify the following mixtures as heterogeneous or homogeneous: clear apple juice homogeneous; oil and vinegar heterogeneous. L2 LS **Linguistic**

Teacher FYI

Homogeneous Mixtures Homogeneous mixtures are defined by the sizes of the particles that make them up. A solution has particles less than 10^{-7} cm in size. A homogeneous mixture with particles between 10^{-7} and 10^{-4} cm in size is called a colloid. An emulsion is a colloid consisting of two liquids. An aerosol is a colloid in which either a solid is dispersed in a gas (smoke) or a liquid is dispersed in a gas (fog).

Quick Demo

Properties of Mixtures

Materials sugar cubes, marbles, water, transparent container

Estimated Time five minutes

Procedure Place a few marbles and several sugar cubes into a transparent container. Add enough water to make the sugar dissolve. Explain to the students that while the sugar and water have combined to form a homogeneous mixture, the marbles combine with the other materials as a heterogeneous mixture.

Figure 27 Mixtures are part of your everyday life.

Science Online

Topic: Mixtures
Visit bookk.msscience.com for Web links to information about separating mixtures.

Activity Describe how chemists separate the components of a mixture.

Your blood is a mixture made up of elements and compounds. It contains white blood cells, red blood cells, water, and a number of dissolved substances. The different parts of blood can be separated and used by doctors in different ways. The proportions of the substances in your blood change daily, but the mixture does not change its identity.

Separating Mixtures Sometimes you can use a liquid to separate a mixture of solids. For example, if you add water to a mixture of sugar and sand, only the sugar dissolves in the water. The sand then can be separated from the sugar and water by pouring the mixture through a filter. Heating the remaining solution will separate the water from the sugar.

At other times, separating a mixture of solids of different sizes might be as easy as pouring them through successively smaller sieves or filters. A mixture of marbles, pebbles, and sand could be separated in this way.

Curriculum Connection

Art Have students make collages that demonstrate the difference between a homogeneous and a heterogeneous mixture. Have them search through magazines to collect illustrations for their collages. Images could include: homogeneous—any type of solution; heterogeneous—strawberry ice cream, salad, chocolate chip cookie. L1 LS **Visual-Spatial** P

Homogeneous or Heterogeneous

Mixtures, such as the ones shown in **Figure 27,** can be classified as homogeneous or heterogeneous. *Homogeneous* means "the same throughout." You can't see the different parts in this type of mixture. In fact, you might not always know that homogeneous mixtures are mixtures because you can't tell by looking. Which mixtures in **Figure 27** are homogeneous? No matter how closely you look, you can't see the individual parts that make up air or the parts of the mixture called brass in the lamp shown. Homogeneous mixtures can be solids, liquids, or gases.

A heterogeneous mixture has larger parts that are different from each other. You can see the different parts of a heterogeneous mixture, such as sand and water. How many heterogeneous mixtures are in **Figure 27?** A pepperoni and mushroom pizza is a tasty kind of heterogeneous mixture. Other examples of this kind of mixture include tacos, vegetable soup, a toy box full of toys, or a tool box full of nuts and bolts.

INTEGRATE Earth Science

Rocks and Minerals
Scientists called geologists study rocks and minerals. A mineral is composed of a pure substance. Rocks are mixtures and can be described as being homogeneous or heterogeneous. Research to learn more about rocks and minerals and note some examples of homogeneous and heterogeneous rocks in your Science Journal.

Rocks and Minerals The term *rocks* applies to the solid materials that make up Earth's crust. These materials have no definite chemical composition. Minerals have more or less definite chemical compositions, crystal structures, and properties. Heterogeneous rocks include granite, gneiss, and conglomerate. Homogeneous rocks include obsidian, some limestones, and basalt.

DAILY INTERVENTION

Check for Understanding
Logical-Mathematical The compound hydrochloric acid can be written HCl. What elements does it contain? hydrogen and chlorine How many atoms of each element are in a molecule of hydrochloric acid? one atom of hydrogen and one atom of chlorine Hydrochloric acid reacts with sodium hydroxide to form table salt and water. The reaction can be written $HCl + NaOH = NaCl + H_2O$. What is the chemical formula for table salt? NaCl L2

Reteach
Blood Ask a medical technologist to make a class presentation explaining the different parts of the mixture known as human blood and describing how these parts can be separated by physical means. L1 IS **Auditory-Musical**

---

section 3 review

Summary

Substances
- A substance can be either an element or a compound.
- A compound contains more than one kind of element bonded together.
- A chemical formula shows which elements and how many atoms of each make up a compound.

Mixtures
- A mixture contains substances that are not chemically bonded together.
- There are many ways to separate mixtures based on their physical properties.
- Homogeneous mixtures are those that are the same throughout. These types of mixtures can be solids, liquids, or gases.
- Heterogeneous mixtures have larger parts that are different from each other.

Self Check

1. **List** three examples of compounds and three examples of mixtures. Explain your choices.
2. **Describe** a procedure that can be used to separate a liquid homogenous mixture of salt and water.
3. **Identify** the elements that make up the following compounds: H_2SO_4 and $CHCl_3$.
4. **Think Critically** Explain whether your breakfast was a compound, a homogeneous mixture, or a heterogeneous mixture.

Applying Skills

5. **Compare and contrast** compounds and mixtures based on what you have learned from this section.
6. **Use a Database** Use a computerized card catalog or database to find information about one element from the periodic table. Include information about the properties and the uses of the mixtures and/or compounds in which the element is frequently found.

Assessment

Process Have students design an experimental procedure that they could use to separate a mixture of white sand and sugar. Use **Performance Assessment in the Science Classroom,** p. 95.

---

section 3 review

1. Possible answers: Compounds— water, carbon dioxide, table salt; mixtures—air, ocean water, brass; mixtures can be separated by physical means; compounds can't.
2. Evaporation, possibly speeded up by boiling, separates them.
3. hydrogen, sulfur, and oxygen; carbon, hydrogen, and chlorine
4. Answers will vary, but most breakfasts, such as orange juice and cold cereal with milk, are heterogeneous mixtures.
5. Compounds are pure substances whose properties vary from the elements they are made from. Mixtures are made from different parts and can be physically separated.
6. Sample answer: Carbon is found in the sun, stars, comets, and in most planets. It is also present as carbon dioxide in the atmosphere and dissolved in water. It is also a component of rocks.

BENCH TESTED

▶ **Real-World Question**

Purpose Students test for certain compounds and decide which are present in a mystery mixture. L2 ELL IS **Kinesthetic**

Process Skills form a hypothesis, communicate, observe and infer, recognize cause and effect, separate and control variables, interpret data

Time Required 45 minutes

▶ **Procedure**

Materials Compounds used are a cornstarch, powdered sugar, and baking soda. Combine any two of these compounds to make the mystery mixture. Prepare iodine test solution by adding 7 g of iodine and 5 g of potassium iodide to 5 mL of water, then diluting to 100 mL with denatured alcohol.

Safety Precautions Students must wear goggles and aprons. Remind students that when heating a test tube, the opening of the tube should never be pointed at themselves or others.

Iodine is poisonous and will stain clothing.

Remind students that test tubes should not be touched while they are hot.

Mystery Mixtures

Goals
- **Test** for the presence of certain compounds.
- **Decide** which of these compounds are present in an unknown mixture.

Materials
test tubes (4)
cornstarch
powdered sugar
baking soda
mystery mixture
small scoops (3)
dropper bottles (2)
iodine solution
white vinegar
hot plate
250-mL beaker
water (125 mL)
test-tube holder
small pie pan

Safety Precautions

WARNING: *Use caution when handling hot objects. Substances could stain or burn clothing. Be sure to point the test tube away from your face and your classmates while heating.*

▶ **Real-World Question**

You will encounter many compounds that look alike. For example, a laboratory stockroom is filled with white powders. It is important to know what each is. In a kitchen, cornstarch, baking powder, and powdered sugar are compounds that look alike. To avoid mistaking one for another, you can learn how to identify them. Different compounds can be identified

by using chemical tests. For example, some compounds react with certain liquids to produce gases. Other combinations produce distinctive colors. Some compounds have high melting points. Others have low melting points. How can the compounds in an unknown mixture be identified by experimentation?

Alternative Inquiry Lab

Further Exploration To extend this Lab into an Inquiry Lab, allow students to explore related topics. Possibilities include ores in mining, petroleum refinement, separating mixtures by solubility, fractional distillation, and crystallization. Students could develop research reports or lab demonstrations of their own, or you could prepare a simple separation by solubility lab by mixing a soluble and insoluble ionic salt. A fractional distillation is also easy to set up, if you have the equipment, by mixing two molecular liquids of very different boiling points. Have students check their experiment plans with you before conducting the research.

Using Scientific Methods

◉ Procedure

1. Copy the data table into your Science Journal. Record your results carefully for each of the following steps.

2. Again place a small scoopful of cornstarch on the pie pan. Do the same for the sugar and baking soda maintaining separate piles. Add a drop of vinegar to each. Wash and dry the pan after you record your observations.

3. Again place a small scoopful of cornstarch, sugar, and baking soda on the pie pan. Add a drop of iodine solution to each one.

4. Place a small scoopful of each compound in a separate test tube. Hold the test tube with the test-tube holder and with an oven mitt. Gently heat the test tube in a beaker of boiling water on a hot plate.

5. Follow steps 2 through 4 to test your mystery mixture for each compound.

Identifying Presence of Compounds			
Substance to Be Tested	Fizzes with Vinegar	Turns Blue with Iodine	Melts When Heated
Cornstarch	No	Yes	No
Sugar	No	No	Yes
Baking soda	Yes	No	No
Mystery mix	Answers will vary.		

◉ Analyze Your Data

1. **Identify** from your data table which compound(s) you have.

2. **Describe** how you decided which substances were in your unknown mixture.

◉ Conclude and Apply

1. **Explain** how you would be able to tell if all three compounds were not in your mystery substance.

2. **Draw a Conclusion** What would you conclude if you tested baking powder from your kitchen and found that it fizzed with vinegar, turned blue with iodine, and did not melt when heated?

Make a different data table to display your results in a new way. **For more help, refer to the** Science Skill Handbook.

✔ Assessment

Performance After students have determined the two compounds that were present in the mystery mixture, have them determine other possible two-material combinations and explain how the combinations would react when tested. Use **Performance Assessment in the Science Classroom**, p. 93. [L2]

Students could add illustrations, chemical symbols, or color to their data tables. [L2]

◉ Procedure

Teaching Strategies

- In Steps 2 and 3, have students use only sufficient amounts of solids to produce satisfactory test results. Test your scoops to determine how much to use.

- In Step 4, have students use only enough solid to fill the bottom rounded portion of the test tubes.

Expected Outcome Cornstarch will react with iodine to make a blue color. Sugar will melt when heated. Baking soda will fizz in the presence of vinegar.

◉ Analyze Your Data

1. Answers will vary depending on the two compounds used for the mystery mixture.

2. Students should include data they gather.

Error Analysis If students let their experiments run together or do not clean their equipment, they may get erroneous results. Have students compare their results with the results of other groups. If results differ, discuss errors that could have caused the difference.

◉ Conclude and Apply

1. If the mixture did not turn blue in the presence of iodine, did not melt when heated, and did not fizz with vinegar, you would know that all three compounds were absent from the mystery mixture.

2. It contained baking soda and cornstarch.

TIME

Content Background

Kashyapa lived during the 6th century B.C., and was the first to use the word *parmanu*, derived from the two Sanskrit words *param*, meaning "beyond," and *anu*, meaning "atom." Among other things, he proposed that two different classes of parmanu could combine to form what he called *dwinuka*, or binary molecules, of new substances.

The Chinese term for the five material agents of matter, as they called the five elements, is *wu hsing*. The Chinese believed that these material agents took part in cyclical patterns of change that resulted in the opposites, yin and yang.

Discussion

Atomic Theory Do you think Kashyapa's ideas were known to Democritus when he developed his theory of the atom? Why or why not? Accept all well-supported answers. Point out to students on a globe the relative locations of Greece and India and remind them of the means of transportation and communication available at the time these two men lived. L2

Historical Significance

Both the Chinese and Indian philosophies have roots in ancient history. Encourage students to choose a current scientific theory and use a variety of research tools to trace the idea back to its earliest origins. Make sure students understand that a theory may have origins in ideas that arose independently in several different cultures. This activity will help students become aware that our modern theories have had a long history of development.

TIME > SCIENCE AND HISTORY

SCIENCE CAN CHANGE THE COURSE OF HISTORY!

Ancient Views of Matter

Two cultures observed the world around them differently

Water

Air & ether

The world's earliest scientists were people who were curious about the world around them and who tried to develop explanations for the things they observed. This type of observation and inquiry flourished in ancient cultures such as those found in India and China. Read on to see how the ancient Indians and Chinese defined matter.

Indian Ideas

To Indians living about 3,000 years ago, the world was made up of five elements: fire, air, earth, water, and ether, which they thought of as an unseen substance that filled the heavens. Building upon this concept, the early Indian philosopher Kashyapa (kah SHI ah pah) proposed that the five elements could be broken down into smaller units called parmanu (par MAH new). Parmanu were similar to atoms in that they were too small to be seen but still retained the properties of the original element. Kashyapa also believed that each type of parmanu had unique physical and chemical properties.

Metal

Parmanu of earth elements, for instance, were heavier than parmanu of air elements. The different properties of the parmanu determined the characteristics of a substance. Kashyapa's ideas about matter are similar to those of the Greek philosopher Democritus, who lived centuries after Kashyapa.

Chinese Ideas

The ancient Chinese also broke matter down into five elements: fire, wood, metal, earth, and water. Unlike the early Indians, however, the Chinese believed that the elements constantly changed form. For example, wood can be burned and thus changes to fire. Fire eventually dies down and becomes ashes, or earth. Earth gives forth metals from the ground. Dew or water collects on these metals, and the water then nurtures plants that grow into trees, or wood.

This cycle of constant change was explained in the fourth century B.C. by the philosopher Tsou Yen. Yen, who is known as the founder of Chinese scientific thought, wrote that all changes that took place in nature were linked to changes in the five elements.

Fire

Earth

Research Write a brief paragraph that compares and contrasts the ancient Indian and Chinese views of matter. How are they different? Similar? Which is closer to the modern view of matter? Explain.

Science Online

For more information, visit
bookk.msscience.com/time

Research As a prewriting activity have students discuss similarities and differences in the two theories presented here. Select a volunteer to record suggestions. Have students use this information in their paragraphs and reexamine it as they compare the historical perspectives with the modern view of matter, which they studied earlier in the chapter.

Resources for Teachers and Students

Chemistry in Action, by Nina Morgan, Oxford University Press, 1995

The Periodic Kingdom, by P.W. Atkins, Basic Books, 1995

Reviewing Main Ideas

Section 1 Models of the Atom

1. Matter is made up of very small particles called atoms.

2. Atoms are made of smaller parts called protons, neutrons, and electrons.

3. Many models of atoms have been created as scientists try to discover and define the atom's internal structure. Today's model has a central nucleus with the protons and neutrons, and an electron cloud surrounding it that contains the electrons.

Section 2 The Simplest Matter

1. Elements are the basic building blocks of matter.

2. An element's atomic number tells how many protons its atoms contain, and its atomic mass tells the average atomic mass of its atoms.

3. Isotopes are two or more atoms of the same element that have different numbers of neutrons.

Section 3 Compounds and Mixtures

1. Compounds are substances that are produced when elements combine. Compounds contain specific proportions of the elements that make them up.

2. Mixtures are combinations of compounds and elements that have not formed new substances. Their proportions can change.

Visualizing Main Ideas

Copy and complete this concept map.

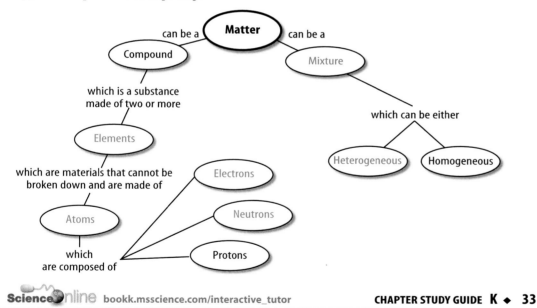

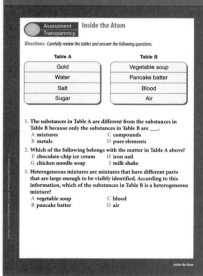

Science Online bookk.msscience.com/interactive_tutor

CHAPTER STUDY GUIDE K ◆ 33

Reviewing Main Ideas

Summary statements can be used by students to review the major concepts of the chapter.

Visualizing Main Ideas

See student page.

Visit bookk.msscience.com
/self_check_quiz
/interactive_tutor
/vocabulary_puzzlemaker
/chapter_review
/standardized_test

Assessment Transparency

For additional assessment questions, use the *Assessment Transparency* located in the transparency book.

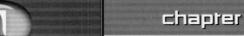

Using Vocabulary

1. proton
2. compound
3. atomic number
4. neutrons
5. metals

Checking Concepts

6. D	11. B
7. C	12. C
8. B	13. C
9. C	14. B
10. D	15. D

Thinking Critically

16. one sulfur and two oxygen atoms
17. Nitrogen; the number of protons determines the identity of an atom.
18. The element loses its characteristics and a new substance is formed.
19. Cobalt-60 and cobalt-59 both have 27 protons in their nuclei, so they are both cobalt, but they have different numbers of neutrons so they have different mass numbers.
20. Rutherford's gold foil experiment showed that the atom contains a small, dense, positively charged structure, which he called the nucleus.
21. He would get the same results because his conclusion about a dense nucleus surrounded by almost empty space was true for all atoms, including aluminum atoms.

Using Vocabulary

atomic mass p. 22	metal p. 22
atomic number p. 21	metalloid p. 23
compound p. 25	mixture p. 27
electron p. 11	neutron p. 15
electron cloud p.17	nonmetal p. 23
element p. 9	proton p. 14
isotope p. 21	substance p. 25
mass number p. 21	

Fill in the blanks with the correct word.

1. The _____ is the particle in the nucleus of the atom that carries a positive charge and is counted to identify the atomic number.

2. The new substance formed when elements combine chemically is a(n) _____.

3. The _____ is equal to the number of protons in an atom.

4. The particles in the atom that account for most of the mass of the atom are protons and _____.

5. Elements that are shiny, malleable, ductile, good conductors of heat and electricity, and make up most of the periodic table are _____.

Checking Concepts

Choose the word or phrase that best answers the question.

6. What is a solution an example of?
   A) element
   B) heterogeneous mixture
   C) compound
   D) homogeneous mixture

7. The nucleus of one atom contains 12 protons and 12 neutrons, while the nucleus of another atom contains 12 protons and 16 neutrons. What are the atoms?
   A) chromium atoms
   B) two different elements
   C) two isotopes of an element
   D) negatively charged

8. What is a compound?
   A) a mixture of chemicals and elements
   B) a combination of two or more elements
   C) anything that has mass and occupies space
   D) the building block of matter

9. What does the atom consist of?
   A) electrons, protons, and alpha particles
   B) neutrons and protons
   C) electrons, protons, and neutrons
   D) elements, protons, and electrons

10. In an atom, where is an electron located?
    A) in the nucleus with the proton
    B) on the periodic table of the elements
    C) with the neutron
    D) in a cloudlike formation surrounding the nucleus

11. How is mass number defined?
    A) the negative charge in an atom
    B) the number of protons and neutrons in an atom
    C) the mass of the nucleus
    D) an atom's protons

12. What are two atoms that have the same number of protons called?
    A) metals   C) isotopes
    B) nonmetals   D) metalloids

13. Which is a heterogeneous mixture?
    A) air   C) a salad
    B) brass   D) apple juice

 Science Online bookk.msscience.com/vocabulary_puzzlemaker

Use the Exam*View*® Pro Testmaker CD-ROM to:
• create multiple versions of tests
• create modified tests with one mouse click for inclusion students
• edit existing questions and add your own questions
• build tests aligned with state standards using built-in State Curriculum Tags
• change English tests to Spanish with one mouse click and vice versa

Use the illustration below to answer questions 14 and 15.

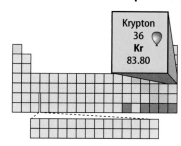

Krypton
36
Kr
83.80

14. According to the figure above, krypton has
  A) an atomic number of 84.
  B) an atomic number of 36.
  C) an atomic mass of 36.
  D) an atomic mass of 72.

15. From the figure, the element krypton is
  A) a solid.   **C)** a mixture.
  B) a liquid.   **D)** a gas.

Thinking Critically

16. Analyze Information A chemical formula is written to indicate the makeup of a compound. What is the ratio of sulfur atoms to oxygen atoms in SO_2?

17. Determine which element contains seven electrons and seven protons. What element is this atom?

18. Describe what happens to an element when it becomes part of a compound.

19. Explain how cobalt-60 and cobalt-59 can be the same element but have different mass numbers.

20. Analyze Information What did Rutherford's gold foil experiment tell scientists about atomic structure?

21. Predict Suppose Rutherford had bombarded aluminum foil with alpha particles instead of the gold foil he used in his experiment. What observations do you predict Rutherford would have made? Explain your prediction.

22. Compare and Contrast Aluminum is close to carbon on the periodic table. List the properties that make aluminum a metal and carbon a nonmetal.

23. Draw Conclusions You are shown a liquid that looks the same throughout. You're told that it contains more than one type of element and that the proportion of each varies throughout the liquid. Is this an element, a compound, or a mixture.

Use the illustration below to answer question 24.

24. Interpret Scientific Illustrations Look at the two carbon atoms above. Explain whether or not the atoms are isotopes.

25. Explain how the atomic mass of krypton was determined.

Performance Activities

26. Newspaper Article Research the source, composition, and properties of asbestos. Why was it used in the past? Why is it a health hazard now? What is being done about it? Write a newspaper article to share your findings.

Applying Math

27. Calculate Krypton has six naturally occurring isotopes with atomic masses of 78, 80, 82, 83, 84, and 86. Make a table of the number of protons, electrons, and neutrons in each isotope.

22. Aluminum is shiny, solid at room temperature, and malleable. Carbon is dull and is neither malleable nor ductile.

23. mixture

24. They are isotopes as they have the same number of protons but different numbers of neutrons. The atom on the left has 6 protons and 6 neutrons whereas the one on the right has 6 protons and 8 neutrons.

25. The atomic mass of krypton was determined by using the weighed average of the isotopes of krypton.

Performance Activities

26. Asbestos is a hydrous magnesium silicate—$Mg_3Si_2O_5(OH)_4$. It occurs as fibers, which are spun into yarn or mixed with other materials to form cement board or other fireproof building materials. When asbestos fibers become airborne, they can be inhaled. The sharp fibers penetrate the lungs, and can cause a form of lung cancer. Use **Performance Assessment in the Science Classroom,** p. 141.

Applying Math

National Math Standards
5

27.

u	Protons	Neutrons	Electrons
78	36	42	36
80	36	44	36
82	36	46	36
83	36	47	36
84	36	48	36
86	36	50	36

☑ Assessment   Resources

Reproducible Masters
Chapter Fast File Resources
  Chapter Review, pp. 33–34
  Chapter Tests, pp. 35–38
  Assessment Transparency Activity, p. 45
Glencoe Science Web site
  Chapter Review Test
  Standardized Test Practice

Glencoe Technology
  🖋 Assessment Transparency
  🌐 ExamView® Pro Testmaker
  📼 MindJogger Videoquiz
  🌐 Interactive Chalkboard

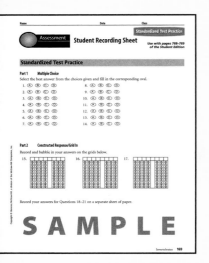

Answer Sheet A practice answer sheet can be found at bookk.msscience.com/answer_sheet.

S A M P L E

Part 1 Multiple Choice

1. A   5. C
2. D   6. D
3. A   7. C
4. B   8. B

Part 2 Short Response

9. They are more likely to be close to the nucleus because they are attracted to the positive charges of the protons.

10. 90

11. nonmetals

12. $6H_2O_2$

13. electrons

14. mixture

15. substance

Record your answers on the answer sheet provided by your teacher or on a sheet of paper.

1. Which of the following has the smallest size?
   A. electron   C. proton
   B. nucleus   D. neutron

Use the illustration below to answer questions 2 and 3.

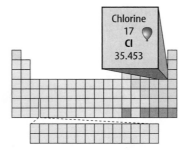

Chlorine
17
Cl
35.453

2. The periodic table block shown above lists properties of the element chlorine. What does the number 35.453 mean?
   A. the number of neutrons and in every chlorine atom
   B. the number of neutrons and protons in every chlorine atom
   C. the average number of neutrons in a chlorine atom
   D. the average number of neutrons and protons in a chlorine atom

3. According to the periodic table block, how many electrons does an uncharged atom of chlorine have?
   A. 17   C. 35
   B. 18   D. 36

Test-Taking Tip

Answer Each Question Never leave any constructed-response answer blank. Answer each question as best as you can. You can receive partial credit for partially correct answers.

4. Which of the following scientists envisioned the atom having a hard sphere that is the same throughout?
   A. Crookes   C. Thomson
   B. Dalton   D. Rutherford

Use the illustration below to answer questions 5 and 6.

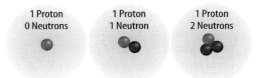

| 1 Proton
0 Neutrons | 1 Proton
1 Neutron | 1 Proton
2 Neutrons |

5. Which of the following correctly identifies the three atoms shown in the illustration above?
   A. hydrogen, lithium, sodium
   B. hydrogen, helium, lithium
   C. hydrogen, hydrogen, hydrogen
   D. hydrogen, helium, helium

6. What is the mass number for each of the atoms shown in the illustration?
   A. 0, 1, 2   C. 1, 2, 2
   B. 1, 1, 1   D. 1, 2, 3

7. Which of the following are found close to the right side of the periodic table?
   A. metals   C. nonmetals
   B. lanthanides   D. metalloids

8. Which of the following best describes a neutron?
   A. positive charge; about the same mass as an electron
   B. no charge; about the same mass as a proton
   C. negative charge; about the same mass as a proton
   D. no charge; about the same mass as an electron

Part 3 Open Ended

16. Dalton thought that matter was made up of atoms, and the atoms could not be divided into smaller pieces. He proposed that all atoms of an element are exactly alike. Different elements, he said, are made of different kinds of atoms. Dalton pictured the atom as a hard sphere that was the same throughout.

17. A source of alpha particles was aimed at a thin sheet of gold foil. The foil was surrounded by a fluorescent screen that emitted a flash of light each time it was hit by a charged particle. Rutherford thought most of the alpha particles would pass straight through the foil. He didn't think the foil contained enough matter to stop or deflect the particles. He thought the positive charge in the gold might cause a few small changes in the paths of the alpha particles.

18. The particles that reflected at large angles showed that Thomson's model of the atom was incorrect. The positive charge in the gold was

Part 2 | Short Response/Grid In

Record your answers on the answer sheet provided by your teacher or on a sheet of paper.

9. Are electrons more likely to be close to the nucleus or far away from the nucleus? Why?

10. How many naturally occurring elements are listed on the periodic table?

11. Is the human body made of mostly metal, nonmetals, or metalloids?

12. A molecule of hydrogen peroxide is composed of two atoms of hydrogen and two atoms of oxygen. What is the formula for six molecules of hydrogen peroxide?

13. What is the present-day name for cathode rays?

Use the illustration below to answer questions 14 and 15.

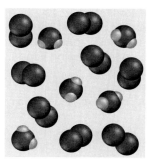

Enclosed sample of air

14. The illustration above shows atoms of an element and molecules of a compound that are combined without making a new compound. What term describes a combination such as this?

15. If the illustration showed only the element or only the compound, what term would describe it?

Part 3 | Open Ended

Record your answers on a sheet of paper.

16. Describe Dalton's ideas about the composition of matter, including the relationship between atoms and elements.

Use the illustration below to answer questions 17 and 18.

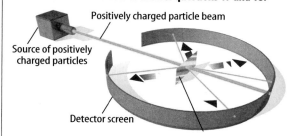

Positively charged particle beam

Source of positively charged particles

Detector screen

17. The illustration above shows Rutherford's gold foil experiment. Describe the setup shown. What result did Rutherford expect from his experiment?

18. What is the significance of the particles that reflected back from the gold foil? How did Rutherford explain his results?

19. Describe three possible methods for separating mixtures. Give an example for each method.

20. Describe the difference between a homogeneous and a heterogeneous mixture.

21. What are the rows and columns on the periodic table called? How are elements in the rows similar, and how are elements in the columns similar?

22. Describe how Thomson was able to show that cathode rays were streams of particles, not light.

23. Describe how the mass numbers, or atomic masses, listed on the periodic table for the elements are calculated.

columns are called groups. Elements in each group have similar properties related to their structure. They also tend to form similar bonds.

22. Thomson repeated Crookes' experiment so that cathode rays moved from the negative electrode to the positive electrode. However, when Thomson placed a magnet near the cathode ray tube, the cathode rays were deflected. Since light is not deflected by a magnet, Thomson deduced that the rays must be made of charged particles.

23. Each atom's mass number is the number of protons plus the number of neutrons. Each isotope has an integer mass number. The mass number for the element is calculated by calculating a weighted average. The weighted average is the sum of each isotope's mass number multiplied by the percentage of isotopes of that kind.

Rubrics

For more help evaluating open-ended assessment questions, see the rubric on p. 10T.

reflecting the particles. Rutherford proposed that almost all the mass of the atom and all of its positive charge was contained in a small nucleus of the atom.

19. A mixture of sugar and sand can be separated by adding water. The sugar dissolves in the water and the sand can then be filtered out. A mixture of water and sugar can be separated by heating the water so that the water evaporates, leaving the sugar. Mixtures of different-sized solids, such as pebbles and sand, can be separated by filtering out the larger solid.

20. Mixtures are a combination of two or more substances that come together but don't combine to make a new substance. In a homogeneous mixture, the substances are combined thoroughly so that the mixture is the same throughout. A heterogeneous mixture has larger parts that are different from each other. You can see the different parts of a heterogeneous mixture.

21. The rows are called periods. Elements in a row have the same number of energy levels. The

Section/Objectives	Standards		Labs/Features
Chapter Opener	National	State/Local	**Launch Lab:** Experiment with a Freezing Liquid, p. 39 **Foldables,** p. 39
	See pp. 9T–10T for a Key to Standards.		
Section 1 Matter ⏱ 2 sessions 🧱 1 block 1. **Recognize** that matter is made of particles in constant motion. 2. **Relate** the three states of matter to the arrangement of particles within them.	National Content Standards: UCP.1, UCP.2, UCP.3, UCP.5, A.1, A.2, B.1, B.2, B.3		**Integrate History,** p. 42 **Science Online,** p. 43
Section 2 Changes of State ⏱ 3 sessions 🧱 1.5 blocks 3. **Define and compare** thermal energy and temperature. 4. **Relate** changes in thermal energy to changes of state. 5. **Explain** how atoms have greater energy of motion when temperature increases.	National Content Standards: UCP.1, UCP.2, UCP.3, UCP.5, A.1, A.2, B.1, B.2, B.3		**Integrate Physics,** p. 46 **Visualizing States of Matter,** p. 48 **Science Online,** p. 49 **Applying Science:** How can ice save oranges?, p. 49 **MiniLAB:** Observing Vaporization, p. 50 **Science Online,** p. 51 **Lab:** The Water Cycle, p. 53
Section 3 Behavior of Fluids ⏱ 3 sessions 🧱 1.5 blocks 6. **Explain** why some things float but others sink. 7. **Describe** how pressure is transmitted through fluids.	National Content Standards: UCP.1, UCP.2, UCP.3, UCP.5, A.1, A.2, B.1, B.2, E.1, E.2, F.5, G.3		**MiniLAB:** Predicting a Waterfall, p. 57 **Applying Math:** Calculating Density, p. 59 **Science Online,** p. 61 **Lab:** Design Your Own Ship, p. 62 **Oops! Accidents in Science:** The Incredible Stretching Goo, p. 64

Lab Materials	Reproducible Resources	Section Assessment	Technology
Launch Lab: test tubes, laboratory-grade stearic acid, test-tube rack, thermometer	**Chapter *FAST FILE* Resources** Foldables Worksheet, p. 15 Directed Reading Overview, p. 17 Note-taking Worksheets, pp. 31–32	**GLENCOE'S ASSESSMENT ADVANTAGE**	Teacher**Works** includes: • Interactive Teacher Edition • Lesson Planner with calendar • Access to all program blacklines • Correlations to standards • Web links
Need materials? Contact Science Kit at 1-800-828-7777 or www.sciencekit.com on the Internet.	**Chapter *FAST FILE* Resources** Transparency Activity, p. 42 Enrichment, p. 28 Reinforcement, p. 25 Directed Reading, p. 18 Transparency Activity, pp. 45–46 Lab Activity, pp. 9–10	**Portfolio** Assessment, p. 44 **Performance** Applying Skills, p. 44 **Content** Section Review, p. 44	Section Focus Transparency Teaching Transparency Virtual Labs CD-ROM Guided Reading Audio Program Interactive Chalkboard CD-ROM
MiniLAB: dropper, rubbing alcohol **Lab:** hot plate, ice cubes, thermometer or electronic temperature probe, wall clock or watch with second hand, stirring rod, 250-mL beaker	**Chapter *FAST FILE* Resources** Transparency Activity, p. 43 MiniLAB, p. 3 Enrichment, p. 29 Reinforcement, p. 26 Directed Reading, p. 19 Lab Worksheet, pp. 5–6 Lab Activity, pp. 11–13 **Physical Science Critical Thinking/Problem Solving,** p. 10 **Reading and Writing Skill Activities,** p. 17	**Portfolio** Activity, p. 47 **Performance** Applying Science, p. 49 MiniLAB, p. 50 Applying Math, p. 52 **Content** Section Review, p. 52	Section Focus Transparency Virtual Labs CD-ROM Guided Reading Audio Program Interactive Chalkboard CD-ROM
MiniLAB: plastic cup, water, index card **Lab:** balance, 2 small plastic cups, graduated cylinder, metric ruler, scissors, cupful of marbles, sink or basin	**Chapter *FAST FILE* Resources** Transparency Activity, p. 44 MiniLAB, p. 4 Enrichment, p. 30 Reinforcement, p. 27 Directed Reading, pp. 19–20 Lab Worksheet, pp. 7–8 **Mathematics Skill Activities,** p. 31	**Portfolio** Science Journal, p. 55 **Performance** MiniLAB, p. 57 Applying Math, p. 59 Applying Math, p. 61 **Content** Section Review, p. 61	Section Focus Transparency Virtual Labs CD-ROM Guided Reading Audio Program Interactive Chalkboard CD-ROM Video Lab

End of Chapter Assessment

GLENCOE'S ASSESSMENT ADVANTAGE

Blackline Masters	Technology	Professional Series
Chapter *FAST FILE* Resources Chapter Review, pp. 35–36 Chapter Tests, pp. 37–40 **Standardized Test Practice,** pp. 11–14	MindJogger Videoquiz Virtual Labs CD-ROM Exam*View*® Pro Testmaker TeacherWorks CD-ROM Interactive Chalkboard CD-ROM	**Performance Assessment in the Science Classroom (PASC)**

Transparencies

Section Focus

Section Focus Transparency 1 — Bummer

If you found a rock like one of these, what would you think? A lot of people would think they had found gold. Unfortunately, this rock is really a mineral called pyrite, or fool's gold.

1. What can you determine about pyrite from this picture?
2. How is pyrite similar to gold? How might pyrite and gold differ?

L2

Section Focus Transparency 2 — Looking forward to some ice water, are you?

Be sure not to forget about any water you put in the freezer to cool quickly. You might come back to a big ice cube.

1. What state of matter was the water in before it was put into the freezer? What happened in the freezer?
2. Compared to liquid water, how much space does solid water take up?
3. What are some examples of the effects of water expanding as it freezes?

L2

Section Focus Transparency 3 — Up or Down?

Submarines have the ability to float on top of the ocean as well as dive beneath its surface. They accomplish this by taking water into holding tanks to dive and releasing it to surface.

1. The shape of a submarine is similar to an airplane's body. Why is this so?
2. Name some metal objects that float. Name some metal objects that sink. Why might metal sometimes float and sometimes sink?
3. How are submarines and hot air balloons similar in the way they ascend and descend?

L2

This is a representation of key blackline masters available in the Teacher Classroom Resources. See Resource Manager boxes within the chapter for additional information.

Assessment

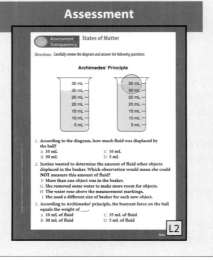

Assessment Transparency — States of Matter

Directions: Carefully review the diagram and answer the following questions.

Archimedes' Principle

1. According to the diagram, how much fluid was displaced by the ball?
   A 35 mL   C 10 mL.
   B 30 mL   D 5 mL.
2. Justine wanted to determine the amount of fluid other objects displaced in the beaker. Which observation would mean she could NOT measure this amount of fluid?
   F More than one object was in the beaker.
   G She removed some water to make more room for objects.
   H The water rose above the measurement markings.
   J She used a different size of beaker for each new object.
3. According to Archimedes' principle, the buoyant force on the ball equals the weight of ___.
   A 10 mL of fluid   C 35 mL of fluid
   B 30 mL of fluid   D 5 mL of fluid

L2

Teaching

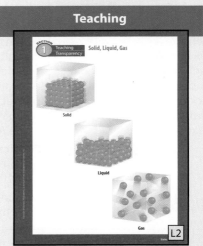

Teaching Transparency — Solid, Liquid, Gas

Solid

Liquid

Gas

L2

Key to Teaching Strategies

The following designations will help you decide which activities are appropriate for your students.

L1 — Level 1 activities should be appropriate for students with learning difficulties.

L2 — Level 2 activities should be within the ability range of all students.

L3 — Level 3 activities are designed for above-average students.

ELL — ELL activities should be within the ability range of English-Language Learners.

COOP LEARN — Cooperative Learning activities are designed for small group work.

LS — Multiple Learning Styles logos, as described on page 6T, are used throughout to indicate strategies that address different learning styles.

P — These strategies represent student products that can be placed into a best-work portfolio.

PBL — Problem-Based Learning activities apply real-world situations to learning.

Hands-on Activities

Student Text Lab Worksheet

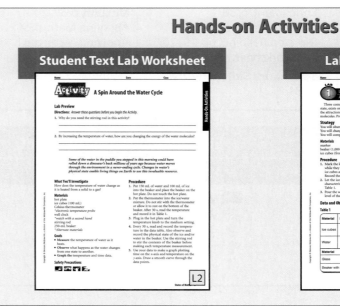

Activity — A Spin Around the Water Cycle

Lab Preview

Directions: Answer these questions before you begin the Activity.

1. Why do you need the stirring rod in this activity?

2. By increasing the temperature of water, how are you changing the energy of the water molecules?

Some of the water in the puddle you stepped in this morning could have rolled down a dinosaur's back millions of years ago because water moves through the environment in a never-ending cycle. Changes in water's physical state enable living things on Earth to use this invaluable resource.

What You'll Investigate

How does the temperature of water change as it is heated from a solid to a gas?

Materials
hot plate
ice cubes (100 mL)
Celsius thermometer
*electronic temperature probe
wall clock
*watch with a second hand
stirring rod
250-mL beaker
*Alternate materials

Goals
• Measure the temperature of water as it heats.
• Observe what happens as the water changes from one state to another.
• Graph the temperature and time data.

Safety Precautions

Procedure
1. Put 150 mL of water and 100 mL of ice into the beaker and place the beaker on the hot plate. Do not touch the hot plate.
2. Put the thermometer into the ice/water mixture. Do not stir with the thermometer or allow it to rest on the bottom of the beaker. After 30 s, read the temperature and record it in Table 1.
3. Plug in the hot plate and turn the temperature knob to the medium setting.
4. Every 30 s, read and record the temperature in the data table. Also observe and record the physical state of the ice and/or water in the beaker. Use the stirring rod to stir the contents of the beaker before making each temperature measurement.
5. Use your data to make a graph plotting time on the x-axis and temperature on the y-axis. Draw a smooth curve through the data points.

L2

Laboratory Activities

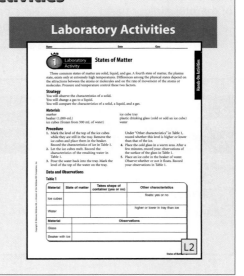

Laboratory Activity 1 — States of Matter

Three common states of matter are solid, liquid, and gas. A fourth state of matter, the plasma state, exists only at extremely high temperatures. Differences among the physical states depend on the attractions between the atoms or molecules and on the rate of movement of the atoms or molecules. Pressure and temperature control these two factors.

Strategy
You will observe the characteristics of a solid.
You will change a gas to a liquid.
You will compare the characteristics of a solid, a liquid, and a gas.

Materials
marker
beaker (1,000-mL)
ice cubes (frozen from 500 mL of water)
ice cube tray
plastic drinking glass (cold or add an ice cube)
water

Procedure
1. Mark the level of the top of the ice cubes while they are still in the tray. Remove the ice cubes and place them in the beaker. Record the characteristics of ice in Table 1.
2. Let the ice cubes melt. Record the characteristics of the resulting water in Table 1.
3. Pour the water back into the tray. Mark the level of the top of the water on the tray.

   Under "Other characteristics" in Table 1, record whether this level is higher or lower than that of the ice.
4. Place the cold glass in a warm area. After a few minutes, record your observations of the surface of the glass in Table 1.
5. Place an ice cube in the beaker of water. Observe whether or not it floats. Record your observations in Table 1.

Data and Observations

Table 1

Material	State of matter	Takes shape of container (yes or no)	Other characteristics
Ice cubes			floats: yes or no
Water			higher or lower in tray than ice

Material	Observations
Glass	
Beaker with ice	

L2

Meeting Different Ability Levels

Content Outline

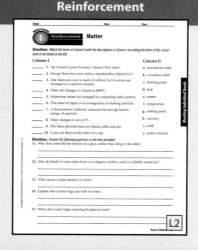

Reinforcement

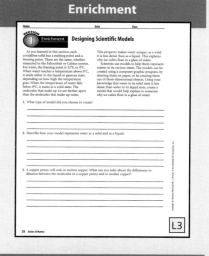

Enrichment

Directed Reading (English/Spanish)

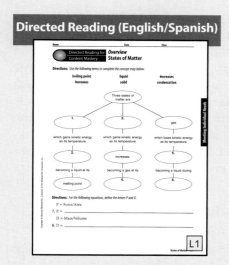

Study Guide

Reading Essentials

Assessment

Test Practice Workbook

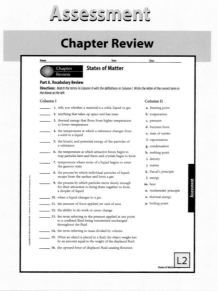

Chapter Review

Chapter Tests

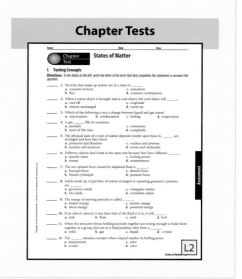

Science Content Background

section **1**

Matter

Understanding Matter

Matter is made of tiny moving particles separated by space. The three states of matter that people mainly encounter are gases, liquids, and solids. In gases, the separation of the particles is the greatest because these particles are moving the fastest. Decreasing the spaces between gas molecules by decreasing the temperature or increasing the pressure can turn gases into liquids and liquids into solids.

section **2**

Changes of State

Forces Between Molecules

When a liquid is poured into a container such as a glass test tube, the liquid's surface is called the meniscus. The shape of the meniscus depends on the relative strength of the cohesive forces between liquid particles and the adhesive forces between particles of the liquid and the container. If the adhesive forces are greater, the meniscus is concave. Water in a glass tube has a concave meniscus. If the cohesive forces are greater, the meniscus is convex. Mercury in a glass tube has a convex meniscus.

Temperature

The Kelvin temperature scale is an absolute scale. It begins at absolute zero, or 0 K. Each degree on the Kelvin scale is the same magnitude as a degree on the Celsius temperature scale. The freezing point of water on the Celsius scale is 0°C; the freezing point of water on the Kelvin scale is 273 K. The average kinetic energy of the particles that make up a substance is directly proportional to its Kelvin temperature. Although particles should not be moving at absolute zero, they have a small amount of motion called the zero point energy.

Heat

Heat is energy transferred from matter at a higher temperature to matter at a lower temperature. Objects do not contain heat; they contain internal energy, which is the sum of the kinetic and potential energies of their particles. Heat can be transferred three ways: radiation is the emission of electromagnetic waves, conduction is the transfer of heat by direct contact, and convection is heat transfer by warmer matter flowing into regions of colder matter.

section **3**

Behavior of Fluids

Atmospheric Pressure

Air pressure decreases rapidly with altitude. At the top of Mount Everest, 8.85 km above sea level, the pressure is only 33% of atmospheric pressure at sea level. This difference in pressure demonstrates how effectively gravity contains Earth's atmosphere.

chapter content resources

Internet Resources
For additional content background, visit
bookk.msscience.com to:
- access your book online
- find references to related articles in popular science magazines
- access Web links with related content background
- access current events with science journal topics

Print Resources
Chemistry; The Molecular Nature of Matter and Change, Martin S. Silberberg, McGraw-Hill, 2003
Chemistry, Steve S. Zumdahl, Susan A. Zumdahl, Houghton Mifflin Company, 2003
Chemistry, Raymond Chang, McGraw-Hill College, 2001

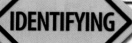

IDENTIFYING Misconceptions

Find Out What Students Think

Students may think that . . .

Matter does not include liquids or gases.

Forms of energy such as heat and light are matter.

Since solids are easy to see and feel, students usually understand easily that these materials are matter. Most gases are not directly observed, either through vision or other senses, so students may have difficulty categorizing gases as matter. Some students, however, may have too inclusive a view of matter. They fail to realize that energy may affect particles but is not composed of particles. These misunderstandings about matter can interfere with acquisition of new concepts.

Discussion

Ask students to divide a page in their Science Journals into two columns, one headed *Matter* and the other headed *Not Matter.* Read the following terms, and have students write each one in the appropriate column: *oxygen gas, orange juice, science book, pencil, electricity, carbon dioxide gas, water, heat, and light.* [L2]

Superstock

Promote Understanding

Demonstration

Explain that matter is composed of molecules.

• Hold up an ice cube, and establish that it is matter and is made of H_2O molecules.

• Allow the ice cube to melt. Point to the water. Is this matter? Establish that it is matter and that it is still made of H_2O molecules.

• Boil the water on a hot plate to produce steam. Is the steam matter? Establish that it is and that it is still made of H_2O molecules. Matter includes solids, liquids, and gases.

• Move your hand over the hot plate, and say that it feels warm. Is heat matter? Let students discuss this.

• Does heat have particles? Make sure students realize that heat affects particles but is not composed of particles. Heat is a form of energy, just as light and X rays are forms of energy. Energy is not matter.

Have students go back to their charts and move any terms that are not in the proper columns. [L2]

Assess

After completing the chapter, see *Identifying Misconceptions* in the Study Guide at the end of the chapter.

chapter 2

Chapter Vocabulary

matter, p. 40
solid, p. 41
liquid, p. 42
viscosity, p. 43
surface tension, p. 43
gas, p. 44
thermal energy, p. 45
temperature, p. 46
heat, p. 46
melting, p. 47
freezing, p. 49
vaporization, p. 50
condensation, p. 51
pressure, p. 54
buoyant force, p. 58
Archimedes' principle, p. 59
density, p. 59
Pascal's principle, p. 60

Science Journal The students may have questions about the source of the water, why the water is warm, why the snow hasn't melted, and how they would feel in the spring.

INTERACTIVE CHALKBOARD
with Image Bank

PowerPoint® Presentations

This CD-ROM is an editable Microsoft® PowerPoint® presentation that includes:
- a pre-made presentation for every chapter
- interactive graphics
- animations
- audio clips
- image bank
- all new section and chapter questions
- Standardized Test Practice
- transparencies
- pre-lab questions for all labs
- Foldables directions
- links to bookk.msscience.com

chapter 2

States of Matter

chapter preview

sections

1 **Matter**

2 **Changes of State**
   Lab   *The Water Cycle*

3 **Behavior of Fluids**
   Lab   *Design Your Own Ship*

⊙ *Virtual Lab How does thermal energy affect the state of a substance?*

Ahhh!

A long, hot soak on a snowy day! This Asian monkey called a macaque is experiencing the effects of heat—the transfer of thermal energy from a warmer object to a colder object. In this chapter, you will learn about heat and the three common states of matter on Earth.

Science Journal   Write about what you think is the source of the warm water.

Theme Connection

Systems and Interactions The structure and motion of particles of matter can be analyzed to explain many properties of systems containing huge numbers of particles. Powerful changes can be caused when energy is absorbed or released by these systems. Earth's weather offers many examples of changes involving the absorption or release of energy.

About the Photo

Heat Transfer The photo may help the students think about "the why" of every day events, such as putting ice cubes in a liquid or taking aluminum foil from a hot oven. While we observe the properties of matter daily, the students may have many misconceptions about the properties and characteristics that define matter.

Start-Up Activities

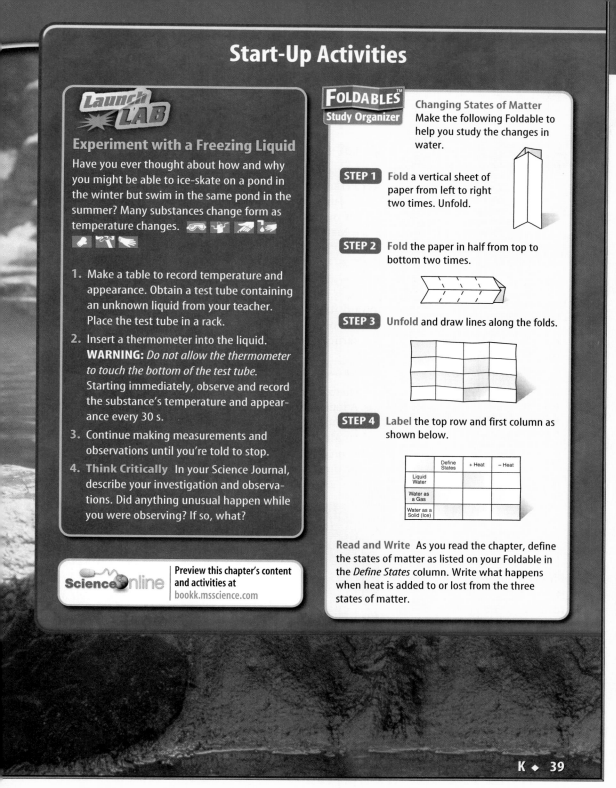

Launch LAB

Experiment with a Freezing Liquid

Have you ever thought about how and why you might be able to ice-skate on a pond in the winter but swim in the same pond in the summer? Many substances change form as temperature changes.

1. Make a table to record temperature and appearance. Obtain a test tube containing an unknown liquid from your teacher. Place the test tube in a rack.

2. Insert a thermometer into the liquid. **WARNING:** *Do not allow the thermometer to touch the bottom of the test tube.* Starting immediately, observe and record the substance's temperature and appearance every 30 s.

3. Continue making measurements and observations until you're told to stop.

4. **Think Critically** In your Science Journal, describe your investigation and observations. Did anything unusual happen while you were observing? If so, what?

Science Online Preview this chapter's content and activities at bookk.msscience.com

FOLDABLES Study Organizer

Changing States of Matter
Make the following Foldable to help you study the changes in water.

STEP 1 Fold a vertical sheet of paper from left to right two times. Unfold.

STEP 2 Fold the paper in half from top to bottom two times.

STEP 3 Unfold and draw lines along the folds.

STEP 4 Label the top row and first column as shown below.

	Define States	+ Heat	– Heat
Liquid Water			
Water as a Gas			
Water as a Solid (Ice)			

Read and Write As you read the chapter, define the states of matter as listed on your Foldable in the *Define States* column. Write what happens when heat is added to or lost from the three states of matter.

K ◆ 39

Launch LAB

Purpose Use the Launch Lab to help students discover that temperature remains constant as a substance freezes. [L2] COOP LEARN [IS] **Kinesthetic**

Preparation When students arrive, have test tubes half-filled with molten stearic acid sitting in a hot water bath in a hood at a temperature of approximately 75°C. Keep test tubes in hood until needed.

Materials laboratory-grade stearic acid, glass test tube, Celsius thermometer, watch or clock with a second hand, test-tube rack or jar

Teaching Strategy Suggest that student groups divide the responsibilities of tracking time, taking temperature readings, and recording data. Students then can graph and analyze the data individually.

Safety Precautions
• Caution students to be careful with the thermometer and wear safety glasses while working with the liquid.
• Do NOT let students remove thermometers from solid stearic acid. Breaking can occur. At the end of lab, have students return all materials to you. Reheat test tubes to remove thermometers.

Think Critically
The liquid's temperature fell gradually, remained the same as the liquid formed a white solid, then fell again. Heat was given off by the freezing liquid.

Sample Data

Time(s)	Temperature (°C)
0	74.0
30	72.5
60	70.0
90	69.5
120	69.5
150	69.5
180	69.5
210	69.0
240	68.5

FOLDABLES Study Organizer — Dinah Zike Study Fold

Student preparation materials for this Foldable are available in the **Chapter *FAST FILE* Resources.**

Assessment

Performance Have students predict what would happen if they were given twice as much of the unknown liquid. Use **Performance Assessment in the Science Classroom,** p. 89.

Matter

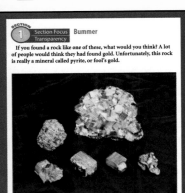
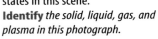
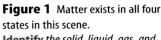
as you read

What You'll Learn
- **Recognize** that matter is made of particles in constant motion.
- **Relate** the three states of matter to the arrangement of particles within them.

Why It's Important
Everything you can see, taste, and touch is matter.

🔁 Review Vocabulary
atom: a small particle that makes up most types of matter

New Vocabulary
- matter
- solid
- liquid
- viscosity
- surface tension
- gas

Figure 1 Matter exists in all four states in this scene.
Identify *the solid, liquid, gas, and plasma in this photograph.*

What is matter?

Take a look at the beautiful scene in **Figure 1.** What do you see? Perhaps you notice the water and ice. Maybe you are struck by the Sun in the background. All of these images show examples of matter. **Matter** is anything that takes up space and has mass. Matter doesn't have to be visible—even air is matter.

States of Matter All matter is made up of tiny particles, such as atoms, molecules, or ions. Each particle attracts other particles. In other words, each particle pulls other particles toward itself. These particles also are constantly moving. The motion of the particles and the strength of attraction between the particles determine a material's state of matter.

✔ Reading Check *What determines a material's state of matter?*

There are three familiar states of matter—solid, liquid, and gas. A fourth state of matter known as plasma occurs at extremely high temperatures. Plasma is found in stars, lightning, and neon lights. Although plasma is common in the universe, it is not common on Earth. For that reason, this chapter will focus only on the three states of matter that are common on Earth.

40 ◆ K

Solids

What makes a substance a solid? Think about some familiar solids. Chairs, floors, rocks, and ice cubes are a few examples of matter in the solid state. What properties do all solids share? A **solid** is matter with a definite shape and volume. For example, when you pick up a rock from the ground and place it in a bucket, it doesn't change shape or size. A solid does not take the shape of a container in which it is placed. This is because the particles of a solid are packed closely together, as shown in **Figure 2.**

Particles in Motion The particles that make up all types of matter are in constant motion. Does this mean that the particles in a solid are moving too? Although you can't see them, a solid's particles are vibrating in place. The particles do not have enough energy to move out of their fixed positions.

✔ **Reading Check** *What motion do solid particles have?*

Crystalline Solids In some solids, the particles are arranged in a repeating, three-dimensional pattern called a crystal. These solids are called crystalline solids. In **Figure 3** you can see the arrangement of particles in a crystal of sodium chloride, which is table salt. The particles in the crystal are arranged in the shape of a cube. Diamond, another crystalline solid, is made entirely of carbon atoms that form crystals that look more like pyramids. Sugar, sand, and snow are other crystalline solids.

Solid

Figure 2 The particles in a solid vibrate in place while maintaining a constant shape and volume.

Figure 3 The particles in a crystal of sodium chloride (NaCl) are arranged in an orderly pattern.

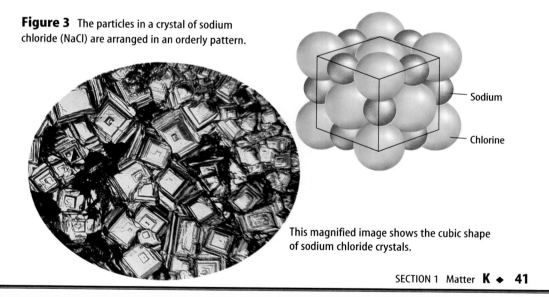

Sodium

Chlorine

This magnified image shows the cubic shape of sodium chloride crystals.

Differentiated Instruction

Different Solids The particles in a crystalline solid occupy defined spaces, like eggs in an egg carton. In an amorphous solid the particles are in a random arrangement, more like lemons in a bowl.

Answer The particles in amorphous solids have a random arrangement instead of an ordered arrangement.

Fresh Water What waterways, if any, are near your home and school? Are the waterways still being used? Are they natural or man-made, like canals? Find out how the waterways were used by the early settlers of your town.

Activity

States of Matter Have students create a Venn diagram of the properties of water as a solid, a liquid, and a gas. The diagrams should include characteristics such as shape, volume, and particle motion. L2

INTEGRATE History

Fresh Water Early settlers have always decided to build their homes near water. The rivers provided ways for people to travel, drinking water for themselves and their animals, and irrigation for farming. Over time, small communities became larger communities with industry building along the same water.

Figure 4 The particles in a liquid stay close together, although they are free to move past one another.

Amorphous Solids Some solids come together without forming crystal structures. These solids often consist of large particles that are not arranged in a repeating pattern. Instead, the particles are found in a random arrangement. These solids are called amorphous (uh MOR fuhs) solids. Rubber, plastic, and glass are examples of amorphous solids.

Reading Check *How is a crystalline solid different from an amorphous solid?*

Liquids

From the orange juice you drink with breakfast to the water you use to brush your teeth at night, matter in the liquid state is familiar to you. How would you describe the characteristics of a liquid? Is it hard like a solid? Does it keep its shape? A **liquid** is matter that has a definite volume but no definite shape. When you pour a liquid from one container to another, the liquid takes the shape of the container. The volume of a liquid, however, is the same no matter what the shape of the container. If you pour 50 mL of juice from a carton into a pitcher, the pitcher will contain 50 mL of juice. If you then pour that same juice into a glass, its shape will change again but its volume will not.

Free to Move The reason that a liquid can have different shapes is because the particles in a liquid move more freely, as shown in **Figure 4,** than the particles in a solid. The particles in a liquid have enough energy to move out of their fixed positions but not enough energy to move far apart.

Liquid

Differentiated Instruction

English-Language Learners Have English-Language Learners create the Venn diagram in the activity on this page in their native language. Ask them to translate the diagram into English. Then have the students share the translated version with a classmate. L2 **ELL**

Viscosity Do all liquids flow the way water flows? You know that honey flows more slowly than water and you've probably heard the phrase "slow as molasses." Some liquids flow more easily than others. A liquid's resistance to flow is known as the liquid's **viscosity.** Honey has a high viscosity. Water has a lower viscosity. The slower a liquid flows, the higher its viscosity is. The viscosity results from the strength of the attraction between the particles of the liquid. For many liquids, viscosity increases as the liquid becomes colder.

Surface Tension If you're careful, you can float a needle on the surface of water. This is because attractive forces cause the particles on the surface of a liquid to pull themselves together and resist being pushed apart. You can see in **Figure 5** that particles beneath the surface of a liquid are pulled in all directions. Particles at the surface of a liquid are pulled toward the center of the liquid and sideways along the surface. No liquid particles are located above to pull on them. The uneven forces acting on the particles on the surface of a liquid are called **surface tension.** Surface tension causes the liquid to act as if a thin film were stretched across its surface. As a result you can float a needle on the surface of water. For the same reason, the water strider can move around on the surface of a pond or lake. When a liquid is present in small amounts, surface tension causes the liquid to form small droplets.

Science Online

Topic: Plasma
Visit bookk.msscience.com for Web links to information about the states of matter.

Activity List four ways that plasma differs from the other three states of matter

Figure 5 Surface tension exists because the particles at the surface experience different forces than those at the center of the liquid.

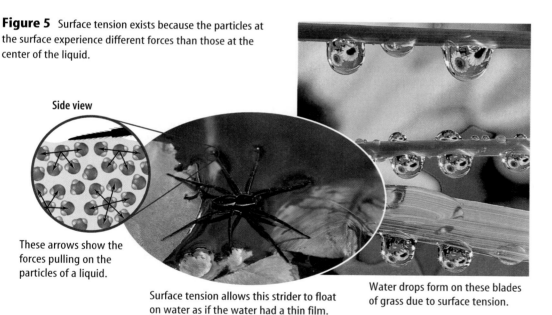

Side view

These arrows show the forces pulling on the particles of a liquid.

Surface tension allows this strider to float on water as if the water had a thin film.

Water drops form on these blades of grass due to surface tension.

SECTION 1 Matter **K** ◆ **43**

LAB DEMONSTRATION

Purpose to show how temperature affects the viscosity of a liquid

Materials 2 jars, syrup or molasses, refrigerator, 2 small beakers, stopwatch

Preparation Add 10 mL of syrup to each jar. Place one jar in a refrigerator overnight, and allow the other to stand at room temperature.

Procedure Have one student pour all the cold syrup into one beaker while another student pours all the room-temperature syrup into the other beaker. Have remaining students record the time it takes to empty each jar.

Expected Outcome The cold syrup takes longer to pour.

Assessment

Why does the cold syrup have higher viscosity than the warmer syrup? The particles in the cold syrup are closer together and exert a stronger force upon each other than do the warmer particles.

Quick Demo

Movement of Gases

Materials can of air freshener

Estimated Time five minutes

Procedure Demonstrate that gases spread out to fill all available space by spraying a small amount of air freshener in one corner of the room. Have students raise their hands when they first smell the scent. Have students explain the movement of the particles.

3 Assess

DAILY INTERVENTION

Check for Understanding

Logical-Mathematical Have students explain why motor oil is made in a wide range of viscosities. Motor oil must remain fluid enough to protect a car engine in a wide range of weather conditions. L2

Reteach

Compression of Gases Blow up a balloon and tie it closed at the neck. Use the balloon to illustrate to students that a gas can be compressed. Ask students what happens to the gas in the balloon if you twist the balloon at the center. Some gas moves into each end of the balloon, where it is compressed into a smaller space. L1 LS **Visual-Spatial**

☑ Assessment

Content Have students prepare cartoons that compare and contrast the properties of solids, liquids, and gases. Use **Performance Assessment in the Science Classroom,** p. 133. P

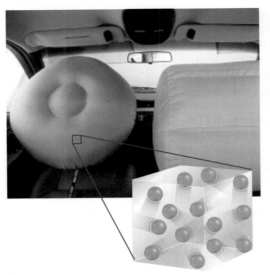

Figure 6 The particles in gas move at high speeds in all directions. The gas inside these air bags spreads out to fill the entire volume of the bag.

Gases

Unlike solids and liquids, most gases are invisible. The air you breathe is a mixture of gases. The gas in the air bags in **Figure 6** and the helium in some balloons are examples of gases. **Gas** is matter that does not have a definite shape or volume. The particles in gas are much farther apart than those in a liquid or solid. Gas particles move at high speeds in all directions. They will spread out evenly, as far apart as possible. If you poured a small volume of a liquid into a container, the liquid would stay in the bottom of the container. However, if you poured the same volume of a gas into a container, the gas would fill the container completely. A gas can expand or be compressed. Decreasing the volume of the container squeezes the gas particles closer together.

Vapor Matter that exists in the gas state but is generally a liquid or solid at room temperature is called vapor. Water, for example, is a liquid at room temperature. Thus, water vapor is the term for the gas state of water.

section ① review

Summary

What is matter?
- Matter is anything that takes up space and has mass. Solid, liquid, and gas are the three common states of matter.

Solids
- Solids have a definite volume and shape.
- Solids with particles arranged in order are called crystalline solids. The particles in amorphous solids are not in any order.

Liquids
- Liquids have definite volume but no defined shape.
- Viscosity is a measure of how easily liquids flow.

Gases
- Gases have no definite volume or shape.
- Vapor refers to gaseous substances that are normally liquids or solids at room temperature.

Self Check

1. **Define** the two properties of matter that determine its state.
2. **Describe** the movement of particles within solids, liquids, and gases.
3. **Name** the property that liquids and solids share. What property do liquids and gases share?
4. **Infer** A scientist places 25 mL of a yellow substance into a 50-mL container. The substance quickly fills the entire container. Is it a solid, liquid, or gas?
5. **Think Critically** The particles in liquid A have a stronger attraction to each other than the particles in liquid B. If both liquids are at the same temperature, which liquid has a higher viscosity? Explain.

Applying Skills

6. **Concept Map** Draw a Venn diagram in your Science Journal and fill in the characteristics of the states of matter.

  Science Online bookk.msscience.com/self_check_quiz

section ① review

1. motion of particles and strength of attraction between particles
2. solids: particles are very close together and vibrate back and forth; liquids: particles are farther apart and individual particles can flow past each other; gases: particles are very far apart and move quickly
3. solid—liquid—constant volume liquid—gas—take on shape of container
4. Gas state, the particles take the shape and volume of their container.
5. Liquid A—greater attraction among molecules, the greater the viscosity
6. Check students' work for characteristics that are shared and not shared by states of matter.

Changes of State

Thermal Energy and Heat

Shards of ice fly from the sculptor's chisel. As the crowd looks on, a swan slowly emerges from a massive block of ice. As the day wears on, however, drops of water begin to fall from the sculpture. Drip by drip, the sculpture is transformed into a puddle of liquid water. What makes matter change from one state to another? To answer this question, you need to think about the particles that make up matter.

Energy Simply stated, energy is the ability to do work or cause change. The energy of motion is called kinetic energy. Particles within matter are in constant motion. The amount of motion of these particles depends on the kinetic energy they possess. Particles with more kinetic energy move faster and farther apart. Particles with less energy move more slowly and stay closer together.

The total kinetic energy of all the particles in a sample of matter is called **thermal energy.** Thermal energy, an extensive property, depends on the number of particles in a substance as well as the amount of energy each particle has. If either the number of particles or the amount of energy in each particle changes, the thermal energy of the sample changes. With identically sized samples, the warmer substance has the greater thermal energy. In **Figure 7,** the particles of hot water from the hot spring have more thermal energy than the particles of snow on the surrounding ground.

as you read

What You'll Learn

- **Define and compare** thermal energy and temperature.
- **Relate** changes in thermal energy to changes of state.
- **Explore** energy and temperature changes on a graph.

Why It's Important

Matter changes state as it heats up or cools down.

Review Vocabulary
energy: the ability to do work or cause change

New Vocabulary
- thermal energy
- temperature
- heat
- melting
- freezing
- vaporization
- condensation

Figure 7 These girls are enjoying the water from the hot spring. **Infer** why the girls appear to be comfortable in the hot spring while there is snow on the ground.

Caption Answer
Figure 8 the hot tea

INTEGRATE Physics

Types of Energy All types of energy can cause change. What changes can each of the forms of energy listed in the Integrate Physics cause? thermal energy—make particles move faster; chemical energy—make and break chemical bonds; electrical energy—illuminate light bulbs, turn motors; electromagnetic energy of light—stimulate cells so we can see; nuclear energy—change mass to energy.

L2 IS **Logical-Mathematical**
Research Have students research geothermal energy. Topics that should be included are a definition of the term, how geothermal energy is being used for household applications and how geothermal energy is being used to generate electricity. L2

✔ Reading Check

Answer When a substance is heated, it gains thermal energy; therefore, its particles move faster and its temperature rises.

IDENTIFYING Misconceptions

Thermal Energy Students may not realize that two systems at the same temperature can have different amounts of thermal energy. For example, a cup of boiling water and a pot of boiling water may have the same temperature, but the pot of water has more thermal energy and can transfer more heat.

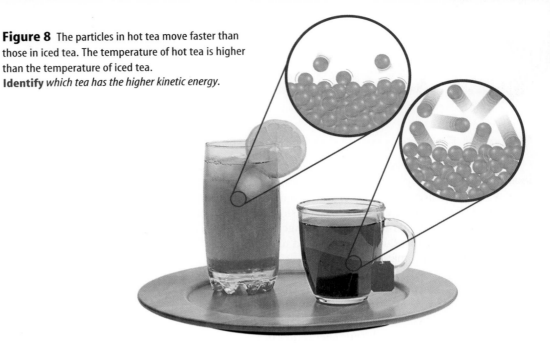

Figure 8 The particles in hot tea move faster than those in iced tea. The temperature of hot tea is higher than the temperature of iced tea.
Identify *which tea has the higher kinetic energy.*

INTEGRATE Physics

Types of Energy Thermal energy is one of several different forms of energy. Other forms include the chemical energy in chemical compounds, the electrical energy used in appliances, the electromagnetic energy of light, and the nuclear energy stored in the nucleus of an atom. Make a list of examples of energy that you are familiar with.

Temperature Not all of the particles in a sample of matter have the same amount of energy. Some have more energy than others. The average kinetic energy of the individual particles is the **temperature,** an intensive property, of the substance. You can find an average by adding up a group of numbers and dividing the total by the number of items in the group. For example, the average of the numbers 2, 4, 8, and 10 is $(2 + 4 + 8 + 10) \div 4 = 6$. Temperature is different from thermal energy because thermal energy is a total and temperature is an average.

You know that the iced tea is colder than the hot tea, as shown in **Figure 8.** Stated differently, the temperature of iced tea is lower than the temperature of hot tea. You also could say that the average kinetic energy of the particles in the iced tea is less than the average kinetic energy of the particles in the hot tea.

Heat When a warm object is brought near a cooler object, thermal energy will be transferred from the warmer object to the cooler one. The movement of thermal energy from a substance at a higher temperature to one at a lower temperature is called **heat.** When a substance is heated, it gains thermal energy. Therefore, its particles move faster and its temperature rises. When a substance is cooled, it loses thermal energy, which causes its particles to move more slowly and its temperature to drop.

✔ Reading Check *How is heat related to temperature?*

Science Journal

Thermal Energy on the Move Ask students to pay attention to the transfer of thermal energy around them and record all the examples they observe in one 24-hour period. Have them write their observations in their Science Journals. They should include for each example where the thermal energy came from and where it went. L2 IS **Naturalist**

Specific Heat

As you study more science, you will discover that water has many unique properties. One of those is the amount of heat required to increase the temperature of water as compared to most other substances. The specific heat of a substance is the amount of heat required to raise the temperature of 1 g of a substance 1°C.

Substances that have a low specific heat, such as most metals and the sand in **Figure 9,** heat up and cool down quickly because they require only small amounts of heat to cause their temperatures to rise. A substance with a high specific heat, such as the water in **Figure 9,** heats up and cools down slowly because a much larger quantity of heat is required to cause its temperature to rise or fall by the same amount.

Changes Between the Solid and Liquid States

Matter can change from one state to another when thermal energy is absorbed or released. This change is known as change of state. The graph in **Figure 11** shows the changes in temperature as thermal energy is gradually added to a container of ice.

Melting As the ice in **Figure 11** is heated, it absorbs thermal energy and its temperature rises. At some point, the temperature stops rising and the ice begins to change into liquid water. The change from the solid state to the liquid state is called **melting.** The temperature at which a substance changes from a solid to a liquid is called the melting point. The melting point of water is 0°C.

Amorphous solids, such as rubber and glass, don't melt in the same way as crystalline solids. Because they don't have crystal structures to break down, these solids get softer and softer as they are heated, as you can see in **Figure 10.**

Figure 9 The specific heat of water is greater than that of sand. The energy provided by the Sun raises the temperature of the sand much faster than the water.

Figure 10 Rather than melting into a liquid, glass gradually softens. Glass blowers use this characteristic to shape glass into beautiful vases while it is hot.

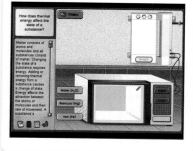
Activity

Specific Heat Between 0°C and 100°C the specific heat of water is about 4.18 J/g°C. Ask students to find the specific heats of several metals and compare them with the specific heat of water. Have them make a table from their findings. The specific heat of silver between these temperatures is 0.235 J/g°C. Between 20°C and 100°C the specific heat of aluminum is 0.903 J/g°C, the specific heat of copper is 0.385 J/g°C, and the specific heat of iron is 0.449 J/g°C. These range from about one-twentieth that of water to about one-fifth that of water.

L3 LS **Logical-Mathematical** P

IDENTIFYING Misconceptions

Changing States Students may think particles of a substance can change state only at the melting point or boiling point of the substance. In fact, at any temperature different particles of a substance have different amounts of kinetic energy and may have enough energy to change state. Melting and boiling occur when the number of particles with enough energy to change state is great enough that the average kinetic energy of the particles is at the melting point or the boiling point of the substance.

Curriculum Connection

Geography Earth's temperature has increased during the past few decades. Have students research how this increase could cause changes in the state of water and the effects these changes could have on a specific geographic region. For example, melting of the polar ice caps is causing erosion along coastlines.

L3 LS **Linguistic**

Visualizing States of Matter

Have students examine the pictures and read the captions. Then ask the following questions.

During the melting and vaporization process the temperature remains constant. Look at the graph and identify which factor continues to increase. thermal energy

What changes in molecular attraction occur as water goes from a solid to a liquid to a gas? As a solid, the molecules have the most attraction for each other. As a liquid, the molecular attraction has decreased. As a gas, there is no longer any molecular attraction between the molecules.

During condensation, what must be removed from the gas in order for the gas to become a liquid? thermal energy

Activity

Water Molecule Have the students write a letter about the life of a water molecule as it goes from a solid to a gas. How free and what will it see as a molecule that's part of a solid, liquid, or vapor? L2 IN **Linguistic**

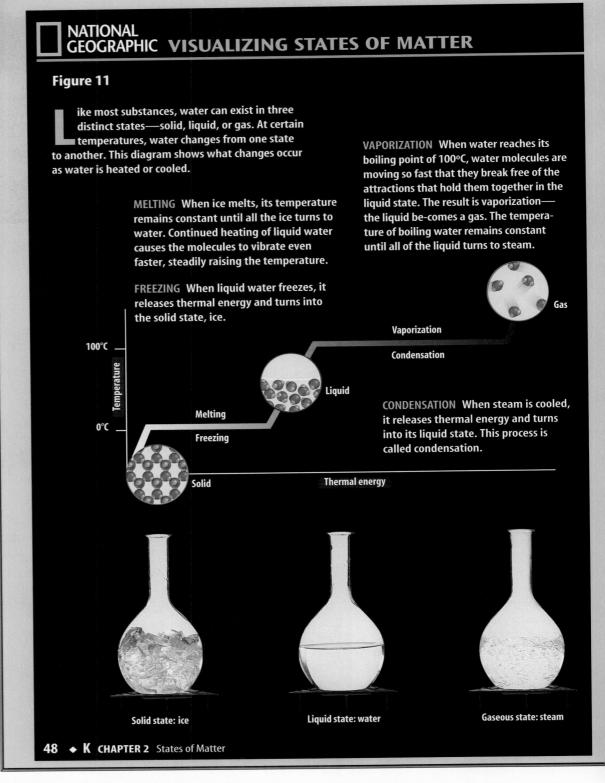

NATIONAL GEOGRAPHIC VISUALIZING STATES OF MATTER

Figure 11

Like most substances, water can exist in three distinct states—solid, liquid, or gas. At certain temperatures, water changes from one state to another. This diagram shows what changes occur as water is heated or cooled.

MELTING When ice melts, its temperature remains constant until all the ice turns to water. Continued heating of liquid water causes the molecules to vibrate even faster, steadily raising the temperature.

FREEZING When liquid water freezes, it releases thermal energy and turns into the solid state, ice.

VAPORIZATION When water reaches its boiling point of 100°C, water molecules are moving so fast that they break free of the attractions that hold them together in the liquid state. The result is vaporization—the liquid be-comes a gas. The temperature of boiling water remains constant until all of the liquid turns to steam.

CONDENSATION When steam is cooled, it releases thermal energy and turns into its liquid state. This process is called condensation.

Solid state: ice

Liquid state: water

Gaseous state: steam

Differentiated Instruction

Challenge Have students find out the energy changes that occur during the refrigeration cycle. Have them also find the properties of environmentally safe refrigerants and share the information with the class. L3

Freezing The process of melting a crystalline solid can be reversed if the liquid is cooled. The change from the liquid state to the solid state is called **freezing.** As the liquid cools, it loses thermal energy. As a result, its particles slow down and come closer together. Attractive forces begin to trap particles, and the crystals of a solid begin to form. As you can see in **Figure 11,** freezing and melting are opposite processes.

The temperature at which a substance changes from the liquid state to the solid state is called the freezing point. The freezing point of the liquid state of a substance is the same temperature as the melting point of the solid state. For example, solid water melts at 0°C and liquid water freezes at 0°C.

During freezing, the temperature of a substance remains constant while the particles in the liquid form a crystalline solid. Because particles in a liquid have more energy than particles in a solid, energy is released during freezing. This energy is released into the surroundings. After all of the liquid has become a solid, the temperature begins to decrease again.

Science Online

Topic: Freezing Point Study
Visit bookk.msscience.com for Web links to information about freezing.

Activity Make a list of several substances and the temperatures at which they freeze. Find out how the freezing point affects how the substance is used.

Discussion

Energy Since temperature doesn't change as a substance is freezing, the kinetic energy of its particles doesn't change. But the substance is losing energy. What kind of energy is the substance losing? It is losing the potential energy of the attraction between the particles. L3 [LS] **Logical-Mathematical**

Applying Science

How can ice save oranges?

During the spring, Florida citrus farmers carefully watch the fruit when temperatures drop close to freezing. When the temperatures fall below 0°C, the liquid in the cells of oranges can freeze and expand. This causes the cells to break, making the oranges mushy and the crop useless for sale. To prevent this, farmers spray the oranges with water just before the temperature reaches 0°C. How does spraying oranges with water protect them?

Identifying the Problem
Using the diagram in **Figure 11,** consider what is happening to the water at 0°C. Two things occur. What are they?

Solving the Problem
1. What change of state and what energy changes occur when water freezes?
2. How does the formation of ice on the orange help the orange?

Applying Science

Teaching Strategies
Show students the difference between an orange that has been frozen below 0°C (-2.2°C) and one that has not been frozen. The layer of ice on top protects the orange from the colder air temperatures. Point out that this is also what occurs when a lake freezes over. The ice on top protects the water beneath, so fish can survive.

Answers
1. The two changes that occur are the phase change from water to ice and the loss of energy (exothermic) when the phase change occurs.
2. The ice forms at 0°C forming a coating on the orange that acts as insulation against the colder air temperature. Some of the energy that is released when the ice forms goes into the orange.

Differentiated Instruction

Learning Disabled Help students analyze the questions posed in Applying Science by breaking down the process that occurs as the water sprayed on the oranges freezes. Draw diagrams and use arrows to show the energy transfers involved and relate them to the graphs on the previous page. L2 [LS] **Logical-Mathematical**

Mini LAB

Purpose Students observe that a liquid absorbs heat from its surroundings as it evaporates.

[L1] [IS] **Kinesthetic**

Materials dropper, rubbing alcohol

Teaching Strategy Prevent waste by providing students with small amounts of alcohol.

Safety Precautions Students should wear goggles when performing this MiniLAB. Alcohol is flammable. There should be no open flames in the lab.

Analysis

1. The alcohol evaporated.
2. The hand felt cool where the alcohol was located. The alcohol removed heat from the skin as it evaporated, and then the hand warmed up again.
3. Sweating alone will not cool the body. The sweat has to evaporate for the body to feel cooler.

Assessment

Content Explain how the body is cooled by perspiration. Heat from the body is absorbed as perspiration evaporates from the skin. Use **Performance Assessment in the Science Classroom**, p. 89.

Caption Answer

Figure 12 Vaporization describes a liquid changing to a gas.

Visual Learning

Figure 12 Discuss with students the difference between evaporation and boiling. Could both occur at the same time? Yes; while some particles are becoming gas inside the liquid, other liquid particles can become gas at the surface. [L2] [IS] **Logical-Mathematical**

Mini LAB

Observing Vaporization

Procedure

1. Use a **dropper** to place one drop of **rubbing alcohol** on the back of your hand.
2. Describe how your hand feels during the next 2 min.
3. Wash your hands.

Analysis

1. What changes in the appearance of the rubbing alcohol did you notice?
2. What sensation did you feel during the 2 min? How can you explain this sensation?
3. Infer how sweating cools the body.

Changes Between the Liquid and Gas States

After an early morning rain, you and your friends enjoy stomping through the puddles left behind. But later that afternoon when you head out to run through the puddles once more, the puddles are gone. The liquid water in the puddles changed into a gas. Matter changes between the liquid and gas states through vaporization and condensation.

Vaporization As liquid water is heated, its temperature rises until it reaches 100°C. At this point, liquid water changes into water vapor. The change from a liquid to a gas is known as **vaporization** (vay puh ruh ZAY shun). You can see in **Figure 11** that the temperature of the substance does not change during vaporization. However, the substance absorbs thermal energy. The additional energy causes the particles to move faster until they have enough energy to escape the liquid as gas particles.

Two forms of vaporization exist. Vaporization that takes place below the surface of a liquid is called boiling. When a liquid boils, bubbles form within the liquid and rise to the surface, as shown in **Figure 12.** The temperature at which a liquid boils is called the boiling point. The boiling point of water is 100°C.

Vaporization that takes place at the surface of a liquid is called evaporation. Evaporation, which occurs at temperatures below the boiling point, explains how puddles dry up. Imagine that you could watch individual water molecules in a puddle. You would notice that the molecules move at different speeds. Although the temperature of the water is constant, remember that temperature is a measure of the average kinetic energy of the molecules. Some of the fastest-moving molecules overcome the attractive forces of other molecules and escape from the surface of the water.

Figure 12 During boiling, liquid changes to gas, forming bubbles in the liquid that rise to the surface.
Define the word that describes a liquid changing to the gas.

Teacher FYI

Maxwell-Boltzmann Distribution At a given temperature, the motions of the particles in a substance vary according to a well-defined distribution of particle speeds called the Maxwell-Boltzmann distribution. This distribution looks similar to a bell curve but is not as symmetrical. The limit on the fastest speeds is the speed of light, while zero is the lowest speed a particle can have.

Figure 13 The drops of water on these glasses and pitcher of lemonade were formed when water vapor in the air lost enough energy to return to the liquid state. This process is called condensation.

Location of Molecules It takes more than speed for water molecules to escape the liquid state. During evaporation, these faster molecules also must be near the surface, heading in the right direction, and they must avoid hitting other water molecules as they leave. With the faster particles evaporating from the surface of a liquid, the particles that remain are the slower, cooler ones. Evaporation cools the liquid and anything near the liquid. You experience this cooling effect when perspiration evaporates from your skin.

Condensation Pour a nice, cold glass of lemonade and place it on the table for a half hour on a warm day. When you come back to take a drink, the outside of the glass will be covered by drops of water, as shown in **Figure 13.** What happened? As a gas cools, its particles slow down. When particles move slowly enough for their attractions to bring them together, droplets of liquid form. This process, which is the opposite of vaporization, is called **condensation.** As a gas condenses to a liquid, it releases the thermal energy it absorbed to become a gas. During this process, the temperature of the substance does not change. The decrease in energy changes the arrangement of particles. After the change of state is complete, the temperature continues to drop, as you saw in **Figure 11.**

 *What energy change occurs during condensation?*

Condensation formed the droplets of water on the outside of your glass of lemonade. In the same way, water vapor in the atmosphere condenses to form the liquid water droplets in clouds. When the droplets become large enough, they can fall to the ground as rain.

Science Online

Topic: Condensation
Visit bookk.msscience.com for Web links to information about how condensation is involved in weather.

Activity Find out how condensation is affected by the temperature as well as the amount of water in the air.

☑ **Reading Check**

Answer During condensation, a gas releases energy as its particles become more ordered.

Visual Learning

Figure 13 Have students describe the various places that heat transfer is occurring in **Figure 13.** L2
LS **Visual-Spatial**

Quick Demo
Condensation
Materials hot plate, beaker, water, small mirror, thermal mitt
Estimated Time 10 minutes
Procedure Place a beaker half to three-quarters full of water on a hot plate. Have the water heating on a high temperature, but not boiling before the students arrive. Increase the temperature so that the water boils. While wearing the thermal mitt, hold the mirror over the boiling beaker. Hold this position until there is condensation on the mirror. Have the students explain condensation in terms of energy loss and gain.

Curriculum Connection

Geography Have students research how changes of state contribute to the formation of deserts near the Tropic of Cancer. Ask students to make posters with diagrams illustrating their findings. Warm moist air from the equator rises and flows northward and southward. As this moist air cools it loses its moisture. This dry air then descends over the Tropics of Capricorn and Cancer pulling moisture out of the ground by evaporation and drying out the land. This pattern has produced a belt of deserts along the Tropics of Capricorn and Cancer. L2 LS **Linguistic**

DAILY INTERVENTION

Check for Understanding

Logical-Mathematical If you have an automatic ice-cube maker in your freezer, you may have noticed that the older ice cubes at the bottom of the tray are much smaller than the newer cubes at the top. Use what you have learned to explain why. The faster molecules on the surface of an ice cube can escape from the cube and become a gas. Over time, the ice cube will completely sublimate away. L2 LS

Reteach

Evaporation and Boiling Have students explain the difference between evaporation and boiling. Boiling occurs when particles below the surface of a liquid change from liquid to gas. Evaporation occurs when particles at the surface of a liquid change from liquid to gas. L2 LS **Logical-Mathematical**

✓ Assessment

Oral Have students hypothesize what would happen if the unknown substance from the Launch Lab were reheated. The substance would melt at the same temperature at which it froze. The temperature would remain constant while the substance was melting, then increase gradually. Use **Performance Assessment in the Science Classroom,** p. 93.

Figure 14 The solid carbon dioxide (dry ice) at the bottom of this beaker of water is changing directly into gaseous carbon dioxide. This process is called sublimation.

Changes Between the Solid and Gas States

Some substances can change from the solid state to the gas state without ever becoming a liquid. During this process, known as sublimation, the surface particles of the solid gain enough energy to become a gas. One example of a substance that undergoes sublimation is dry ice. Dry ice is the solid form of carbon dioxide. It often is used to keep materials cold and dry. At room temperature and pressure, carbon dioxide does not exist as a liquid. Therefore, as dry ice absorbs thermal energy from the objects around it, it changes directly into a gas. When dry ice becomes a gas, it absorbs thermal energy from water vapor in the air. As a result, the water vapor cools and condenses into liquid water droplets, forming the fog you see in **Figure 14.**

section 2 review

Summary

Thermal Energy and Heat
- Thermal energy depends on the amount of the substance and the kinetic energy of particles in the substance.
- Heat is the movement of thermal energy from a warmer substance to a cooler one.

Specific Heat
- Specific heat is a measure of the amount of energy required to raise 1 g of a substance 1°C.

Changes Between Solid and Liquid States
- During all changes of state, the temperature of a substance stays the same.

Changes Between Liquid and Gas States
- Vaporization is the change from the liquid state to a gaseous state.
- Condensation is the change from the gaseous state to the liquid state.

Changes Between Solid and Gas States
- Sublimation is the process of a substance going from the solid state to the gas state without ever being in the liquid state.

Self Check

1. **Describe** how thermal energy and temperature are similar. How are they different?
2. **Explain** how a change in thermal energy causes matter to change from one state to another. Give two examples.
3. **List** the three changes of state during which energy is absorbed.
4. **Describe** the two types of vaporization.
5. **Think Critically** How can the temperature of a substance remain the same even if the substance is absorbing thermal energy?
6. **Write** a paragraph in your Science Journal that explains why you can step out of the shower into a warm bathroom and begin to shiver.

Applying Math

7. **Make and Use Graphs** Use the data you collected in the Launch Lab to plot a temperature-time graph. Describe your graph. At what temperature does the graph level off? What was the liquid doing during this time period?
8. **Use Numbers** If sample A requires 10 calories to raise the temperature of a 1-g sample 1°C, how many calories does it take to raise a 5-g sample 10°C?

 bookk.msscience.com/self_check_quiz

section 2 review

1. Thermal energy is the total amount of energy contained in a body whereas temperature measures the average kinetic energy of the particles in the body. Both deal with quantities of energy.
2. As thermal energy changes, the kinetic energy of the particles

changes. If their kinetic energy increases, particles can overcome the attractive forces holding them together. If their kinetic energy decreases, particles can become subject to the forces pulling them together. Examples will vary.
3. melting, vaporization, and sublimation
4. Boiling occurs when particles below

the surface of a liquid change from liquid to gas. Evaporation occurs when particles at the surface of a liquid change from liquid to gas.
5. The temperature remains the same because the absorbed energy is being used to break attractive forces between the particles of a substance as it changes state.
6. The water on your skin absorbs heat

from your body and evaporates.
7. Check students' work. Sample data can be found in the teacher margin of the Launch Lab. Answers may vary, but should be near 69.5°C. The liquid was freezing during this time period.
8. specific heat = cal/(g × °C); 10 cal/(1 g × 1°C) = x cal/(5 g × 10°C), therefore x = 500 cal

The Water Cycle

Water is all around us and you've used water in all three of its common states. This lab will give you the opportunity to observe the three states of matter and to discover for yourself if ice really melts at 0°C and if water boils at 100°C.

◉ Real-World Question

How does the temperature of water change as it is heated from a solid to a gas?

Goals
- **Measure** the temperature of water as it heats.
- **Observe** what happens as the water changes from one state to another.
- **Graph** the temperature and time data.

Materials
hot plate
ice cubes (100 mL)
Celsius thermometer
*electronic temperature probe
wall clock
*watch with second hand
stirring rod
250-mL beaker
*Alternate materials

Safety Precautions

◉ Procedure

1. Make a data table similar to the table shown.
2. Put 150 mL of water and 100 mL of ice into the beaker and place the beaker on the hot plate. Do not touch the hot plate.
3. Put the thermometer into the ice/water mixture. Do not stir with the thermometer or allow it to rest on the bottom of the beaker. After 30 s, read and record the temperature in your data table.

Characteristics of Water Sample		
Time (min)	Temperature (°C)	Physical State
	Answers will vary.	

4. Plug in the hot plate and turn the temperature knob to the medium setting.
5. Every 30 s, read and record the temperature and physical state of the water until it begins to boil. Use the stirring rod to stir the contents of the beaker before making each temperature measurement. Stop recording. Allow the water to cool.

◉ Analyze Your Data

Use your data to make a graph plotting time on the x-axis and temperature on the y-axis. Draw a smooth curve through the data points.

◉ Conclude and Apply

1. **Describe** how the temperature of the ice/water mixture changed as you heated the beaker.
2. **Describe** the shape of the graph during any changes of state.

Communicating Your Data

Add labels to your graph. Use the detailed graph to explain to your class how water changes state. **For more help, refer to the Science Skill Handbook.**

◉ Real-World Question

Purpose Students observe the solid and liquid states of water. L1 LS **Kinesthetic**

Process Skills measure, observe, make and use tables, use numbers, make and use graphs, infer

Time 30 minutes

◉ Procedure

Alternate Materials electronic temperature probe

Safety Precautions Caution students not to use the thermometer as a stirrer or allow it to rest on the bottom of the beaker during heating.

Teaching Strategy Crushed ice or small pieces will give quicker results.

◉ Analyze Your Data

Expected Outcome Students' graphs should show increasing temperature until a change of state occurs and then be level until the next change of state.

◉ Conclude and Apply

1. The temperature increased, stayed the same for a period of time, then increased again.
2. During changes of state, the graph leveled off.

☑ Assessment

Content How would the graphs change if twice as much ice were used? The temperature would rise more slowly and the plateau would be longer. Use **Performance Assessment in the Science Classroom,** p. 101. LS **Logical-Mathematical**

Communicating Your Data

Encourage students to compare graphs with other students and discuss possible reasons for inconsistent data.

1 Motivate

section 3

Behavior of Fluids

Bellringer

INTERACTIVE
CHALKBOARD
PowerPoint® Presentations

Section Focus Transparencies
also are available on the
Interactive Chalkboard CD-ROM.

L2 ELL

1. The shape of a submarine is similar to an airplane's body. Why is this so?
2. Name some metal objects that float. Name some metal objects that sink. Why might metal sometimes float and sometimes sink?
3. How are submarines and hot air balloons similar in the way they ascend and descend?

Tie to Prior Knowledge

Pumping Bicycle Tires Ask students whether they have ever pumped up bicycle tires. Have a volunteer describe what happens during the process. More and more air molecules are pushed into the tire, increasing the pressure inside. Explain that in this section students will explore how the motion of particles of matter is related to different kinds of pressure occurring in fluids.

---

as you read

What You'll Learn
■ **Explain** why some things float but others sink.
■ **Describe** how pressure is transmitted through fluids.

Why It's Important
Pressure enables you to squeeze toothpaste from a tube, and buoyant force helps you float in water.

Review Vocabulary
force: a push or pull

New Vocabulary
● pressure
● buoyant force
● Archimedes' principle
● density
● Pascal's principle

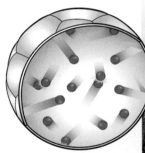

Figure 15 Without the pressure of air inside this volleyball, the ball would be flat.

Pressure

It's a beautiful summer day when you and your friends go outside to play volleyball, much like the kids in **Figure 15.** There's only one problem—the ball is flat. You pump air into the ball until it is firm. The firmness of the ball is the result of the motion of the air particles in the ball. As the air particles in the ball move, they collide with one another and with the inside walls of the ball. As each particle collides with the inside walls, it exerts a force, pushing the surface of the ball outward. A force is a push or a pull. The forces of all the individual particles add together to make up the pressure of the air.

Pressure is equal to the force exerted on a surface divided by the total area over which the force is exerted.

$$\text{pressure} = \frac{\text{force}}{\text{area}}$$

When force is measured in newtons (N) and area is measured in square meters (m^2), pressure is measured in newtons per square meter (N/m^2). This unit of pressure is called a pascal (Pa). A more useful unit when discussing atmospheric pressure is the kilopascal (kPa), which is 1,000 pascals.

54 ◆ K CHAPTER 2 States of Matter

Section 3 Resource Manager

Chapter *FAST FILE* Resources
Directed Reading for Content Mastery, pp. 19, 20
Transparency Activity, p. 44
MiniLab, p. 4
Enrichment, p. 30

Reinforcement, p. 27
Lab Worksheet, pp. 7–8
Mathematics Skill Activities, p. 31
Performance Assessment in the Science Classroom, p. 39
Physical Science Critical Thinking/Problem Solving, p. 3

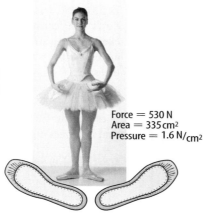

Figure 16 The force of the dancer's weight on pointed toes results in a higher pressure than the same force on flat feet. **Explain** *why the pressure is higher.*

Force = 530 N
Area = 335 cm²
Pressure = 1.6 N/cm²

Force = 530 N
Area = 37 cm²
Pressure = 14 N/cm²

Force and Area You can see from the equation on the opposite page that pressure depends on the quantity of force exerted and the area over which the force is exerted. As the force increases over a given area, pressure increases. If the force decreases, the pressure will decrease. However, if the area changes, the same amount of force can result in different pressure. **Figure 16** shows that if the force of the ballerina's weight is exerted over a smaller area, the pressure increases. If that same force is exerted over a larger area, the pressure will decrease.

✓ Reading Check *What variables does pressure depend on?*

Atmospheric Pressure You can't see it and you usually can't feel it, but the air around you presses on you with tremendous force. The pressure of air also is known as atmospheric pressure because air makes up the atmosphere around Earth. Atmospheric pressure is 101.3 kPa at sea level. This means that air exerts a force of about 101,000 N on every square meter it touches. This is approximately equal to the weight of a large truck.

It might be difficult to think of air as having pressure when you don't notice it. However, you often take advantage of air pressure without even realizing it. Air pressure, for example, enables you to drink from a straw. When you first suck on a straw, you remove the air from it. As you can see in **Figure 17,** air pressure pushes down on the liquid in your glass then forces liquid up into the straw. If you tried to drink through a straw inserted into a sealed, airtight container, you would not have any success because the air would not be able to push down on the surface of the drink.

Figure 17 The downward pressure of air pushes the juice up into the straw.

Air pressure

SECTION 3 Behavior of Fluids **K** ◆ **55**

Caption Answer
Figure 16 The area is different.

✓ Reading Check

Answer force and area

Visual Learning

Figure 17 Have students explain how a drinking straw works. Sucking on the straw creates a difference between the air pressure on the liquid in the cup and the air pressure on the liquid in the straw. The higher pressure outside the straw pushes the liquid up the straw. L2 **LS** **Visual-Spatial**

Discussion
Snow Skis and Snowshoes How does using snow skis or snowshoes enable a person to ski or walk on soft snow? The skis or snowshoes distribute the force of the person's weight over a larger area, decreasing the pressure exerted on the surface of the snow. L2 **LS** **Logical-Mathematical**

Science Journal

Pressure Applied Have each student make a drawing of a balloon in his or her Science Journal and show the molecular forces that are keeping the balloon inflated. Ask students to include captions that explain why the balloon stays inflated. After completing the section, have students compare their drawings and explanations with **Figure 19.** L2 **LS** **Visual-Spatial** **P**

Use Science Words

Word Meaning The word *atmosphere* is formed from the word parts *atmos*, which is Greek for "vapor," and *sphaera*, the Latin word for "sphere." Ask students to explain how these word parts are related to the meaning of *atmosphere*. The atmosphere is the gases (or vapors) that surround Earth (a spherical body). L2 IS **Linguistic**

Discussion

Air Pressure Suppose that instead of a balloon you had a sealed box of air. What would happen to the particles of air as you carried the box up the mountain? Explain. Nothing would happen as long as the box was sealed, because the rigid walls of the box would keep the particles in the box isolated from the changes in air pressure outside the box. L3 IS **Logical-Mathematical**

Caption Answer

Figure 18 The pressure of fluids in her body balances atmospheric pressure.

Figure 18 Atmospheric pressure exerts a force on all surfaces of this dancer's body.
Explain *why she can't feel this pressure.*

Figure 19 Notice how the balloon expands as it is carried up the mountain. The reason is that atmospheric pressure decreases with altitude. With less pressure pushing in on the balloon, the gas particles within the balloon are free to expand.

Balanced Pressure If air is so forceful, why don't you feel it? The reason is that the pressure exerted outward by the fluids in your body balances the pressure exerted by the atmosphere on the surface of your body. Look at **Figure 18.** The atmosphere exerts a pressure on all surfaces of the dancer's body. She is not crushed by this pressure because the fluids in her body exert a pressure that balances atmospheric pressure.

Variations in Atmospheric Pressure
Atmospheric pressure changes with altitude. Altitude is the height above sea level. As altitude increases atmospheric pressure decreases. This is because fewer air particles are found in a given volume. Fewer particles have fewer collisions, and therefore exert less pressure. This idea was tested in the seventeenth century by a French physician named Blaise Pascal. He designed an experiment in which he filled a balloon only partially with air. He then had the balloon carried to the top of a mountain. **Figure 19** shows that as Pascal predicted, the balloon expanded while being carried up the mountain. Although the amount of air inside the balloon stayed the same, the air pressure pushing in on it from the outside decreased. Consequently, the particles of air inside the balloon were able to spread out further.

56 ◆ **K CHAPTER 2** States of Matter

Visual Learning

Figure 19 Discuss with students how the balloon would change if the amount of air pressure exerted on it were increased. The gas inside the balloon would be compressed as it was squeezed by increased air pressure acting on the balloon. This would make the balloon get smaller. L2 IS **Logical-Mathematical**

Teacher FYI

Pascal Blaise Pascal lived from 1623 to 1662. As part of his work with fluids, he formulated Pascal's principle, which will be studied later in this chapter. The unit of pressure, the pascal, was named for him.

Air Travel If you travel to higher altitudes, perhaps flying in an airplane or driving up a mountain, you might feel a popping sensation in your ears. As the air pressure drops, the air pressure in your ears becomes greater than the air pressure outside your body. The release of some of the air trapped inside your ears is heard as a pop. Airplanes are pressurized so that the air pressure within the cabin does not change dramatically throughout the course of a flight.

Changes in Gas Pressure

In the same way that atmospheric pressure can vary as conditions change, the pressure of gases in confined containers also can change. The pressure of a gas in a closed container changes with volume and temperature.

Pressure and Volume If you squeeze a portion of a filled balloon, the remaining portion of the balloon becomes more firm. By squeezing it, you decrease the volume of the balloon, forcing the same number of gas particles into a smaller space. As a result, the particles collide with the walls more often, thereby producing greater pressure. This is true as long as the temperature of the gas remains the same. You can see the change in the motion of the particles in **Figure 20.** What will happen if the volume of a gas increases? If you make a container larger without changing its temperature, the gas particles will collide less often and thereby produce a lower pressure.

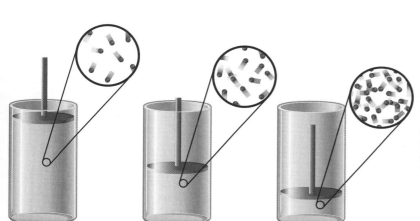

Figure 20 As volume decreases, pressure increases.

As the piston is moved down, the gas particles have less space and collide more often. The pressure increases.

Mini LAB

Predicting a Waterfall

Procedure 🔒👓🧤

1. Fill a **plastic cup** to the brim with **water**.
2. Cover the top of the cup with an **index card**.
3. Predict what will happen if you turn the cup upside down.
4. While holding the index card in place, turn the cup upside down over a sink. Then let go of the card.

Analysis

1. What happened to the water when you turned the cup?
2. How can you explain your observation in terms of the concept of fluid pressure?

Mini LAB

Purpose to observe how air pressure produces enough force to hold water in a cup ☐L2☐ ☐ELL☐ ☐COOP LEARN☐ ☐S☐ **Kinesthetic**

Materials plastic cup, water, index card

Teaching Strategy Tell students to try not to let any water out of the cup as they turn it over.

Troubleshooting The card must be able to make a tight seal with the cup in order for this experiment to work. Any cup used should have a continuously smooth rim.

Analysis

1. The water remained in the cup.
2. The pressure of the molecules in the air pushing up on the card was greater than the pressure of the water pushing down on the card.

Assessment

Process Ask students to form a hypothesis concerning what will happen if some air is included in the cup. Have them try the experiment. As long as the cup contains enough water to make a seal between the rim and the card, the card will remain in place. Use **Performance Assessment in the Science Classroom,** p. 93.

Fun Fact

Relationships between temperature, pressure, and volume in a gas sample were defined by Jacques Charles and Robert Boyle. Charles's law relates temperature and volume. Boyle's law relates pressure and volume.

Warming Gas Provide students with balloons. Have them blow up the balloons and tie them shut. Ask each student to measure the circumference of his or her balloon at its widest point, then hold it over a lit lightbulb for a few minutes and measure the circumference again. What happened to the balloon as it was warmed by the lightbulb? The gas particles inside it started moving faster, pushing out on the balloon and causing it to expand. Extend the activity by placing one or two balloons in the freezer for a short while. L2

 **Kinesthetic**

Caption Answer

Figure 21 The container will explode.

Reading Check

Answer As temperature decreases, pressure decreases. This makes the pressure inside the container lower that the pressure outside the container. The external pressure pushes the container inward.

Discussion

Buoyant Force What do you think will happen if the buoyant force in a fluid is equal to the weight of an object in it? The object will remain suspended in the fluid, neither rising nor falling. L3 **Logical-Mathematical**

Quick Demo

Cartesian Diver

Materials beaker, squeeze condiment packet such as ketchup or soy sauce, empty 2-L bottle with cap, water

Estimated Time 15 minutes

Procedure Fill a beaker with water. Place several types of unopened condiment packets in the water. The one that barely floats will be used for the next step. Fill the 2-L bottle with water to the very top of the bottle. Insert the unopened condiment packet from the first step. Replace the cap on the bottle. Squeezing the bottle will make the condiment packet sink to the bottom. Release the bottle and the packet rises.

Figure 21 Even though the volume of this container does not change, the pressure increases as the substance is heated.
Describe *what will happen if the substance is heated too much.*

Figure 22 The pressure pushing up on an immersed object is greater than the pressure pushing down on it. This difference results in the buoyant force.

Pressure and Temperature When the volume of a confined gas remains the same, the pressure can change as the temperature of the gas changes. You have learned that temperature rises as the kinetic energy of the particles in a substance increases. The greater the kinetic energy is, the faster the particles move. The faster the speed of the particles is, the more they collide and the greater the pressure is. If the temperature of a confined gas increases, the pressure of the gas will increase, as shown in **Figure 21.**

Reading Check *Why would a sealed container of air be crushed after being frozen?*

Float or Sink

You may have noticed that you feel lighter in water than you do when you climb out of it. While you are under water, you experience water pressure pushing on you in all directions. Just as air pressure increases as you walk down a mountain, water pressure increases as you swim deeper in water. Water pressure increases with depth. As a result, the pressure pushing up on the bottom of an object is greater than the pressure pushing down on it because the bottom of the object is deeper than the top.

The difference in pressure results in an upward force on an object immersed in a fluid, as shown in **Figure 22.** This force is known as the **buoyant force.** If the buoyant force is equal to the weight of an object, the object will float. If the buoyant force is less than the weight of an object, the object will sink.

Pressure pushing down

Pressure pushing up

Weight is a force in the downward direction. The buoyant force is in the upward direction. An object will float if the upward force is equal to the downward force.

Weight   Buoyant force

Differentiated Instruction

Challenge Have students construct a neutrally buoyant helium balloon and gondola—one that has the same density as air. When you test the balloon, make sure there are no drafts in the room. Students will have succeeded if the balloon and gondola remain stationary between the ceiling and floor of a room for several minutes or if they ascend or descend slowly. L3 **Kinesthetic**

Archimedes' Principle What determines the buoyant force? According to **Archimedes'** (ar kuh MEE deez) **principle,** the buoyant force on an object is equal to the weight of the fluid displaced by the object. In other words, if you place an object in a beaker that already is filled to the brim with water, some water will spill out of the beaker, as in **Figure 23.** If you weigh the spilled water, you will find the buoyant force on the object.

Density Understanding density can help you predict whether an object will float or sink. **Density** is mass divided by volume.

$$density = \frac{mass}{volume}$$

An object will float in a fluid that is more dense than itself and sink in a fluid that is less dense than itself. If an object has the same density, the object will neither sink nor float but instead stay at the same level in the fluid.

Figure 23 When the golf ball was dropped in the large beaker, it displaced some of the water, which was collected and placed into the smaller beaker. **Communicate** *what you know about the weight and the volume of the displaced water.*

Applying Math — Find an Unknown

CALCULATING DENSITY You are given a sample of a solid that has a mass of 10.0 g and a volume of 4.60 cm³. Will it float in liquid water, which has a density of 1.00 g/cm³?

Solution

1 *This is what you know:*
- mass = 10.0 g
- volume = 4.60 cm³
- density of water = 1.00 g/cm³

2 *This is what you need to find:* the density of the sample

3 *This is the procedure you need to use:*
- density = mass/volume
- density = 10.0 g/4.60 cm³ = 2.17 g/cm³
- The density of the sample is greater than the density of water. The sample will sink.

4 *Check your answer:*
- Find the mass of your sample by multiplying the density and the volume.

Practice Problems

1. A 7.40-cm³ sample of mercury has a mass of 102 g. Will it float in water?

2. A 5.0-cm³ sample of aluminum has a mass of 13.5 g. Will it float in water?

Science Online
For more practice, visit
bookk.msscience.com/
math_practice

SECTION 3 Behavior of Fluids **K ◆ 59**

Curriculum Connection

History Archimedes was one of history's most gifted mathematicians. He very nearly invented calculus, but did not have the notation to describe his ideas. According to legend, he came to an unfortunate end when he yelled at an invading Roman soldier for ruining calculations he was writing in the dirt. The unappreciative soldier killed him with his sword. Have students find out when Archimedes lived. 287–212 B.C. L2

Differentiated Instruction

Learning Disabled Demonstrate to students how density affects the buoyant force. Have two beakers full of the same amount of water. In one beaker add pieces of styrofoam. In the other add several pennies. Ask students to explain why the styrofoam floated, but the pennies sank.

Caption Answer

Figure 23 The volume of the displaced water equals the volume of the golf ball. The weight of the displaced water is less than the weight of the golf ball.

Activity

Soft-Drink Mass Obtain unopened aluminum cans of regular and diet versions of a soft drink. Show the class that the volumes of the cans are equal. Have students predict what will happen when the cans are placed in a sink or aquarium filled with water. Place the cans into the water and observe. The can of diet drink floats, while the can of regular drink sinks. Divide the class in half and have each group measure the masses of the cans with a balance. Ask how the masses compare. The regular drink is heavier. Discuss with students the idea that equal volumes of different substances can have different masses. Explain that the difference in mass is due to sugar. L2 ELL IS Kinesthetic

Applying Math

National Math Standards
Correlation to Mathematics Objectives
1, 6, 7

Teaching Strategy
This is what you know: mass = 102 g, volume = 7.40 cm³, density of water = 1.00 g/cm³
This is what you need to find: density of the sample.
This is the equation you need to use: density = mass/volume
Substitute in the known values: density = 102 g/7.40 cm³ = 13.78 g/cm³

Answers to Practice Problems

1. No; the density of mercury, which is 13.8 g/cm³, is greater than the density of water.

2. No; density of aluminum, which is 2.7 g/cm³, is greater than the density of water.

SECTION 3 Behavior of Fluids **K ◆ 59**

Observing Density

Purpose to explore and observe density by making miniature lava lamps

Possible Materials glass jar or clear drinking glass, vegetable oil, salt, water, food coloring

Estimated Time 20 minutes

Teaching Strategies

• Students make simple lava lamps by pouring about 7.5 cm of water in the bottom of the jar. Then have them pour about 78 mL of vegetable oil into the jar. Add food coloring.

• Students should shake salt on top of oil while slowly counting to 5.

Observe

What happened when salt is added to the oil? Salt is more dense than water. When salt is poured on the oil, it sinks to the bottom of the mixture, carrying some of the oil with it. In the water layer, the salt starts to dissolve. As it dissolves, the oil is released and floats back up to the top of the water.

For additional inquiry activities, see *Science Inquiry Labs.*

Discussion

Ear Pressure Challenge students to use Pascal's principle to explain why their ears may hurt when they swim to the bottom of the deepest part of a swimming pool. The weight of the water above makes the pressure at the bottom of the pool greater than that at the surface. L2

Figure 24 A hydraulic lift utilizes Pascal's principle to help lift this car and this dentist's chair.

Figure 25 By increasing the area of the piston on the right side of the tube, you can increase the force exerted on the piston. In this way a small force pushing down on the left piston can result in a large force pushing up on the right piston. The force can be great enough to lift a car.

Pascal's Principle

What happens if you squeeze a plastic container filled with water? If the container is closed, the water has nowhere to go. As a result, the pressure in the water increases by the same amount everywhere in the container—not just where you squeeze or near the top of the container. When a force is applied to a confined fluid, an increase in pressure is transmitted equally to all parts of the fluid. This relationship is known as **Pascal's principle.**

Hydraulic Systems You witness Pascal's principle when a car is lifted up to have its oil changed or if you are in a dentist's chair as it is raised or lowered, as shown in **Figure 24.** These devices, known as hydraulic (hi DRAW lihk) systems, use Pascal's principle to increase force. Look at the tube in **Figure 25.** The force applied to the piston on the left increases the pressure within the fluid. That increase in pressure is transmitted to the piston on the right. Recall that pressure is equal to force divided by area. You can solve for force by multiplying pressure by area.

$$\text{pressure} = \frac{\text{force}}{\text{area}} \quad \text{or} \quad \text{force} = \text{pressure} \times \text{area}$$

If the two pistons on the tube have the same area, the force will be the same on both pistons. If, however, the piston on the right has a greater surface area than the piston on the left, the resulting force will be greater. The same pressure multiplied by a larger area equals a greater force. Hydraulic systems enable people to lift heavy objects using relatively small forces.

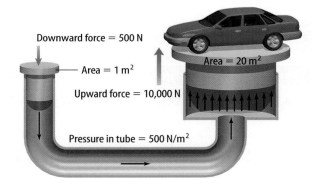

Downward force = 500 N
Area = 1 m²
Area = 20 m²
Upward force = 10,000 N
Pressure in tube = 500 N/m²

Cultural Diversity

Force Pumps Simple piston-type force pumps were known throughout the ancient world. The more efficient double-acting piston bellows were developed by the Chinese, and did not reach Europe until the 1500s. In this device, fluid is pulled in through intake valves on either side and pushed out through a nozzle on both strokes of the piston.

Visual Learning

Figure 25 Review with students the process shown in this figure. Remind students that work equals force times distance. In a hydraulic lift, the force applied to the smaller piston is small, but it is applied over a long distance, so the work done on each side of the lift is the same. L2 **IS** **Visual-Spatial**

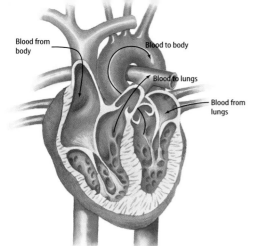

Blood from body
Blood to body
Blood to lungs
Blood from lungs

Figure 26 The heart is responsible for moving blood throughout the body. Two force pumps work together to move blood to and from the lungs and to the rest of the body.

Force Pumps If an otherwise closed container has a hole in it, any fluid in the container will be pushed out the opening when you squeeze it. This arrangement, known as a force pump, makes it possible for you to squeeze toothpaste out of a tube or mustard from a plastic container.

INTEGRATE
Life Science

Your heart has two force pumps. One pump pushes blood to the lungs, where it picks up oxygen. The other force pump pushes the oxygen-rich blood to the rest of your body. These pumps are shown in **Figure 26.**

ScienceOnline

Topic: Blood Pressure
Visit bookk.msscience.com for Web links to information about blood pressure. Find out what the term means, how it changes throughout the human body, and why it is unhealthy to have high blood pressure.

Activity Write a paragraph in your Science Journal that explains why high blood pressure is dangerous.

section ③ review

Summary

Pressure
- Pressure depends on force and area.
- The air around you exerts a pressure.
- The pressure inside your body matches the pressure exerted by air.

Changes in Gas Pressure
- The pressure exerted by a gas depends on its volume and its temperature.

Float or Sink
- Whether an object floats or sinks depends on its density relative to the density of the fluid it's in.

Pascal's Principle
- This principle relates pressure and area to force.

Self Check

1. **Describe** what happens to pressure as the force exerted on a given area increases.
2. **Describe** how atmospheric pressure changes as altitude increases.
3. **State** Pascal's principle in your own words.
4. **Infer** An object floats in a fluid. What can you say about the buoyant force on the object?
5. **Think Critically** All the air is removed from a sealed metal can. After the air has been removed, the can looks as if it were crushed. Why?

Applying Math

6. **Simple Equations** What pressure is created when 5.0 N of force are applied to an area of 2.0 m²? How does the pressure change if the force is increased to 10.0 N? What about if instead the area is decreased to 1.0 m²?

DAILY **INTERVENTION**

Check for Understanding
Logical-Mathematical Have students predict what would happen if a rock punched a small hole in the bottom of an airtight compartment in a ship. As long as no air escaped, the pressure of the air in the compartment would allow little water into the compartment. L3 [LS]

Reteach
Fluids Organize the class into four groups. Assign each group pressure, density, Archimedes' principle, or Pascal's principle. Have each group present to the class its understanding of the assigned term. Each group should be able to define the term and give examples illustrating it. L2 COOP LEARN [LS] **Interpersonal**

✓ **Assessment**

Process Place a beaker of water, a beaker of alcohol, and a beaker of ethylene glycol in front of the class. Challenge students to use buoyancy to put the liquids in order from lowest density to highest density. Students may immerse objects in the liquids to determine the relative densities of the liquids. Use **Performance Assessment in the Science Classroom,** p. 97.

---

section ③ review

1. Pressure increases.
2. Atmospheric pressure decreases.
3. When a force is applied to a confined fluid, an increase in pressure is transmitted equally to all parts of the fluid.
4. The buoyant force is greater than the weight of the object.
5. After the air is removed, the atmospheric pressure on the outside of the can is greater than the pressure on the inside of the can, so the can collapses.
6. 2.5 Pa; the pressure increases to 5 Pa. If the force is 5.0 N and the area is decreased to 1.0 m², the pressure increases to 5 Pa.

LAB

Design Your Own

▶ Real-World Question

Purpose Students apply Archimedes' principle to shipbuilding.

L2 | COOP LEARN | ELL

IS **Logical-Mathematical**

Process Skills observe and infer, design an experiment to test a hypothesis, interpret data, separate and control variables, predict, use numbers

Time Required 90 minutes

Materials balance, 2 small plastic cups, graduated cylinder, metric ruler, scissors, marbles, sink

Alternate Materials basin, pan, or bucket

▶ Form a Hypothesis

Possible Hypothesis Students might hypothesize that a boat floats when the displaced water weighs the same as or more than the boat and its cargo.

▶ Test Your Hypothesis

Possible Procedure Find the mass of the cup and the marbles. Use the density of water (1.00 g/mL) to calculate the volume of water that has the same mass as the cup and marbles, which is the volume of water the boat must displace. Fill the cup with the amount of water that has the same mass as the cup and marbles. Draw a line around the cup at the water line, empty the water, trim the cup to size, and dry the cup. Put the cup into the water in the sink or basin and carefully load the marbles and the trimmed pieces of cup into the floating cup.

Goals

■ **Design** an experiment that uses Archimedes' principle to determine the size of ship needed to carry a given amount of cargo in such a way that the top of the ship is even with the surface of the water.

Possible Materials
balance
small plastic cups (2)
graduated cylinder
metric ruler
scissors
marbles (cupful)
sink
*basin, pan, or bucket
*Alternate materials

Safety Precautions

Design Your ⚓wn Ship

▶ Real-World Question

It is amazing to watch ships that are taller than buildings float easily on water. Passengers and cargo are carried on these ships in addition to the tremendous weight of the ship itself. How can you determine the size of a ship needed to keep a certain mass of cargo afloat?

▶ Form a Hypothesis

Think about Archimedes' principle and how it relates to buoyant force. Form a hypothesis to explain how the volume of water displaced by a ship relates to the mass of cargo the ship can carry.

▶ Test Your Hypothesis

Make a Plan

1. Obtain a set of marbles or other items from your teacher. This is the cargo that your ship must carry. Think about the type of ship

Cargo ship

Alternative Inquiry Lab

Explore Further To extend this Lab into an Inquiry Lab, have students think of similarities and differences between designing a water boat and an airship. What would an airship be filled with? lighter-than-air gases or hot air, like a hot air balloon What shape, material, and design differences are there? Students may enjoy tracing the history of airships, including their role in World War II, researching the different kinds of airships and technologies used in their engineering and construction, and/or experimenting with commercial helium-filled balloons to see how much weight they can carry.

you will design. Consider the types of materials you will use. Decide how your group is going to test your hypothesis.

2. **List** the steps you need to follow to test your hypothesis. Include in your plan how you will measure the mass of your ship and cargo, calculate the volume of water your ship must displace in order to float with its cargo, and measure the volume and mass of the displaced water. Also, explain how you will design your ship so that it will float with the top of the ship even with the surface of the water. Make the ship.

3. **Prepare** a data table in your Science Journal to use as your group collects data. Think about what data you need to collect.

Follow Your Plan

1. Make sure your teacher approves your plan before you start.

2. Perform your experiment as planned. Be sure to follow all proper safety procedures. In particular, clean up any spilled water immediately.

3. Record your observations carefully and complete the data table in your Science Journal.

◉ *Analyze Your Data*

1. **Write** your calculations showing how you determined the volume of displaced water needed to make your ship and cargo float.

2. Did your ship float at the water's surface, sink, or float above the water's surface? Draw a diagram of your ship in the water.

3. **Explain** how your experimental results agreed or failed to agree with your hypothesis.

◉ *Conclude and Apply*

1. If your ship sank, how would you change your experiment or calculations to correct the problem? What changes would you make if your ship floated too high in the water?

2. What does the density of a ship's cargo have to do with the volume of cargo the ship can carry? What about the density of the water?

Communicating
Your Data

Compare your results with other students' data. Prepare a combined data table or summary showing how the calculations affect the success of the ship. **For more help, refer to the** Science Skill Handbook.

Communicating
Your Data

Content Background

Silicon is the second most abundant element in Earth's crust. Rubber is a natural carbon-based polymer that comes from trees. Polymers are large molecules made from many small molecules linked together. During World War II, scientists were trying to replace carbon in organic molecules such as rubber with silicon. Silicones are polymers made up of silicon atoms linked to oxygen atoms. Various organic compounds are often attached to the polymer to control and change its physical properties. Some silicones form rubbery elastic compounds, while others are designed to act as lubricants.

Activity

Make Your Own "Goo" Allow small groups of students to investigate how the addition of a compound can change the properties of a polymer. Dissolve 2 mL of borax in 125 mL of water in a beaker. Have students pour 15 mL of white glue (a polymer) into a paper cup. Then have them add 15 mL of the borax solution to the glue and stir it with a craft stick. The borax cross-links the glue polymers, making the resulting compound thicker and more rubbery. Tell students to remove the polymer from the cup and knead it for a few minutes. As a class, discuss the properties of the new polymer. L2 LS **Kinesthetic**

Analyze the Event

Why do this? Ask students to brainstorm possible reasons scientists tried unusual experiments when working to come up with an inexpensive alternative to synthetic rubber.

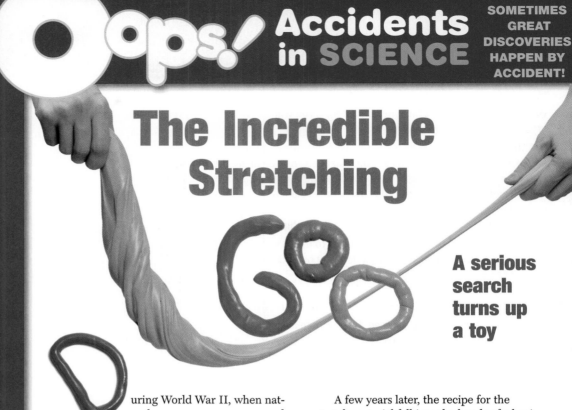

The Incredible Stretching Goo

A serious search turns up a toy

uring World War II, when natural resources were scarce and needed for the war effort, the U.S. government asked an engineer to come up with an inexpensive alternative to synthetic rubber. While researching the problem and looking for solutions, the engineer dropped boric acid into silicone oil. The result of these two substances mixing together was—a goo!

Because of its molecular structure, the goo could bounce and stretch in all directions. The engineer also discovered the goo could break into pieces. When strong pressure is applied to the substance, it reacts like a solid and breaks apart. Even though the combination was versatile—and quite amusing, the U.S. government decided the new substance wasn't a good substitute for synthetic rubber.

A few years later, the recipe for the stretch material fell into the hands of a businessperson, who saw the goo's potential—as a toy. The toymaker paid $147 for rights to the boric acid and silicone oil mixture. And in 1949 it was sold at toy stores for the first time. The material was packaged in a plastic egg and it took the U.S. by storm. Today, the acid and oil mixture comes in a multitude of colors and almost every child has played with it at some time.

The substance can be used for more than child's play. Its sticky consistency makes it good for cleaning computer keyboards and removing small specks of lint from fabrics.

People use it to make impressions of newspaper print or comics. Athletes strengthen their grips by grasping it over and over. Astronauts use it to anchor tools on spacecraft in zero gravity. All in all, a most *eggs-cellent* idea!

Research As a group, examine a sample of the colorful, sticky, stretch toy made of boric acid and silicone oil. Then brainstorm some practical—and impractical—uses for the substance.

Science Online
For more information, visit bookk.msscience.com/oops

Research Ask students in each group to describe the list of uses they came up with for the goo. Ask students in other groups to comment on whether or not they think the proposed uses would actually work. If possible, allow students to demonstrate some of the uses they brainstormed. L2

Resources for Teachers and Students

Super Science Concoctions, by Jill Frankel Hauser, Williamson Publishing, 1997

They All Laughed . . . From Light Bulbs to Lasers: The Fascinating Stories Behind Great Inventions That Have Changed Our Lives, by Ira Flatow, Harper Perennial, 1992

Reviewing Main Ideas

Section 1 Matter

1. All matter is composed of tiny particles that are in constant motion.

2. In the solid state, the attractive force between particles holds them in place to vibrate.

3. Particles in the liquid state have defined volumes and are free to move about within the liquid.

Section 2 Changes of State

1. Thermal energy is the total energy of the particles in a sample of matter. Temperature is the average kinetic energy of the particles in a sample.

2. An object gains thermal energy when it changes from a solid to a liquid, or when it changes from a liquid to a gas.

3. An object loses thermal energy when it changes from a gas to a liquid, or when it changes from a liquid to a solid.

Section 3 Behavior of Fluids

1. Pressure is force divided by area.

2. Fluids exert a buoyant force in the upward direction on objects immersed in them.

3. An object will float in a fluid that is more dense than itself.

4. Pascal's principle states that pressure applied to a liquid is transmitted evenly throughout the liquid.

Visualizing Main Ideas

Copy and complete the following concept map on matter.

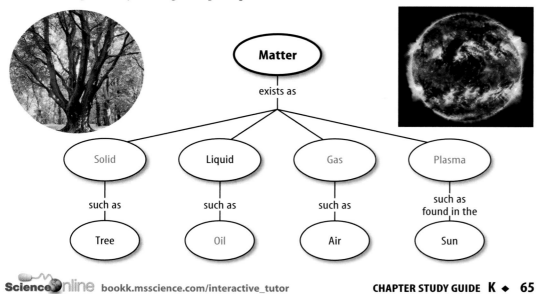

Matter — exists as — Solid / Liquid / Gas / Plasma

Solid — such as — Tree
Liquid — such as — Oil
Gas — such as — Air
Plasma — such as found in the — Sun

Reviewing Main Ideas

Summary statements can be used by students to review the major concepts of the chapter.

Visualizing Main Ideas

See student page.

Visit bookk.msscience.com
/self_check_quiz
/interactive_tutor
/vocabulary_puzzlemaker
/chapter_review
/standardized_test

Assessment Transparency

For additional assessment questions, use the *Assessment Transparency* located in the transparency book.

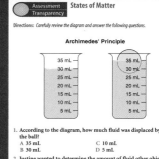

Assessment

Assessment Transparency — States of Matter

Directions: Carefully review the diagram and answer the following questions.

Archimedes' Principle

35 mL / 30 mL / 25 mL / 20 mL / 15 mL / 10 mL / 5 mL

1. According to the diagram, how much fluid was displaced by the ball?
   A 35 mL   C 10 mL
   B 30 mL   D 5 mL
2. Justine wanted to determine the amount of fluid other objects displaced in the beaker. Which observation would mean she could NOT measure this amount of fluid?
   F More than one object was in the beaker.
   G She removed some water to make more room for objects.
   H The water rose above the measurement markings.
   J She used a different size of beaker for each new object.
3. According to Archimedes' principle, the buoyant force on the ball equals the weight of ___.
   A 10 mL of fluid   C 35 mL of fluid
   B 30 mL of fluid   D 5 mL of fluid

Use the assessment as follow-up to page F at the beginning of the chapter after students have completed the chapter.

Materials paper, pencil

Procedure Have students work in groups to make cartoon posters of sporting events in which the Matter Team plays the Non-Matter Team. Students should choose a team sport and create each team. For instance in a baseball game there can be an Iron Infielder and Plastic Pitcher on the Matter Team and Light Left fielder and Kinetic Energy Catcher on the Non-Matter Team. L2

Expected Outcome Students should realize that matter includes solids, liquids, and gases and does not include types of energy.

Using Vocabulary

1. gas
2. liquid
3. Heat
4. Temperature
5. condensation
6. vaporization
7. Density
8. Pressure
9. Pascal's Principle

Checking Concepts

10. B	16. D
11. A	17. B
12. C	18. C
13. D	19. C
14. B	20. B
15. C	

Using Vocabulary

Archimedes' principle p. 59	melting p. 47
buoyant force p. 58	Pascal's principle p. 60
condensation p. 51	pressure p. 54
density p. 59	solid p. 41
freezing p. 49	surface tension p. 43
gas p. 44	temperature p. 46
heat p. 46	thermal energy p. 45
liquid p. 42	vaporization p. 50
matter p. 40	viscosity p. 43

Fill in the blanks with the correct vocabulary word.

1. A(n) _____ can change shape and volume.

2. A(n) _____ has a different shape but the same volume in any container.

3. _____ is thermal energy moving from one substance to another.

4. _____ is a measure of the average kinetic energy of the particles of a substance.

5. A substance changes from a gas to a liquid during the process of _____.

6. A liquid becomes a gas during _____.

7. _____ is mass divided by volume.

8. _____ is force divided by area.

9. _____ explains what happens when force is applied to a confined fluid.

Checking Concepts

Choose the word or phrase that best answers the question.

10. Which of these is a crystalline solid?
   A) glass   C) rubber
   B) sugar   D) plastic

11. Which description best describes a solid?
   A) It has a definite shape and volume.
   B) It has a definite shape but not a definite volume.
   C) It adjusts to the shape of its container.
   D) It can flow.

12. What property enables you to float a needle on water?
   A) viscosity   C) surface tension
   B) temperature   D) crystal structure

13. What happens to an object as its kinetic energy increases?
   A) It holds more tightly to nearby objects.
   B) Its mass increases.
   C) Its particles move more slowly.
   D) Its particles move faster.

14. During which process do particles of matter release energy?
   A) melting   C) sublimation
   B) freezing   D) boiling

15. How does water vapor in air form clouds?
   A) melting   C) condensation
   B) evaporation   D) sublimation

16. Which is a unit of pressure?
   A) N   C) g/cm^3
   B) kg   D) N/m^2

17. Which change results in an increase in gas pressure in a balloon?
   A) decrease in temperature
   B) decrease in volume
   C) increase in volume
   D) increase in altitude

18. In which case will an object float on a fluid?
   A) Buoyant force is greater than weight.
   B) Buoyant force is less than weight.
   C) Buoyant force equals weight.
   D) Buoyant force equals zero.

 bookk.msscience.com/vocabulary_puzzlemaker

Use the Exam*View*® Pro Testmaker CD-ROM to:
- create multiple versions of tests
- create modified tests with one mouse click for inclusion students
- edit existing questions and add your own questions
- build tests aligned with state standards using built-in State Curriculum Tags
- change English tests to Spanish with one mouse click and vice versa

Use the photo below to answer question 19.

19. In the photo above, the water in the small beaker was displaced when the golf ball was added to the large beaker. What principle does this show?
A) Pascal's principle
B) the principle of surface tension
C) Archimedes' principle
D) the principle of viscosity

20. Which is equal to the buoyant force on an object?
A) volume of the object
B) weight of the displaced fluid
C) weight of object
D) volume of fluid

Thinking Critically

21. Explain why steam causes more severe burns than boiling water.

22. Explain why a bathroom mirror becomes fogged while you take a shower.

23. Form Operational Definitions Write operational definitions that explain the properties of and differences among solids, liquids, and gases.

24. Determine A king's crown has a volume of 110 cm^3 and a mass of 1,800 g. The density of gold is 19.3 g/cm^3. Is the crown pure gold?

25. Infer Why do some balloons pop when they are left in sunlight for too long?

 Science Online bookk.msscience.com/chapter_review

Performance Activities

26. Storyboard Create a visual-aid storyboard to show ice changing to steam. There should be a minimum of five frames.

Applying Math

Use the graph below to answer question 27.

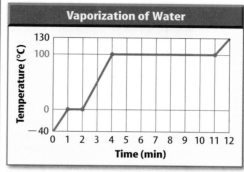

27. Explain how this graph would change if a greater volume of water were heated. How would it stay the same?

Use the table below to answer question 28.

Water Pressure

Depth (m)	Pressure (atm)	Depth (m)	Pressure (atm)
0	1.0	100	11.0
25	3.5	125	13.5
50	6.0	150	16.0
75	8.5	175	18.5

28. Make and Use Graphs In July of 2001, Yasemin Dalkilic of Turkey dove to a depth of 105 m without any scuba equipment. Make a depth-pressure graph for the data above. Based on your graph, how does water pressure vary with depth? Note: The pressure at sea level, 101.3 kPa, is called one atmosphere (atm).

CHAPTER REVIEW K ◆ 67

Thinking Critically

21. Steam contains more thermal energy than boiling water.

22. Some of the hot water from the shower evaporates into the air. It condenses on the mirror because the mirror is cooler than the air.

23. Solids are materials with particles that are very close together. Solids have a definite shape and volume and can be crystalline or amorphous. Liquids are materials in which particles are farther apart than in solids. The individual particles in liquids can flow past each other and have an attraction to each other that gives liquids viscosity and surface tension. Liquids have a definite volume and take the shape of their containers. Gases have particles that are very far apart, move quickly, and lack an attraction to each other. Gases have no definite shape or volume.

24. Check student work. Answers should include changes in temperature and changes in thermal energy.

25. The pressure of the gas inside the balloon increases as the air in the balloon heats up.

Performance Activities

26. Ice should change first to liquid water, then to steam as heat is added to the system and the water molecules move faster. Use **PASC**, p. 135.

Applying Math

National Math Standards
5, 10

27. The melting and boiling points would remain the same. However, the temperature would rise more slowly and the time required for melting and boiling would increase. Therefore, the slopes during the temperature increases would be less.

28. Water pressure increases as the depth increases.

CHAPTER REVIEW K ◆ 67

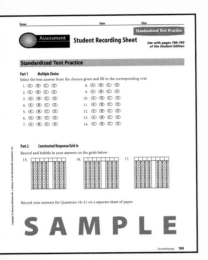

FAST FILE

Answer Sheet A practice answer sheet can be found at bookk.msscience.com/answer_sheet.

S A M P L E

Part 1 | Multiple Choice

1. D
2. A
3. D
4. A
5. C
6. B
7. C
8. B
9. B

Part 2 | Short Response

10. The helium will expand to occupy the volume and shape of the room.

11. The pressure she exerts is 1.52 N/cm^2 on the left and 13 N/cm^2 on the right.

12. Large clown shoes would increase the area over which she exerts force, so the force would be divided by a larger area, which would mean the pressure she exerted would be less.

Part 1 | Multiple Choice

1. In which state of matter do particles stay close together, yet are able to move past one another?
  A. solid   **C.** liquid
  B. gas   **D.** plasma

Use the illustration below to answer questions 2 and 3.

2. Which of the following statements is true about the volume of the water displaced when the golf ball was dropped into the large beaker?
  A. It is equal to the volume of the golf ball.
  B. It is greater than the volume of the golf ball.
  C. It is less than the volume of the golf ball.
  D. It could be greater or less than the volume of the golf ball.

3. What do you know about the buoyant force on the golf ball?
  A. It is equal to the density of the water displaced.
  B. It is equal to the volume of the water displaced.
  C. It is less than the weight of the water displaced.
  D. It is equal to the weight of the water displaced.

4. What is the process called when a gas cools to form a liquid?
  A. condensation   **C.** boiling
  B. sublimation   **D.** freezing

5. Which of the following is an amorphous solid?
  A. diamond   **C.** glass
  B. sugar   **D.** sand

6. Which description best describes a liquid?
  A. It has a definite shape and volume.
  B. It has a definite volume but not a definite shape.
  C. It expands to fill the shape and volume of its container.
  D. It cannot flow.

7. During which processes do particles of matter absorb energy?
  A. freezing and boiling
  B. condensation and melting
  C. melting and vaporization
  D. sublimation and freezing

Use the illustration below to answer questions 8 and 9.

8. What happens as the piston moves down?
  A. The volume of the gas increases.
  B. The volume of the gas decreases.
  C. The gas particles collide less often.
  D. The pressure of the gas decreases.

9. What relationship between the volume and pressure of a gas does this illustrate?
  A. As volume decreases, pressure decreases.
  B. As volume decreases, pressure increases.
  C. As volume decreases, pressure remains the same.
  D. As the volume increases, pressure remains the same.

13. The gas in the balloon will expand. As the temperature is increased, the particles of air in the balloon have more kinetic energy. They collide with one another more frequently and increase the pressure on the inside of the balloon.

14. Thermal energy is the total kinetic energy of all the particles in a sample of matter. Heat is the movement of thermal energy from a substance of higher energy to one of lower energy.

15. Attractive forces cause the particles on the surface of a liquid to pull themselves together and resist being pushed apart. This surface tension causes the water to act as

if a thin film were stretched across it surface. The insects are able to move around on this "film."

16. The upward buoyant force is equal to the downward force of the object's weight.

17. 12 g

Part 2 | Short Response/Grid In

10. A balloon filled with helium bursts in a closed room. What space will the helium occupy?

Use the illustration below to answer questions 11 and 12.

11. If the force exerted by the dancer is 510 N, what is the pressure she exerts if the area is 335 cm² on the left and 37 cm² on the right?

12. Compare the pressure the dancer would exert on the floor if she were wearing large clown shoes to the photo on the left.

13. If a balloon is blown up and tied closed, air is held inside it. What will happen to the balloon if it is then pushed into hot water or held over a heater? Why does this happen?

14. What is the relationship of heat and thermal energy?

15. Why are some insects able to move around on the surface of a lake or pond?

16. How does the weight of a floating object compare with the buoyant force acting on the object?

17. What is the mass of an object that has a density of 0.23 g/cm³ and whose volume is 52 cm³?

 bookk.msscience.com/standardized_test

Part 3 | Open Ended

18. Compare and contrast evaporation and boiling.

Use the illustration below to answer questions 19 and 20.

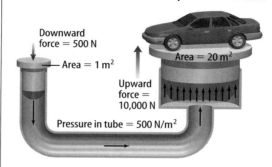

Downward force = 500 N
Area = 1 m²
Area = 20 m²
Upward force = 10,000 N
Pressure in tube = 500 N/m²

19. Name and explain the principle that is used in lifting the car.

20. Explain what would happen if you doubled the area of the piston on the right side of the hydraulic system.

21. Explain why a woman might put dents in a wood floor when walking across it in high-heeled shoes, but not when wearing flat sandals.

22. Explain why the tires on a car might become flattened on the bottom after sitting outside in very cold weather.

23. Compare the arrangement and movement of the particles in a solid, a liquid, and a gas.

24. Explain why the water in a lake is much cooler than the sand on beach around it on a sunny summer day.

> **Test-Taking Tip**
>
> **Show Your Work** For open-ended questions, show all of your work and any calculations on your answer sheet.
>
> **Hint:** In question 20, the pressure in the tube does not change.

STANDARDIZED TEST PRACTICE **K ◆ 69**

21. High-heeled shoes have a smaller area than sandals do. The force the woman exerts on the floor would be greater when she is wearing high-heeled shoes than when she is wearing sandals. This greater force might be enough to put dents in the wood floor.

22. When the temperature of a confined gas decreases, the speed of the gas particles slow down and the less kinetic energy they have. The particles collide less, so they exert less pressure on the inside of the tire making the tire look flat instead of round.

23. Solid particles are very close together and vibrate in place. Liquid particles move more freely than solid particles and have enough energy to move from their fixed positions. Gas particles are much further apart than solid or liquid particles and spread out evenly as far apart as possible.

24. Water has a higher specific heat than sand does. It takes a much larger quantity of heat to make the temperature of the water rise as much as the sand. So the water heats up more slowly than the sand.

Rubrics

For more help evaluating open-ended assessment questions, see the rubric on p. 10T.

Part 3 | Open Ended

18. Both are forms of vaporization where a liquid changes to a gas. Evaporation is vaporization that takes place at the surface of a liquid and occurs at temperatures below the boiling point. Boiling is vaporization that takes place below the surface of a liquid. During boiling, bubbles form within the liquid and rise to the surface. Boiling takes place at a particular temperature called the boiling point of the liquid.

19. Pascal's principle is used in lifting the car. Pascal's principle says that when a force is applied to a confined fluid, an increase in pressure is transmitted equally to all parts of the fluid.

20. By doubling the area of the piston on the right side, the force exerted on the piston would also be doubled. This is because the pressure on the piston would still be 500 N/m², but the piston would have an area of 40 m². This means the force on the piston would be 500 N/m² × 40 m² or 20,000 N.

Section/Objectives	Standards		Labs/Features
	National	State/Local	
Chapter Opener	See pp. 9T–10T for a Key to Standards.		**Launch Lab:** The Changing Face of a Volcano, p. 71 **Foldables,** p. 71
Section 1 Physical and Chemical Properties ⏱ 3 sessions 📦 1.5 blocks 1. **Identify** physical and chemical properties of matter.	National Content Standards: UCP.1, UCP.2, UCP.3, UCP.5, A.1, A.2, B.1		**MiniLAB:** Measuring Properties, p. 74 **MiniLAB:** Identifying an Unknown Substance, p. 75 **Science Online,** p. 76 **Lab:** Finding the Difference, p. 77
Section 2 Physical and Chemical Changes ⏱ 4 sessions 📦 2 blocks 2. **Compare** several physical and chemical changes. 3. **Identify** examples of physical and chemical changes.	National Content Standards: UCP.1, UCP.2, UCP.3, UCP.5, A.1, A.2, B.1, B.3, E.3, G.3		**MiniLAB:** Comparing Changes, p. 81 **Science Online,** p. 81 **Integrate Astronomy,** p. 83 **Applying Math,** p. 84 **Visualizing Recycling,** p. 86 **Lab:** Battle of the Toothpastes, p. 88 **Science Stats:** Strange Changes, p. 90

Lab Materials	Reproducible Resources	Section Assessment	Technology
Launch Lab: samples of obsidian and pumice, clear container, water	**Chapter** *FAST FILE* **Resources** Foldables Worksheet, p. 17 Directed Reading Overview, p. 19 Note-taking Worksheets, pp. 31–32	GLENCOE'S ASSESSMENT ADVANTAGE	TeacherWorks includes: • Interactive Teacher Edition • Lesson Planner with calendar • Access to all program blacklines • Correlations to standards • Web links
MiniLAB: 10-mL graduated cylinder, balance **Lab:** meterstick, spring scale, block of wood, metal bar or ruler, plastic bin, drinking glass, water, rubber ball, paper, carpet, magnet, rock, plant or flower, soil, sand, apple, vegetable, slice of bread, dry cereal, egg, feather	**Chapter** *FAST FILE* **Resources** Transparency Activity, p. 42 MiniLAB, p. 3 Enrichment, p. 29 Reinforcement, p. 27 Directed Reading, p. 20 Lab Worksheet, pp. 5–6 Lab Activity, pp. 9–10 **Reading and Writing Skill Activities,** p. 17	**Portfolio** Assessment, p. 76 **Performance** MiniLAB, p. 74 MiniLAB, p. 75 Applying Math, p. 76 **Content** Section Review, p. 76	♪ Section Focus Transparency ⊙ Virtual Labs CD-ROM ∩ Guided Reading Audio Program ⊙ Interactive Chalkboard CD-ROM
MiniLAB: a piece of fine steel wool, paper plate, tap water **Lab:** 3 or 4 different brands of toothpaste, drinking glasses or bowls, hard-boiled eggs, concentrated lemon juice, apple juice, water, artist's paint brush *Need materials?* Contact Science Kit at 1-800-828-7777 or www.sciencekit.com on the Internet.	**Chapter** *FAST FILE* **Resources** Transparency Activity, p. 43 MiniLAB, p. 4 Enrichment, p. 30 Reinforcement, p. 28 Directed Reading, pp. 21, 22 Transparency Activity, pp. 45–46 Lab Worksheet, pp. 7–8 Lab Activity, pp. 13–16 **Mathematics Skill Activities,** p. 9 **Science Inquiry Labs,** pp. 37–38 **Home and Community Involvement,** p. 27 **Cultural Diversity,** p. 5 **Life Science Critical Thinking/ Problem Solving,** p. 8 **Lab Management and Safety,** p. 67	**Portfolio** Differentiated Instruction, p. 81 **Performance** MiniLAB, p. 81 Applying Math, p. 84 **Content** Applying Math, p. 87 Section Review, p. 87	♪ Section Focus Transparency ♪ Teaching Transparency ⊙ Virtual Labs CD-ROM ∩ Guided Reading Audio Program ⊙ Interactive Chalkboard CD-ROM 📼 Video Lab

End of Chapter Assessment

GLENCOE'S ASSESSMENT ADVANTAGE

Blackline Masters	Technology	Professional Series
Chapter *FAST FILE* **Resources** Chapter Review, pp. 35–36 Chapter Tests, pp. 37–40 **Standardized Test Practice,** pp. 15–18	📼 MindJogger Videoquiz ⊙ Virtual Labs CD-ROM ⊙ ExamView® Pro Testmaker ⊙ TeacherWorks CD-ROM ⊙ Interactive Chalkboard CD-ROM	**Performance Assessment in the Science Classroom (PASC)**

Transparencies

Section Focus

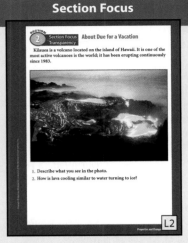

This is a representation of key blackline masters available in the Teacher Classroom Resources. See Resource Manager boxes within the chapter for additional information.

Assessment

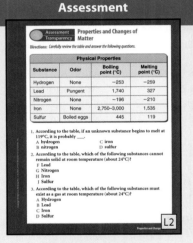

Teaching

Key to Teaching Strategies

The following designations will help you decide which activities are appropriate for your students.

L1 Level 1 activities should be appropriate for students with learning difficulties.

L2 Level 2 activities should be within the ability range of all students.

L3 Level 3 activities are designed for above-average students.

ELL ELL activities should be within the ability range of English Language Learners.

COOP LEARN Cooperative Learning activities are designed for small group work.

LS Multiple Learning Styles logos, as described on page 6T, are used throughout to indicate strategies that address different learning styles.

P These strategies represent student products that can be placed into a best-work portfolio.

PBL Problem-Based Learning activities apply real-world situations to learning.

Hands-on Activities

Student Text Lab Worksheet

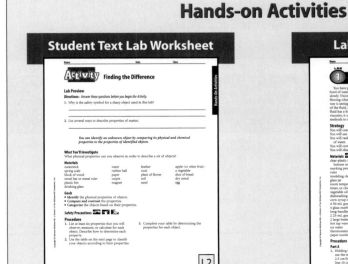

Laboratory Activities

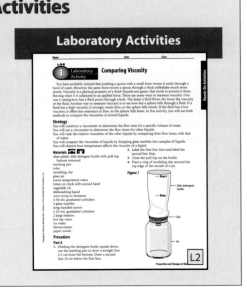

Meeting Different Ability Levels

Content Outline

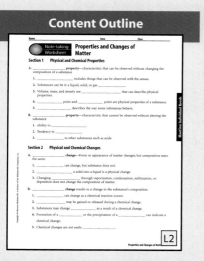

L2

Reinforcement

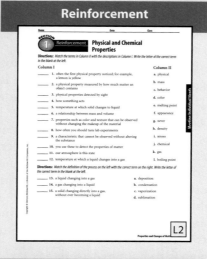

L2

Enrichment

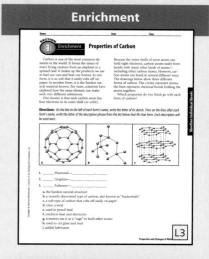

L3

Directed Reading (English/Spanish)

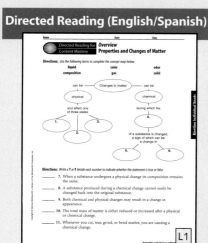

L1

Study Guide

Study Guide

Features
- Contains a study guide page for each section of the chapter
- Reviews key concepts
- Includes answer pages

L2

Reading Essentials

Reading Essentials for Glencoe Science
An Interactive Student Workbook

Features
- Condensed core content
- Actively involves students in reading
- Reinforces key vocabulary

L1

Assessment

Test Practice Workbook

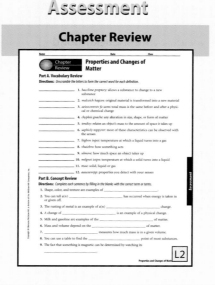

L2

Chapter Review

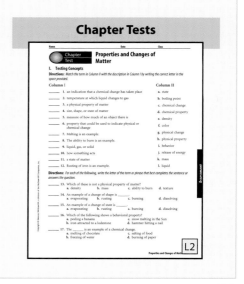

L2

Chapter Tests

L2

Science Content Background

section 1 Physical and Chemical Properties

Physical Properties

You must be careful in describing some physical properties, particularly properties such as solubility. Describing solubility can involve a reaction and, for that reason, may not be a true physical property. For example, if you say that sodium is soluble in water that would imply that the sodium simply dissolves in water. Instead, sodium reacts with water to form hydrogen gas and an aqueous sodium hydroxide solution.

Chemical Properties

A substance's chemical properties describe its ability to react with other substances or to decompose. For example, one chemical property of limestone, or calcium carbonate, is its ability to react with hydrochloric acid, producing carbon dioxide, water, and calcium chloride.

Another chemical property of calcium carbonate is the ability to decompose, forming calcium oxide and carbon dioxide when heated.

The ability to corrode many metals is a chemical property of some acids. For example, when sulfuric acid corrodes aluminum, the aluminum atoms are oxidized (lose electrons) to form positively charged aluminum ions, while the hydrogen ions in the sulfuric acid are reduced (gain electrons) to form hydrogen atoms.

Intensive and Extensive Properties

Properties can also be classified as either intensive or extensive, depending on whether their value changes with the size of the sample. Intensive properties, like melting point and temperature, have values that do not depend on the amount of the sample. Extensive properties, like mass, length, and volume, have values that do depend on the sample size. Density is an

Charles D. Winters/Photo Researchers, Inc.

intensive physical property that relates the mass of an object to its volume. Density is temperature dependent because most substances change in volume when heated or cooled.

section 2 Physical and Chemical Changes

Physical Changes

Knowledge of physical changes and the circumstances under which they occur can be used to separate mixtures. Distillation is a change-of-state operation that is used to separate substances with different boiling points. Distillation is used to separate drinking water from seawater and hydrocarbons, such as gasoline and kerosene, from petroleum.

Chemical Changes

Chemical reaction is another term for chemical change. In a chemical change, atoms are rearranged. If a precipitate, gas, color, or energy change occurs, a chemical change probably has taken place. Almost all chemical changes involve either taking in (endothermic) or giving off (exothermic) energy. However, not all changes that absorb or release energy are chemical. A cold pack is an example of physical change, dissolution, that absorbs heat.

> **Teacher to Teacher**
> Elaine Pietka
> Public School #56
> Buffalo, NY
>
> "To demonstrate the physical changes associated with matter, I give my students a balance and some bubble gum. I tell them to hypothesize what happens to the mass of the bubble gum after it has been chewed for ten minutes. Although the size and shape of the gum changes, the mass remains the same."
>
> *Elaine Pietka*

Conservation of Mass

The French chemist, Antoine Lavoisier (1743–1794), found that when a chemical reaction was carried out in a closed system, the total mass of the system was not changed. Perhaps the most important chemical reaction Lavoisier performed was the decomposition of the red oxide of mercury to form metallic mercury and a gas he named oxygen. This reaction had been carried out by other scientists, but he was the first to weigh all the substances present before and after the reaction. He was also the first to interpret the reaction correctly. Lavoisier carried out many quantitative experiments, even those with animals. Lavoisier summarized all of his findings in the law of conservation of mass.

Jeff Greenberg/PhotoEdit

Chapter Vocabulary

physical property, p. 72
chemical property, p. 76
physical change, p. 78
condensation, p. 79
sublimation, p. 79
vaporization, p. 79
chemical change, p. 80
law of conservation of mass,
   p. 87

Science Journal Possible answers: chemical changes indicated by a change of color, emittance of light, and difficulty of reversal of the reaction

PowerPoint® Presentations

This CD-ROM is an editable Microsoft® PowerPoint® presentation that includes:
• a pre-made presentation for every chapter
• interactive graphics
• animations
• audio clips
• image bank
• all new section and chapter questions
• Standardized Test Practice
• transparencies
• pre-lab questions for all labs
• Foldables directions
• links to bookk.msscience.com

Properties and Changes of Matter

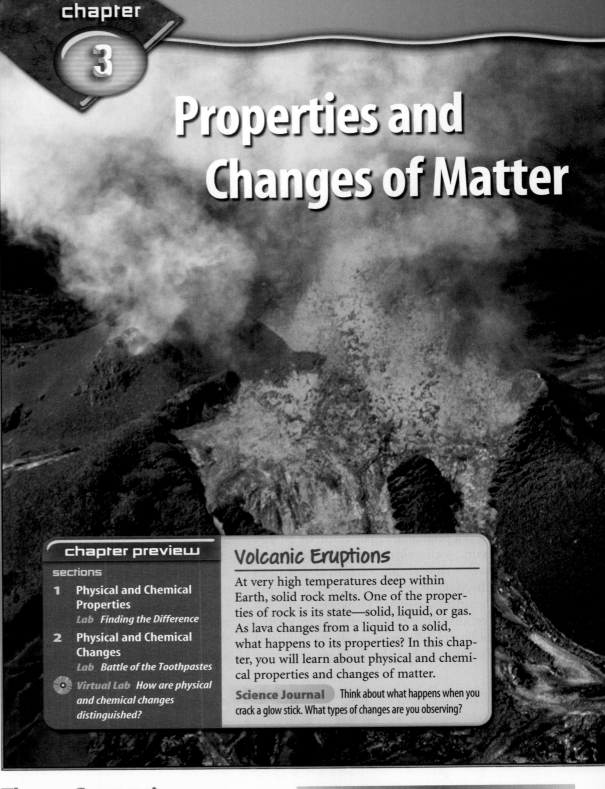

chapter preview

sections

1 **Physical and Chemical Properties**
   Lab Finding the Difference

2 **Physical and Chemical Changes**
   Lab Battle of the Toothpastes

   Virtual Lab How are physical and chemical changes distinguished?

Volcanic Eruptions

At very high temperatures deep within Earth, solid rock melts. One of the properties of rock is its state—solid, liquid, or gas. As lava changes from a liquid to a solid, what happens to its properties? In this chapter, you will learn about physical and chemical properties and changes of matter.

Science Journal Think about what happens when you crack a glow stick. What types of changes are you observing?

Theme Connection

Stability and Change Matter can be described by its physical and chemical properties. These properties determine the physical and chemical changes that different types of matter can undergo.

About the Photo

Volcanoes According to the Smithsonian Institute, approximately 1,500 above-sea volcanoes have been active over the past 10,000 years. Many of these volcanoes are formed by the accumulation of magma under Earth's surface. In 79 A.D., Mount Vesuvius erupted and covered the city of Pompeii with over 13 feet of ash.

Start-Up Activities

Launch LAB

The Changing Face of a Volcano

When a volcano erupts, it spews lava and gases. Lava is hot, melted rock from deep within the Earth. After it reaches the Earth's surface, the lava cools and hardens into solid rock. The minerals and gases within the lava, as well as the rate at which it cools, determine the characteristics of the resulting rocks. In this lab, you will compare two types of volcanic rock.

1. Obtain similar-sized samples of the rocks obsidian (ub SIH dee un) and pumice (PUH mus) from your teacher.
2. Compare the colors of the two rocks.
3. Decide which sample is heavier.
4. Look at the surfaces of the two rocks. How are the surfaces different?
5. Place each rock in water and observe.
6. **Think Critically** What characteristics are different about these rocks? In your Science Journal, make a table that compares your observations.

Science Online
Preview this chapter's content and activities at
bookk.msscience.com

FOLDABLES™
Study Organizer

Changes of Matter Make the following Foldable to help you organize your thoughts about properties and changes.

STEP 1 Fold a sheet of paper in half lengthwise. Make the back edge about 1.25 cm longer than the front edge.

STEP 2 Fold in half, then fold in half again to make three folds.

STEP 3 Unfold and cut only the top layer along the three folds to make four tabs.

STEP 4 Label the tabs as shown.

| Physical Properties | Physical Changes | Chemical Properties | Chemical Changes |

Find Main Ideas As you read the chapter, write information about matter's physical and chemical properties and changes.

Launch LAB

Purpose Use the Launch Lab to help students understand that obsidian and pumice, two rocks formed from volcanic lava, have different properties. L1 ELL IS **Kinesthetic**

Preparation Obtain pumice and obsidian samples and a clear container.

Materials pumice and obsidian samples, a clear cup or container that will hold each sample, water

Teaching Strategy In Step 5, advise students to lower the obsidian and pumice samples into the cup slowly to avoid splashing.

Think Critically

Tables should show that pumice has a rough surface while obsidian is smooth. For a similar-sized sample, the obsidian is much heavier. Pumice floats in water (or at least is more buoyant) while obsidian sinks.

Assessment

Process Have students use a balance to determine the mass of their rock samples and use water displacement in a graduated cylinder to determine the volume of each rock sample. Explain what density is, and show students how to calculate the densities of the pumice and obsidian. Use **Performance Assessment in the Science Classroom,** p. 101.

FOLDABLES™
Study Organizer

Dinah Zike Study Fold

Student preparation materials for this Foldable are available in the Chapter *FAST FILE* Resources.

K ◆ 71

Physical and Chemical Properties

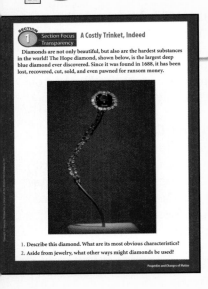

SECTION 1 Section Focus Transparency A Costly Trinket, Indeed

Diamonds are not only beautiful, but also are the hardest substances in the world! The Hope diamond, shown below, is the largest deep blue diamond ever discovered. Since it was found in 1688, it has been lost, recovered, cut, sold, and even pawned for ransom money.

1. Describe this diamond. What are its most obvious characteristics?
2. Aside from jewelry, what other ways might diamonds be used?

Properties and Changes of Matter

Tie to Prior Knowledge

Using Senses Have students re-call occasions when they had to describe an object using their senses.

Reading Check

Answer a characteristic that can be observed without changing the composition of a substance

Caption Answer
Figure 1 Answers will vary.

---

as you read

What **You'll Learn**
- **Identify** physical and chemical properties of matter.
- **Classify** objects based on physi-cal properties.

Why **It's Important**
Understanding the different proper-ties of matter will help you to better describe the world around you.

Review Vocabulary
matter: anything that has mass and takes up space

New Vocabulary
- physical property
- chemical property

Figure 1 All matter can be described by physical properties that can be observed using the five senses.
Identify *the types of matter you think you could see, hear, taste, touch, and smell at the fair.*

Physical Properties

It's a busy day at the state fair as you and your classmates navigate your way through the crowd. While you follow your teacher, you can't help but notice the many sights and sounds that surround you. Eventually, you fall behind the group as you spot the most amazing ride you have ever seen. You inspect it from one end to the other. How will you describe it to the group when you catch up to them? What features will you use in your description?

Perhaps you will mention that the ride is large, blue, and made of wood. These features are all physical properties, or characteris-tics, of the ride. A **physical property** is a characteristic that you can observe without changing or trying to change the composition of the substance. How something looks, smells, sounds, or tastes are all examples of physical properties. In **Figure 1** you can describe and differentiate all types of matter by observing their properties.

Reading Check *What is a physical property of matter?*

Section 1 Resource Manager

Chapter *FAST FILE* Resources
Note-taking Worksheets, p. 42
Directed Reading for Content Mastery, pp. 19, 20
Note-taking Worksheets, pp. 31–32
MiniLAB, p. 3

Enrichment, p. 29
Lab Activity, pp. 9–12
Lab Worksheet, pp. 5–6
Reinforcement, p. 27
Reading and Writing Skill Activities, p. 17
Mathematics Skill Activities, p. 39

Using Your Senses Some physical properties describe the appearance of matter. You can detect many of these properties with your senses. For example, you can see the color and shape of the ride at the fair. You can also touch it to feel its texture. You can smell the odor or taste the flavor of some matter. (You should never taste anything in the laboratory.) Consider the physical properties of the items in **Figure 2.**

State To describe a sample of matter, you need to identify its state. Is the ride a solid, a liquid, or a gas? This property, known as the state of matter, is another physical property that you can observe. The ride, your chair, a book, and a pen are examples of matter in the solid state. Milk, gasoline, and vegetable oil are examples of matter in the liquid state. The helium in a balloon, air in a tire, and neon in a sign are examples of matter in the gas state. You can see examples of solids, liquids, and gases in **Figure 3.**

Perhaps you are most familiar with the three states of water. You can drink or swim in liquid water. You use the solid state of water, which is ice, when you put ice cubes in a drink or skate on a frozen lake. Although you can't see it, water in the gas state is all around you in the air.

Figure 2 Some matter has a characteristic color, such as this sulfur pile. You can use a characteristic smell or taste to identify these fruits. Even if you didn't see it, you could probably identify this sponge by feeling its texture.

Figure 3 The state of a sample of matter is an important physical property.

This colorful sign uses the element neon, which is generally found in the gaseous state.

This rock formation is in the solid state.

The oil flowing out of a bottle is in the liquid state.

Teacher FYI

Plasma State In addition to solid, liquid, and gas, there is a state of matter called plasma. Plasma exists when high energies strip electrons from atomic nuclei, so the nuclei and the electrons exist separately. Matter in the Sun is in the plasma state, as is matter in lightning.

Differentiated Instruction

Challenge Have students break into groups to make picture books that explain physical and chemical properties to students who have not studied these concepts. Information displayed should include a general list of physical and chemical properties as well as an explanation of the property being illustrated in each picture. L2

Make a Model

Water Molecule Have each student make a model of a water molecule by using a large circle to represent oxygen and two small circles to represent hydrogen. Direct them to connect the small circles to the large circle with chenille stems and glue. As you discuss solids, liquids, and gasses, collect students' molecules and arrange them on a large piece of construction paper. Glue some of them closely together in a hexagonal arrangement to represent the molecules in solid ice. Arrange the next set more randomly and with spaces between them to represent liquid water. Then lay out a few molecules with large spaces between them to represent gaseous water vapor. Keep these models on the wall to remind students that the molecule for water did not change; instead the arrangement of the molecules determined state. L1
ELL IS Kinesthetic

Visual Learning

Figure 3 Have students describe the physical properties shown in the pictures. rock formation: brown, orange, sharp, sandy, solid; oil: brown, thick, liquid; neon sign: bright, colorful, yellow L2

Discussion

Colors Sulfur has a characteristic yellow color. What other elements have characteristic colors or smells? Possible answers: chlorine smells like the pool, sulfur smells like rotten eggs, lead is gray, calcium is white, cobalt is blue, silver, or gold L2

Mini LAB

Purpose Students measure mass and volume of a water sample and determine its density.

Materials 10-mL graduated cylinder, balance

Teaching Strategy Review with students how to read the volume of a liquid in a graduated cylinder using the meniscus.

Answers to Analysis
1. The mass of the water could not be measured unless the water is in a container. The mass of the container is subtracted from the total mass.
2. It would be unchanged.

Assessment

Performance Using their calculated density, have students calculate the mass of water that would have a volume of 7.5 mL and perform an experiment to confirm the answer. Use **Performance Assessment in the Science Classroom,** p. 97.

Activity

Calculate Volume Give students classroom objects that are rectangular solids, such as a chalkboard eraser, and have them calculate the volume of each by finding the product of the width, height, and depth. L2 LS
Logical-Mathematical

Mini LAB

Measuring Properties

Procedure
1. Measure the mass of a **10-mL graduated cylinder.**
2. Fill the graduated cylinder with **water** to the 10-mL mark and remeasure the mass of the graduated cylinder with the water.
3. Determine the mass of the water by subtracting the mass of the graduated cylinder from the mass of the graduated cylinder and water.
4. Determine the density of water by dividing the mass of the water by the volume of the water.

Analysis
1. Why did you need to measure the mass of the empty graduated cylinder?
2. How would your calculated density be affected if you added more than 10 mL of water?

Figure 4 A spring scale is used to measure an object's weight.

Size-Dependent Properties Some physical properties depend on the size of the object. Suppose you need to move a box. The size of the box would be important in deciding if you need to use your backpack or a truck. You begin by measuring the width, height, and depth of the box. If you multiply them together, you calculate the box's volume. The volume of an object is the amount of space it occupies.

Another physical property that depends on size is mass. Recall that the mass of an object is a measurement of how much matter it contains. A bowling ball has more mass than a basketball. Weight is a measurement of force. Weight depends on the mass of the object and on gravity. If you were to travel to other planets, your weight would change but your size and mass would not. Weight is measured using a spring scale like the one in **Figure 4.**

Size-Independent Properties Another physical property, density, does not depend on the size of an object. Density measures the amount of mass in a given volume. To calculate the density of an object, divide its mass by its volume. The density of water is the same in a glass as it is in a tub. The density of an object will change, however, if the mass changes and the volume remains the same. Another property, solubility, also does not depend on size. Solubility is the number of grams of one substance that will dissolve in 100 g of another substance at a given temperature. The amount of drink mix that can be dissolved in 100 g of water is the same in a pitcher as it is when it is poured into a glass. Size-dependent and independent properties are shown in **Table 1.**

Melting and Boiling Point Melting and boiling point also do not depend upon an object's size. The temperature at which a solid changes into a liquid is called its melting point. The temperature at which a liquid changes into a gas is called its boiling point. The melting and boiling points of several substances, along with some of their other physical properties, are shown in **Table 2.**

Table 1 Properties of Matter	
Physical Properties	
Dependent on sample size	mass, weight, volume
Independent of sample size	density, melting/boiling point, solubility, ability to attract a magnet, state of matter, color

---

 LAB DEMONSTRATION

Purpose to measure the melting and boiling points of water

Materials large beaker, several ice cubes made from distilled water, thermometer, hot plate, hot pad

Procedure Place the ice in the container, then measure the temperature of the ice.

Heat the ice, then measure the mixture's temperature. Continue heating until boiling and remeasure the temperature. Write all three temperatures on the board.

Expected Outcome Students observe the temperatures for the melting and boiling points of water.

Assessment

What happened to the ice between the first and second temperature checks? Its molecules gained energy and broke apart to change the ice to a liquid. What is the second temperature called? melting point What happened to the water at its boiling point? It turned to gas. L2

Table 2 Physical Properties of Several Substances

Substance	State	Density (g/cm³)	Melting point (°C)	Freezing point (°C)	Solubility in cold water (g/100 mL)
Ammonia	gas	0.7710	-78	-33	89.9
Bromine	liquid	3.12	-7	59	4.17
Calcium carbonate	solid	2.71	1,339	898	0.0014
Iodine	solid	4.93	113.5	184	0.029
Potassium hydroxide	solid	2.044	360	1,322	107
Sodium chloride	solid	2.17	801	1,413	35.7
Water	liquid	1	0	100	—

Magnetic Properties Some matter can be described by the specific way in which it behaves. For example, some materials pull iron toward them. These materials are said to be magnetic. The lodestone in **Figure 5** is a rock that is naturally magnetic.

Other materials can be made into magnets. You might have magnets on your refrigerator or locker at school. The door of your refrigerator also has a magnet within it that holds the door shut tightly.

Reading Check *What are some examples of physical properties of matter?*

Figure 5 This lodestone attracts certain metals to it. Lodestone is a natural magnet.

Mini LAB

Identifying an Unknown Substance

Procedure
1. Obtain data from your teacher (mass, volume, solubility, melting or boiling point) for an unknown substance(s).
2. Calculate density and solubility in units of g/100 mL for your unknown substance(s).
3. Using Table 2 and the information you have, identify your unknown substance(s).

Analysis
1. Describe the procedure used to determine the density of your unknown substance(s).
2. Identify three characteristics of your substance(s).
3. Explain how the solubility of your substance would be affected if the water was hot.

Check for Understanding

Auditory-Musical Have students break into groups and compose simple songs to illustrate the physical and chemical properties of matter. Students may also compose acronyms to help them remember the properties more easily. L2

Reteach

Properties of Matter Ask students which of the following properties of a liquid would be physical and which would be chemical: color, ability to burn, nutritional value, volume, thickness, boiling point, smell, whether it is poisonous. L2

✔ Assessment

Portfolio Have students make mini-posters on 5-in × 7-in index cards explaining physical properties and chemical properties. Encourage them to put their mini-posters in their portfolios. Use **Performance Assessment in the Science Classroom,** p. 145. L2 P

Quick Demo

Density

Materials a balance, clay, 100-mL graduated cylinder, water

Estimated Time 10 minutes

Procedure Using a balance, measure out 10 g of clay. Pour water into a 100-mL graduated cylinder to the 50-mL mark. Shape the clay to fit into the graduated cylinder. Cut a piece of string and attach it to the clay. Use the string to lower the clay into the graduated cylinder. Be careful not to splash out any water. Explain that the volume of the clay is the volume of the clay plus water minus 50 mL. Using this value for the clay's volume, calculate the clay's density.

Figure 6 Notice the difference between the new matches and the matches that have been burned. The ability to burn is a chemical property of matter.

Science nline
Topic: Measuring Matter
Visit bookk.msscience.com for Web links to information about methods of measuring matter.

Activity Find an object around the house. Use two methods of measuring matter to describe it.

Chemical Properties

Some properties of matter cannot be identified just by looking at a sample. For example, nothing happens if you look at the matches in the first picture. But if someone strikes the matches on a hard, rough surface they will burn, as shown in the second picture. The ability to burn is a chemical property. A **chemical property** is a characteristic that cannot be observed without altering the substance. As you can see in the last picture, the matches are permanently changed after they are burned. Therefore this property can be observed only by changing the composition of the match. Another way to define a chemical property, then, is the ability of a substance to undergo a change that alters its identity. You will learn more about changes in matter in the following section.

section 1 review

Summary

Physical Properties
- Matter exists in solid, liquid, and gaseous states.
- Volume, mass, and weight are size-dependent properties.
- Properties such as density, solubility, boiling and melting points, and ability to attract a magnet are size-independent.
- Density relates the mass of an object to its volume.

Chemical Properties
- Chemical properties have characteristics that cannot be observed without altering the identity of the substance.

Self Check

1. **Infer** How are your senses important for identifying physical properties of matter?
2. **Describe** the physical properties of a baseball.
3. **Think Critically** Explain why solubility is a size-independent physical property.
4. **Compare and Contrast** How do chemical and physical properties differ?

Applying Math

5. **Solve One-Step Equations** The volume of a bucket is 5 L and you are using a cup with a volume of 50 mL. How many cupfuls will you need to fill the bucket? Hint: 1 L = 1,000 mL

Science nline bookk.msscience.com/self_check_quiz

section 1 review

1. It is through the senses that you gather information about the world around you. For example, you use your senses to detect an object's shape, color, texture, taste, sound, temperature, smell, weight, state, and behavior, as well as to make measurements.

2. Possible answers: state (solid), shape (spherical), texture, color, mass, volume, density

3. Solubility is a ratio of two size-dependent properties. As one property increases, so does the other. The ratio doesn't change.

4. A physical property can be observed without changing the composition of the substance. A chemical property cannot be observed without altering the composition of the sample.

5. 100 cups

Finding the Difference

◉ Real-World Question

You can identify an unknown object by comparing its physical and chemical properties to the properties of identified objects.

Goals

- **Identify** the physical properties of objects.
- **Compare and contrast** the properties.
- **Categorize** the objects based on their properties.

Materials

meterstick	rock
spring scale	plant or flower
block of wood	soil
metal bar or metal ruler	sand
plastic bin	apple (or other fruit)
drinking glass	vegetable
water	slice of bread
rubber ball	dry cereal
paper	egg
carpet	feather
magnet	

Safety Precautions

◉ Procedure

1. List at least six properties that you will observe, measure, or calculate for each object. Describe how to determine each property.
2. In your Science Journal, create a data table with a column for each property and rows for the objects.
3. Complete your table by determining the properties for each object.

◉ Conclude and Apply

1. **Describe** Which properties were you able to observe easily? Which required making measurements? Which required calculations?
2. **Compare and contrast** the objects based on the information in your table.
3. **Draw Conclusions** Choose a set of categories and group your objects into those categories. Some examples of categories are large/medium/small, heavy/moderate/light, bright/moderate/dull, solid/liquid/gas, etc. Were the categories you chose useful for grouping your objects? Why or why not?

Communicating Your Data

Compare your results with those of other students in your class. **Discuss** the properties of objects that different groups included on their tables. Make a large table including all of the objects that students in the class studied.

Communicating Your Data

Students may want to use a computer database to organize their class table.

◉ Real-World Question

Purpose Students will identify physical characteristics and classify objects based on these characteristics. L2 IS **Kinesthetic**

Process Skills collect data, observe, classify, compare and contrast, make and use tables, draw conclusions

Time Required 40 minutes

◉ Procedure

Safety Precautions Students should wear goggles and aprons during this lab.

Teaching Strategy Set up an area where students can get a few items at a time.

◉ Conclude and Apply

1. easy to identify: possible answers: color, texture, physical state; required measurements: possible answers: mass, length; required calculations: possible answer: density
2. Answers will vary.
3. Answers will vary.

✓ Assessment

Oral Ask students the following questions. What are some physical properties that depend on the amount of material present? Possible answers: mass, length, volume What are some physical properties that are independent of the amount of material present? Possible answers: density, boiling point, melting point. Use **Performance Assessment in the Science Classroom,** p. 89.

1   Motivate

Bellringer

PowerPoint® Presentations

Section Focus Transparencies also are available on the Interactive Chalkboard CD-ROM.
[L2] **ELL**

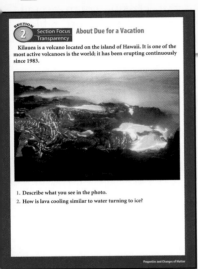

SECTION
2 Section Focus Transparency   About Due for a Vacation

Kilauea is a volcano located on the island of Hawaii. It is one of the most active volcanoes in the world; it has been erupting continuously since 1983.

1. Describe what you see in the photo.
2. How is lava cooling similar to water turning to ice?

Properties and Changes of Matter

Tie to Prior Knowledge

Property Examples Review the concepts of physical properties and chemical properties. Ask students to give an example of each. Explain that in this section they will learn some ways to distinguish between physical and chemical changes. [L2]

Fun Fact

In black and white photographic film, a chemical change occurs when silver bromide (AgBr) is exposed to light and turns dark.

Physical and Chemical Changes

as you read

What You'll Learn
- **Compare** several physical and chemical changes.
- **Identify** examples of physical and chemical changes.

Why It's Important
From modeling clay to watching the leaves turn colors, physical and chemical changes are all around us.

Review Vocabulary
solubility: the amount of a substance that will dissolve in a given amount of another substance

New Vocabulary
- physical change
- vaporization
- condensation
- sublimation
- deposition
- chemical change
- law of conservation of mass

Physical Changes

What happens when the artist turns the lump of clay shown in **Figure 7** into bowls and other shapes? The composition of the clay does not change. Its appearance, however, changes dramatically. The change from a lump of clay to different shapes is a physical change. A **physical change** is one in which the form or appearance of matter changes, but not its composition. The lake in **Figure 7** also experiences a physical change. Although the water changes state due to a change in temperature, it is still made of the elements hydrogen and oxygen.

Changing Shape Have you ever crumpled a sheet of paper into a ball? If so, you caused physical change. Whether it exists as one flat sheet or a crumpled ball, the matter is still paper. Similarly, if you cut fruit into pieces to make a fruit salad, you do not change the composition of the fruit. You change only its form. Generally, whenever you cut, tear, grind, or bend matter, you are causing a physical change.

Figure 7 Although each sample looks quite different after it experiences a change, the composition of the matter remains the same. These changes are examples of physical changes.

Section 2 Resource Manager

Chapter *FAST FILE* Resources
Transparency Activity, pp. 43, 45–46
Directed Reading for Content Mastery, pp. 21, 22
MiniLAB, p. 4
Lab Activity, pp. 13–16
Enrichment, p. 30
Reinforcement, p. 28

Physical Science Critical Thinking/Problem Solving, p. 10
Earth Science Critical Thinking/Problem Solving, p. 15
Performance Assessment in the Science Classroom, p. 44
Science Inquiry Labs, pp. 37–38

Dissolving What type of change occurs when you add sugar to iced tea, as shown in **Figure 8?** Although the sugar seems to disappear, it does not. Instead, the sugar dissolves. When this happens, the particles of sugar spread out in the liquid. The composition of the sugar stays the same, which is why the iced tea tastes sweet. Only the form of the sugar has changed.

Figure 8 Physical changes are occurring constantly. The sugar blending into the iced tea is an example of a physical change. **Define** *What is a physical change?*

Changing State Another common physical change occurs when matter changes from one state to another. When an ice cube melts, for example, it becomes liquid water. The solid ice and the liquid water have the same composition. The only difference is the form.

Matter can change from any state to another. Freezing is the opposite of melting. During freezing, a liquid changes into a solid. A liquid also can change into a gas. This process is known as **vaporization.** During the reverse process, called **condensation,** a gas changes into a liquid. **Figure 9** summarizes these changes.

In some cases, matter changes between the solid and gas states without ever becoming a liquid. The process in which a solid changes directly into a gas is called **sublimation.** The opposite process, in which a gas changes into a solid, is called **deposition.**

Figure 9 Look at the photographs below to identify the different physical changes that bromine undergoes as it changes from one state to another.

Solid state

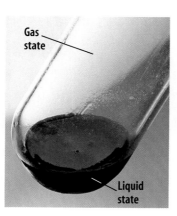
Gas state
Liquid state

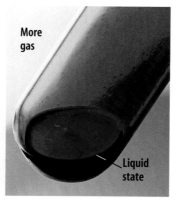
More gas
Liquid state

Caption Answer
Figure 8 a change in which the form or appearance of matter changes but not its composition

Use Science Words
Word Usage Have students use the word *dissolve* in a sentence that describes its meaning and type of change. Possible answer: A substance dissolves when its particles spread out in a liquid; this is a physical change. L2 ELL LS **Linguistic**

Quick Demo
Chemical Change
Materials dry ice, zipper-closure plastic bag
Estimated Time 10 minutes
Procedure Weigh out a 20-g to 30-g sample of dry ice. Place the sample in the zipper-closure plastic bag and allow students to observe it. Release gas from the bag periodically as students observe. A physical change is observed as the dry ice sublimates into a gas.

Make a Model
Changing Clay Give each student a small lump of clay and an index card. Have them divide the clay in half and create small sculptures with one-half of the clay. Tell them to leave the other half of the clay in a lump and to place both pieces on the index card with the label *Physical Change.* L1 ELL LS **Kinesthetic**

Curriculum Connection

History Intense heating caused chemical and physical changes that harden clay into a form that can be used for pottery. Because pottery does not easily decompose, historians have used pottery remains to study ancient civilizations. Ask students to research one early civilization and give a short presentation about the pottery it produced. Civilizations include Maya, Toltec, Inca, Aztec, Cush, Olmec and Cretan. L3

Differentiated Instruction

English-Language Learners Help these students by assigning each one a partner who can assist them with unfamiliar vocabulary. Have the student pairs look at objects in the classroom and discuss the physical and chemical changes that took place as they were made. ELL

Visual Learning

Figure 10 Explain to students that in fireworks, different compounds react with oxygen to produce bright colors. Copper acetoarsenate produces blue, anhydrous strontium carbonate produces red, and barium chloride produces green. L2 LS
Visual-Spatial

✔ Reading Check

Answer A chemical change alters the composition of the matter, while a physical change alters appearance but not composition.

Fun Fact

In order for iron to rust, it must be exposed not only to oxygen in air, but also to water, often as humidity in air. The chemical formula for rust is $Fe_2O_3 \cdot H_2O$. Once some rust has formed, it catalyzes the reaction, and causes additional rust to form faster.

Quick Demo

Tarnished Metal

Materials tarnished silver, silver polish
Estimated Time 10 minutes
Procedure Polish the silver in front of the class. A physical change is occurring as the silver polish removes the tarnish by rubbing it off.

Figure 10 These brilliant fireworks result from chemical changes.
Define *What is a chemical change?*

Chemical Changes

It's the Fourth of July in New York City. Brilliant fireworks are exploding in the night sky. When you look at fireworks, such as these in **Figure 10,** you see dazzling sparkles of red and white trickle down in all directions. The explosion of fireworks is an example of a chemical change. During a **chemical change,** substances are changed into different substances. In other words, the composition of the substance changes.

You are familiar with another chemical change if you have ever left your bicycle out in the rain. After awhile, a small chip in the paint leads to an area of a reddish, powdery substance. This substance is rust. When iron in steel is exposed to oxygen and water in air, iron and oxygen atoms combine to form the principle component in rust. In a similar way, silver coins tarnish when exposed to air. These chemical changes are shown in **Figure 11.**

✔ Reading Check
How is a chemical change different from a physical change?

Figure 11 Each of these examples shows the results of a chemical change. In each case, the substances that are present after the change are different from those that were present before the change.

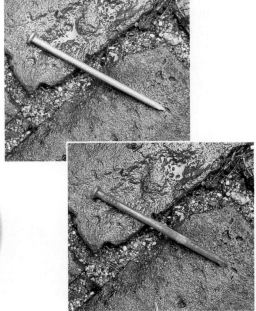

Cultural Diversity

Alchemists Greek, Arabic, and Chinese alchemists began studying chemical changes more than 2,000 years ago. Their work contributed greatly to the understanding of chemical substances and changes. Have students investigate different aspects of alchemy and present their findings to the class. Possible subjects include the processing of metals and the transmutation of metals into gold, the use of minerals and other chemicals for healing, chemical apparatuses developed by alchemists, elements identified by alchemists, and the making of cosmetics and perfumes. L3 LS
Linguistic

Figure 12 In the fall, the chlorophyll in this tree's leaves undergoes a chemical change into colorless chemicals. This allows the red pigment to be seen.

Signs of Chemical Changes

Physical changes are relatively easy to identify. If only the form of a substance changes, you have observed a physical change. How can you tell whether a change is a chemical change? If you think you are unfamiliar with chemical changes, think again.

You have witnessed a spectacular chemical change if you have seen the leaves on a tree change from green to bright yellow, red, or orange. But, it is not a change from a green pigment to a red pigment, as you might think. Pigments are chemicals that give leaves their color. In **Figure 12,** the green pigment that you see during the summer is chlorophyll (KLOHR uh fihl). In autumn, however, changes in temperature and rainfall amounts cause trees to stop producing chlorophyll. The chlorophyll already in the leaves undergoes a chemical change into colorless chemicals. Where do the bright fall colors come from? The pigments that produce fall colors have been present in the leaves all along. However, in the summer, chlorophyll is present in large enough amounts to mask these pigments. In the fall, when chlorophyll production stops, the bright pigments become visible.

Color Perhaps you have found that a half-eaten apple turns brown. The reason is that a chemical change occurs when the apple is exposed to air. Maybe you have toasted a marshmallow or a slice of bread and watched them turn black. In each case, the color of the food changes as it is cooked because a chemical change occurs.

Science Online

Topic: Recognizing Chemical Changes
Visit bookk.msscience.com for Web links to information about how chemical equations can be used to model chemical changes.

Activity Describe the chemical reactions that are involved in making and baking a yeast bread.

Mini LAB

Comparing Changes

Procedure

1. Separate a piece of **fine steel wool** into two halves.
2. Dip one half in **tap water.**
3. Place each piece of steel wool on a separate **paper plate** and let them sit overnight.

Analysis

1. Did you observe any changes in the steel wool? If so, describe them.
2. If you observed changes, were they physical or chemical? How do you know?

Try at Home

Carotenoids The plant pigments that are responsible for the yellow and orange colors of leaves are carotenoids. The pigments responsible for red and purple colors are called anthocyanins. Anthocyanins change color depending on the acidity of the cell sap in the plant.

Career Investigate the qualifications and training of botanists. Working in small groups, design a news interview to present this information to the class.

Discussion

Fruit Changes What evidence do you have that chemical changes occur as fruits and vegetables ripen? Possible answers: apples and tomatoes turn red, pears and bananas become yellow, oranges turn from green to orange

---

Mini LAB

Purpose Students will observe a chemical change with a piece of steel wool. L1 ELL LS
Kinesthetic

Materials piece of fine steel wool, tap water, paper plate

Teaching Strategy Have students tear the steel wool or cut it with tin snips.

Analysis

1. The steel wool dipped in water turned orange.
2. chemical, because the color changed

Assessment

Portfolio Have each student prepare a series of drawings of the steel wool over a two-week period. Students should include descriptions of the chemical changes with the drawings. Use **Performance Assessment in the Science Classroom,** p. 127.

Try at Home

Differentiated Instruction

Challenge Challenge students to investigate reactions that require energy, endothermic, and those that give off energy, exothermic. Where in nature, in the body, or in your house are these types of reactions found? Have students make a poster to illustrate different types of exothermic and endothermic reactions. L3 P

Learning Disabled Have students gather pictures from magazines and newspapers illustrating physical and chemical changes. Have them use these pictures to create one mobile or collage for physical changes and one for chemical changes. They can also use labels to explain the pictures. L2

Visual Learning

Figure 14 Discuss with students the physical and chemical properties of each item. On the board, make a list of the class's observations. L2 ELL LS **Visual-Spatial**

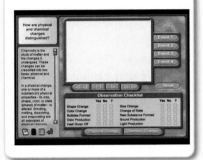
Inquiry Lab

Physical and Chemical Reactions

Purpose Students will explore physical and chemical changes, using substances available in their own kitchen.

Possible Materials salt, baking soda, sugar, flour, vinegar, ice, hot plate, scale

Estimated Time 1 class session

Teaching Strategies

• Challenge students to investigate various solid and liquid mixtures. Which combinations dissolve and which do not? Which combinations cause chemical reactions?

• Students can observe the effect of heating the various solids and solutions. They can further infer if the heat caused a chemical or a physical change.

• Extend the lab by encouraging students to further research the historical use of flour and water as glue. How does it compare to the structure of today's glue?

For additional inquiry activities, see *Science Inquiry Labs.*

Figure 13 Cake batter undergoes a chemical change as it absorbs energy during cooking.

Energy Another sign of a chemical change is the release or gain of energy by an object. Many substances must absorb energy in order to undergo a chemical change. For example, energy is absorbed during the chemical changes involved in cooking. When you bake a cake or make pancakes, energy is absorbed by the batter as it changes from a runny mix into what you see in **Figure 13.**

Another chemical change in which a substance absorbs energy occurs during the production of cement. This process begins with the heating of limestone. Ordinarily, limestone will remain unchanged for centuries. But when it absorbs energy during heating, it undergoes a chemical change in which it turns into lime and carbon dioxide.

Energy also can be released during a chemical change. The fireworks you read about earlier released energy in the form of light that you can see. As shown in **Figure 14,** a chemical change within a firefly releases energy in the form of light. Fuel burned in the camping stove releases energy you see as light and feel as heat. You also can see that energy is released when sodium and chlorine are combined and ignited in the last picture. During this chemical change, the original substances change into sodium chloride, which is ordinary table salt.

Figure 14 Energy is released when a firefly glows, when fuel is burned in a camping stove, and when sodium and chlorine undergo a chemical change to form table salt.

Science Journal

Energy in Physical and Chemical Changes Ask students to list all the changes they can think of that involve the absorption or release of energy and classify each as a chemical or physical change. Changes might include cooking (chemical), boiling water (physical), burning fuel (chemical), and cooling your hand by putting it in cold water (physical). L2 LS **Logical-Mathematical**

Teacher FYI

Heat and Energy Adding energy does not necessarily produce a chemical change. Adding heat to substances can cause them to warm up or to change state, neither of which is a chemical change. In the same way, the release of energy does not necessarily indicate that a chemical change has occurred.

Odor It takes only one experience with a rotten egg to learn that they smell much different than fresh eggs. When eggs and other foods spoil, they undergo chemical change. The change in odor is a clue to the chemical change. This clue can save lives. When you smell an odd odor in foods, such as chicken, pork, or mayonnaise, you know that the food has undergone a chemical change. You can use this clue to avoid eating spoiled food and protect yourself from becoming ill.

Gases or Solids Look at the antacid tablet in **Figure 15.** You can produce similar bubbles if you pour vinegar on baking soda. The formation of a gas is a clue to a chemical change. What other products undergo chemical changes and produce bubbles?

Figure 15 also shows another clue to a chemical change—the formation of a solid. A solid that separates out of a solution during a chemical change is called a precipitate. The precipitate in the photograph forms when a solution containing sodium iodide is mixed with a solution containing lead nitrate.

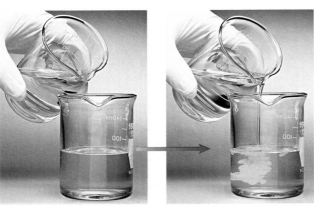

INTEGRATE Astronomy

Meteoroid A meteoroid is a chunk of metal or stone in space. Every day, meteoroids enter Earth's atmosphere. When this happens, the meteoroid burns as a result of friction with gases in the atmosphere. A streak of light produced during this chemical change is known as a meteor, or shooting star. In your Science Journal, infer why most meteoroids never reach Earth's surface.

Figure 15 The bubbles of gas formed when this antacid tablet is dropped into water indicate a chemical change. The solid forming from two liquids is another sign that a chemical change has taken place.

INTEGRATE Astronomy

Meteoroid Answers will vary but should include that during the chemical change that occurs in the atmosphere, most meteors burn up. When a meteoroid burns up in Earth's atmosphere, it is called a meteor; when it strikes Earth, it is called a meteorite. Most meteoroids are debris from asteroid collisions or broken-up comets.

Quick Demo
Gas Release

Materials vinegar, glass container, thermometer, baking soda

Estimated Time 10 minutes

Procedure Pour 10 mL of vinegar into a large glass container. Measure and record the temperature of the vinegar. Add 5 mL of baking soda to the vinegar and take the temperature again. The heat and gas produced are evidence that a chemical reaction has occurred. In this reaction, the baking soda reacted with the vinegar to form sodium acetate, water, and carbon dioxide gas.

IDENTIFYING Misconceptions

Bubbles The production of bubbles of gas does not necessarily mean a chemical change has taken place. In carbonated soft drinks, carbon dioxide gas dissolved in the liquid forms bubbles when the bottle or can is opened. Bubbles also form when a liquid changes state to a gas by boiling.

Teacher FYI

Air Bags The main ingredient in car air bags is sodium azide, NaN_3. Upon impact at speeds above 10–15 mph, a sensor transmits an electrical signal that ignites a detonator compound in the bag. Heat from the detonator causes the sodium azide to decompose into sodium and nitrogen gas.

Caption Answer

Figure 16 No; the ashes are the result of a chemical change.

Reading Check

Answer Possible answers: change in color, loss or gain of energy, odor, production of a gas or solid, the change is not easily reversible

Applying Math

National Math Standards
Correlation to Mathematics Objectives
1, 2, 4, 9

Answers to Practice Problems

1. This is what you know:
temperature $= 156°F$

This is what you need to find out: temperature in degrees Celsius

This is the procedure you need to use:
$(°C × 1.8) + 32 = °F$

Rearrange the equation to solve for °C.
$°C = (°F − 32)/1.8$

Then substitute the known value for °F.
$°C = (156 − 32)/1.8 = 68.9°C$

2. This is what you know:
temperature $= 199°C$

This is what you need to find out: temperature in degrees Fahrenheit

This is the procedure you need to use:
$(199 × 1.8) + 32 = °F$

Solve for °F.
$°F = 390°F$

Figure 16 As wood burns, it turns into a pile of ashes and gases that rise into the air.
Determine *Can you turn ashes back into wood?*

Not Easily Reversed How do physical and chemical changes differ from one another? Think about ice for a moment. After solid ice melts into liquid water, it can refreeze into solid ice if the temperature drops enough. Freezing and melting are physical changes. The substances produced during a chemical change cannot be changed back into the original substances by physical means. For example, the wood in **Figure 16** changes into ashes and gases that are released into the air. After wood is burned, it cannot be restored to its original form as a log.

Think about a few of the chemical changes you just read about to see if this holds true. An antacid tablet cannot be restored to its original form after being dropped in water. Rotten eggs cannot be made fresh again, and pancakes cannot be turned back into batter. The substances that existed before the chemical change no longer exist.

Reading Check *What signs indicate a chemical change?*

Applying Math   Solve for an Unknown

CONVERTING TEMPERATURES Fahrenheit is a non-SI temperature scale. Because it is used so often, it is useful to be able to convert from Fahrenheit to Celsius. The equation that relates Celsius degrees to Fahrenheit degrees is: $(°C × 1.8) + 32 = °F$. What is 15°F on the Celsius scale?

Solution

1 *This is what you know:*
- temperature $= 15°F$
- $(°C × 1.8) + 32 = °F$

2 *This is what you need to find out:*
- temperature in degrees Celsius

3 *This is the procedure you need to use:*
- $(°C × 1.8) + 32 = °F$
- $°C = (°F − 32)/1.8$
- $°C = (15 − 32)/1.8 = −9.4°C$

4 *Check your answer:*
Substitute the Celsius temperature into the original equation. Did you calculate the Fahrenheit temperature that was given?

Practice Problems

1. Water is being heated on the stove at 156°F. What is this temperature on the Celsius scale?

2. The boiling point of ethylene glycol is 199°C. What is the temperature on the Fahrenheit scale?

For more practice, visit
bookk.msscience.com/
math_practice

Active Reading

Reflective Journal In this strategy, have students divide sheets of paper into several columns and record their thoughts, for an activitiy in this section, under headings such as "What I learned," "What surprises did I experience," "What questions do I have," and "Overall response." Have students then write a Reflective Journal entry for this activity. L2

Chemical Versus Physical Change

Now you have learned about many different physical and chemical changes. You have read about several characteristics that you can use to distinguish between physical and chemical changes. The most important point for you to remember is that in a physical change, the composition of a substance does not change and in a chemical change, the composition of a substance does change. When a substance undergoes a physical change, only its form changes. In a chemical change, both form and composition change.

When the wood and copper in **Figure 17** undergo physical changes, the original wood and copper still remain after the change. When a substance undergoes a chemical change, however, the original substance is no longer present after the change. Instead, different substances are produced during the chemical change. When the wood and copper in **Figure 17** undergo chemical changes, wood and copper have changed into new substances with new physical and chemical properties.

Physical and chemical changes are used to recycle or reuse certain materials. **Figure 18** discusses the importance of some of these changes in recycling.

Chemical change

Physical change

Chemical change

Physical change

Figure 17 When a substance undergoes a physical change, its composition stays the same. When a substance undergoes a chemical change, it is changed into different substances.

Indications of Chemical Change
There are situations in which each of the signs of a chemical change discussed in these pages occurs during a physical change. This can cause confusion. A chemical change has occurred only if new substances have been created. Make sure students understand that changes in color and odor, the production of gases or precipitates, the absorption or release of energy, and the fact that a change is difficult to reverse, are indications that they should look further to see whether a new substance has been produced.

Use an Analogy

Basketball Tell students that chemical changes occur and new substances form when electrons interact to form bonds between different kinds of atoms. Discuss the following analogy. Think of the members of a basketball team as electrons associated with a basketball atom. They practice together and play games with other basketball teams. These are analogous to physical changes. The basketball players interact but no new substance is formed. Suppose some of the players decide to join with players from a soccer team to form a sports club. These players are like electrons that have formed bonds with a different kind of atom to form a new substance. L1

Differentiated Instruction

Visually Impaired Describe and discuss in detail with these students each of the photographs in **Figure 17.** Ask another student to describe the observable physical properties in each photo and tell how he or she knows which shows a physical change and which shows a chemical change. L2
IS Visual-Spatial

Visualizing Recycling

Have students examine the pictures and read the captions. Then ask the following questions.

What are some examples of physical changes described in this feature? Possible answers: pulverizing or crushing of glass; melting of plastics and re-forming them; shredding of plastics; shredding of rubber; crushing, flattening, and chopping apart of car bodies; separating iron and steel from other materials with a magnet

Why is it better to remove steel wires from rubber tires? Possible answer: It would prevent pieces of wire from sticking out of pavement where it could damage vehicles' tires or from playground surfaces where it could cause injuries. Also, the steel could then be recycled with the other metal car parts.

Activity

Making Glass Have small groups of students research making new glass bottles from cullet. Have each group make a poster that illustrates the chemical and physical changes that are involved in the process. [L2] COOP LEARN **IS** **Visual-Spatial and Interpersonal**

Figure 18

Recycling is a way to separate wastes into their component parts and then reuse those components in new products. In order to be recycled, wastes need to be physically—and sometimes chemically—changed. The average junked automobile contains about 62 percent iron and steel, 28 percent other materials such as aluminum, copper, and lead, and 10 percent rubber, plastics, and various materials.

Electromagnet ——

Steel ——

◀ Rubber tires can be shredded and added to asphalt pavement and playground surfaces. New recycling processes make it possible to supercool tires to a temperature at which the rubber is shattered like glass. A magnet can then draw out steel from the tires and other parts of the car.

▼ After being crushed and flattened, car bodies are chopped into small pieces. Metals are separated from other materials using physical processes. Some metals are separated using powerful magnets. Others are separated by hand.

◀ Glass can be pulverized and used in asphalt pavement, new glass, and even artwork. This sculpture, named *Groundswell*, was created by artist Maya Lin using windshield glass.

▲ Some plastics can be melted and formed into new products. Others are ground up or shredded and used as fillers or insulating materials.

Conservation of Mass

During a chemical change, the form or the composition of the matter changes. The particles within the matter rearrange to form new substances, but they are not destroyed and new particles are not created. The number and type of particles remains the same. As a result, the total mass of the matter is the same before and after a physical or chemical change. This is known as the **law of conservation of mass.**

This law can sometimes be difficult to believe, especially when the materials remaining after a chemical change might look quite different from those before it. In many chemical changes in which mass seems to be gained or lost, the difference is often due to a gas being given off or taken in. The difference, for example, before and after the candle in **Figure 19** is burned is in the gases released into the air. If the gases could be contained in a chamber around the candle, you would see that the mass does not change.

The scientist who first performed the careful experiments necessary to prove that mass is conserved was Antoine Lavoisier (AN twan • luh VWAH see ay) in the eighteenth century. It was Lavoisier who recognized that the mass of gases that are given off or taken from the air during chemical changes account for any differences in mass.

Figure 19 The candle looks as if it lost mass when it was burned. However, if you could trap and measure the gases given up during burning you would find that the mass of the burnt candle and the gases is equal to the mass of the original candle.

section 2 review

Summary

Physical Changes
- The form of matter, its shape or state, is altered during a physical change.
- The composition of matter remains the same.

Chemical Changes
- Both form and composition of matter are altered during a chemical change.
- Some signs of a chemical change are altered color, energy, odor, and formation of a gas or solid.
- Chemical changes are not easily reversed.

Conservation of Mass
- The total mass of the matter is the same before and after a physical or chemical change.

Self Check

1. **List** five physical changes that you can observe in your home.
2. **Determine** what kind of change occurs on the surface of bread when it is toasted.
3. **Infer** How is mass conserved during a chemical change?
4. **Think Critically** A log is reduced to a small pile of ash when it burns. Explain the difference in mass between the log and the ash.

Applying Math

5. **Solve One-Step Equations** Magnesium and oxygen undergo a chemical change to form magnesium oxide. How many grams of magnesium oxide will be produced when 0.486 g of oxygen completely react with 0.738 g of magnesium?

 Science nline bookk.msscience.com/self_check_quiz SECTION 2 Physical and Chemical Changes **K** ◆ **87**

Use Science Words

Word Origins Tell students that the word *conservation* comes from the Latin prefix *con-*, meaning "with or together," and the Latin verb *servare*, meaning "to keep or guard." Ask how these meanings relate to the law of conservation of mass. Mass is kept or guarded so that it is kept together, or the same. L2 LS

Linguistic

3 Assess

DAILY INTERVENTION

Check for Understanding
Logical-Mathematical Using a large, two-column chart, brainstorm with the class and list physical and chemical changes observed on a daily basis. Discuss why the changes are physical or chemical. L2

Reteach
Properties of Matter Ask students to look at the illustrations on these pages and describe the physical properties, chemical properties, physical changes, and chemical changes that they see. L2

✓ Assessment

Content Have students list five indications that a chemical change may have taken place. Possible answers: changes in color, odor, and energy; the production of gases or solids; the fact that a change is difficult to reverse

section 2 review

1. Examples include cutting paper, pouring milk on cereal, mowing the lawn, and melting ice. These are physical changes because the matter does not change composition.
2. Chemical; the bread changes in color and odor, absorbs heat energy, becomes dark, and cannot be returned to original form.
3. The particles within the matter are rearranged, but the total mass of the matter remains the same.
4. The difference in mass is a result of the mass of gas that was formed in the reaction and escaped.
5. 1.22 g

▶ Real-World Question

Purpose Students will infer the effectiveness of different brands and types of toothpaste in preventing tooth decay. L2 LS **Kinesthetic**

Process Skills design an experiment, form a hypothesis, record and analyze data, compare, infer, predict

Time Required One 45-minute period and daily observations for a week

Alternate Materials You might want to include a tube of toothpaste that does not contain sodium fluoride in its ingredients list.

▶ Form a Hypothesis

Possible Hypothesis Most student hypotheses will reflect that toothpastes containing sodium fluoride will prevent the eggshells from reacting with the acid.

▶ Test Your Hypothesis

Possible Procedures Brush a different brand of toothpaste over each eggshell. Leave two eggshells without toothpaste. Place half the treated eggs in lemon juice and the other half in apple juice. Place one untreated egg in each juice. Observe the eggs each day for one week.

Troubleshooting Students should be sure to coat all parts of the eggs with toothpaste. Any unprotected parts will react with the acid.

LAB Design Your Own

BATTLE OF THE TOOTHPASTES

Goals
- **Observe** how toothpaste helps prevent tooth decay.
- **Design** an experiment to test the effectiveness of various types and brands of toothpaste.

Possible Materials
3 or 4 different brands and types of toothpaste
drinking glasses or bowls
hard-boiled eggs
concentrated lemon juice
apple juice
water
artist's paint brush

Safety Precautions
[safety icons]

▶ Real-World Question

Your teeth are made of a compound called hydroxyapatite (hi DRAHK see A puh tite). The sodium fluoride in toothpaste undergoes a chemical reaction with hydroxyapatite to form a new compound on the surface of your teeth. This compound resists food acids that cause tooth decay, another chemical change. In this lab, you will design an experiment to test the effectiveness of different toothpaste brands. The compound found in your teeth is similar to the mineral compound found in eggshells. Treating hard-boiled eggs with toothpaste is similar to brushing your teeth with toothpaste. Soaking the eggs in food acids such as vinegar for several days will produce similar conditions as eating foods, which contain acids that will produce a chemical change in your teeth, for several months.

▶ Form a Hypothesis

Form a hypothesis about the effectiveness of different brands of toothpaste.

▶ Test Your Hypothesis

Make a Plan

1. **Describe** how you will use the materials to test the toothpaste.
2. **List** the steps you will follow to test your hypothesis.
3. **Decide** on the length of time that you will conduct your experiment.

88 ◆ K CHAPTER 3 Properties and Changes of Matter

Egg	Day 1	Day 2	Day 3
Toothpaste 1			
Toothpaste 2			
No Toothpaste			

Differentiated Instruction

Visually Impaired Be sure that the materials used to hold the eggs can be distinguished by touch. Allow visually impaired students to manipulate the eggs at the start and at the end of the lab. Have peers work with the visually impaired students to assist in describing the effects on the eggshells. L2

4. **Identify** the control and variables you will use in your experiment.

5. **Create** a data table in your Science Journal to record your observations, measurements, and results.

6. **Describe** how you will measure the amount of protection each toothpaste brand provides.

Follow Your Plan

1. Make sure your teacher approves your plan before you start.

2. **Conduct** your experiment as planned. Be sure to follow all proper safety precautions.

3. **Record** your observations in your data table.

Analyze Your Data

1. **Compare** the untreated eggshells with the shells you treated with toothpaste.

2. **Compare** the condition of the eggshells you treated with different brands of toothpaste.

3. **Compare** the condition of the eggshells soaked in lemon juice and in apple juice.

4. **Identify** unintended variables you discovered in your experiment that might have influenced the results.

Conclude and Apply

1. **Identify** Did the results support your hypothesis? Describe the strengths and weaknesses of your hypothesis.

2. **Explain** why the eggshells treated with toothpaste were better-protected than the untreated eggshells.

3. **Identify** which brands of toothpaste, if any, best protected the eggshells from decay.

4. **Evaluate** the scientific explanation for why adding fluoride to toothpaste and drinking water prevents tooth decay.

5. **Predict** what would happen to your protected eggs if you left them in the food acids for several weeks.

6. **Infer** why it is a good idea to brush with fluoride toothpaste.

Communicating Your Data

Compare your results with the results of your classmates. **Create** a poster advertising the benefits of fluoride toothpaste.

Expected Outcome After several days, eggshells coated with a sodium fluoride toothpaste should show little or no reaction. The control eggshell should show evidence of being softened and eaten away.

Analyze Your Data

Answers to Questions

1. The untreated eggshell shows evidence of a chemical reaction, while the treated eggshells do not.

2. Answers will depend on the brands of toothpastes tested.

3. The eggshell in lemon juice should show more evidence of a reaction.

4. Answers will vary.

Error Analysis Have students compare their results and their hypotheses and explain why any differences occurred.

Conclude and Apply

1. Answers will be determined by student hypotheses.

2. The sodium fluoride in the toothpaste prevented the eggshells from chemically reacting with the acid.

3. Answers will vary.

4. Evidence indicates that fluoride prevents a compound similar to that in teeth from reacting with food acids.

5. The protection would lose its effectiveness and the eggshells would react with the acids.

6. Regular brushing with fluoride toothpaste prevents chemicals in teeth from reacting with food acids.

Alternative Inquiry Lab

Experiment Further To extend this Lab into an Inquiry Lab, have students think of other products that people use to produce good chemical reactions in our bodies. They could perform a similar experiment to test the efficiency of antacid brands, using 0.01 mol/L HCl. Students might also think of products that are used to produce good chemical reactions in food.

Communicating Your Data

Encourage students to use a computer graphics program to prepare their posters.

Assessment

Performance Have students make labeled posters of their experimental designs to share with the class and include in their portfolios. Use **Performance Assessment in the Science Classroom,** p. 145.

Content Background

One advantage of hydrogen peroxide over other bleaches is that, as it oxidizes, it breaks down into oxygen and water. Other bleaches might contain materials such as chlorine that can harm the environment if they are present in large quantities.

Discussion

Material Decomposition Contact a local packing store for samples of packing peanuts made from corn and those made from traditional plastic. Show students how the corn-based packing decomposes when placed in water but the plastic packing material does not. How would using such a biodegradable packing material benefit the environment? The material would decompose into an environmentally safe material when it got wet in a landfill. L2

Activity

Recycling Have students keep track of how many soft drink cans they empty in a week. Have them research how much energy is saved when they recycle these cans. Recycling takes only 5% of the energy needed to refine aluminum from ore. Have groups of students prepare posters to place around the school promoting recycling. L3

Applying Math

Answer 0.636 kg/person

Find Out About It

Physical changes include change in state, such as melting. Before investigating chemical changes, ask students, as a class, to brainstorm signs that indicate a chemical change has occurred. Such indications include energy release or absorption and color or odor change. L2

Strange Changes

Did you know...

... A hair colorist is also a chemist!

Colorists use hydrogen peroxide and ammonia to swell and open the cuticle-like shafts on your hair. Once these are open, the chemicals in hair dye can get into your natural pigment molecules and chemically change your hair color. The first safe commercial hair color was created in 1909 in France.

... Americans consume about 175 million kg of sauerkraut each year.
During the production of sauerkraut, bacteria produce lactic acid. The acid chemically breaks down the material in the cabbage, making it translucent and tangy.

Applying Math There are 275 million people in the United States. Calculate the average amount of sauerkraut consumed by each person in the United States in one year.

... More than 450,000 metric tons of plastic packaging are recycled each year in the U.S.
Discarded plastics undergo physical changes including melting and shredding. They are then converted into flakes or pellets, which are used to make new products. Recycled plastic is used to make clothes, furniture, carpets, and even lumber.

Projected Recycling Rates by Material, 2000

Material	1995 Recycling	Proj. Recycling
Paper/Paperboard	40.0%	43 to 46%
Glass	24.5%	27 to 36%
Ferrous metal	36.5%	42 to 55%
Aluminum	34.6%	46 to 48%
Plastics	5.3%	7 to 10%
Yard waste	30.3%	40 to 50%
Total Materials	27.0%	30 to 35%

Find Out About It

Every time you cook, you make physical and chemical changes to food. Visit bookk.msscience.com/science_stats or to your local or school library to find out what chemical or physical changes take place when cooking ingredients are heated or cooled.

Visual Learning

Projected Recycling Rates by Material, 2000 By what percent did the recycling rate increase from 1995 to 2000 for glass and paper? 2.5 to 11.5%; 3.0 to 6.0%, respectively. Have students use a dictionary to find out what *ferrous* means. A ferrous metal is any metal that is primarily iron, such as steel. If 259 kg of aluminum products were used by a family, what mass of that aluminum was likely to be recycled in 1995? 89.6 kg The recycling rate is over 60% for aluminum cans. Why doesn't this percent match those in the table? Aluminum is used in many other products that are not as likely to be recycled. Such products include foil, bicycle parts, and window screen. L2

Reviewing Main Ideas

Section 1 **Physical and Chemical Properties**

1. Matter can be described by its characteristics, or properties, and can exist in different states—solid, liquid, or gas.

2. A physical property is a characteristic that can be observed without altering the composition of the sample.

3. Physical properties include color, shape, smell, taste, and texture, as well as measurable quantities such as mass, volume, density, melting point, and boiling point.

4. A chemical property is a characteristic that cannot be observed without changing what the sample is made of.

Section 2 **Physical and Chemical Changes**

1. During a physical change, the composition of matter stays the same but the appearance changes in some way.

2. Physical changes occur when matter changes from one state to another.

3. A chemical change occurs when the composition of matter changes.

4. Signs of chemical change include changes in energy, color, odor, or the production of gases or solids.

5. According to the law of conservation of mass, mass cannot be created or destroyed.

Visualizing Main Ideas

Copy and complete the following concept map on matter.

Matter
can be described by

Physical properties
such as
- Appearance
- Melting or boiling point
- Density
- State

Chemical properties
such as
- Ability to burn
- Ability to tarnish
- Ability to rust

 bookk.msscience.com/interactive_tutor

CHAPTER STUDY GUIDE **K ◆ 91**

Reviewing Main Ideas

Summary statements can be used by students to review the major concepts of the chapter.

Visualizing Main Ideas

See student page.

Visit bookk.msscience.com
/self_check_quiz
/interactive_tutor
/vocabulary_puzzlemaker
/chapter_review
/standardized_test

Assessment Transparency

For additional assessment questions, use the *Assessment Transparency* located in the transparency book.

Assessment

Properties and Changes of Matter

Directions: *Carefully review the table and answer the following questions.*

Physical Properties

Substance	Odor	Boiling point (°C)	Melting point (°C)
Hydrogen	None	−253	−259
Lead	Pungent	1,740	327
Nitrogen	None	−196	−210
Iron	None	2,750–3,000	1,535
Sulfur	Boiled eggs	445	119

1. According to the table, if an unknown substance begins to melt at 119°C, it is probably ____.
   A hydrogen   C iron
   B nitrogen   D sulfur
2. According to the table, which of the following substances cannot remain solid at room temperature (about 24°C)?
   F Lead
   G Nitrogen
   H Iron
   J Sulfur
3. According to the table, which of the following substances must exist as a gas at room temperature (about 24°C)?
   A Hydrogen
   B Lead
   C Iron
   D Sulfur

Properties and Changes of Matter

Using Vocabulary

1. Color can be observed without changing the object.
2. Melting point, boiling point, and density do not change with the amount of matter.
3. The appearance of matter changes but the composition does not change.
4. A change of state is a physical change.
5. During a chemical change, substances are changed into different substances.
6. Clues that a chemical change has occurred include change in color, loss or gain of energy, change of smell, and production of a gas or solid.
7. Accept all reasonable answers. One example of a chemical change is burning wood.
8. The law of conservation of mass states that the total mass of matter is the same before and after a physical or chemical change.

Checking Concepts

9. C	13. B
10. A	14. C
11. D	15. B
12. C	16. C

17. Cutting cake involved only a physical change since only the cake's appearance changed whereas burning a candle involved a definite chemical change.

Using Vocabulary

chemical change p. 80	physical change p. 78
chemical property p. 76	physical property p. 72
condensation p. 79	sublimation p. 79
deposition p. 79	vaporization p. 79
law of conservation of mass p. 87	

Use what you know about the vocabulary words to answer the following questions. Use complete sentences.

1. Why is color a physical property?
2. What is a physical property that does not change with the amount of matter?
3. What happens during a physical change?
4. What type of change is a change of state?
5. What happens during a chemical change?
6. What are three clues that a chemical change has occurred?
7. What is an example of a chemical change?
8. What is the law of conservation of mass?

Checking Concepts

Choose the word or phrase that best answers the question.

9. What changes when the mass of an object increases while volume stays the same?
   A) color
   B) length
   C) density
   D) height
10. What word best describes the type of materials that attract iron?
    A) magnetic
    B) chemical
    C) mass
    D) physical
11. Which is an example of a chemical property?
    A) color
    B) mass
    C) density
    D) ability to burn

12. Which is an example of a physical change?
    A) metal rusting
    B) silver tarnishing
    C) water boiling
    D) paper burning
13. What characteristic best describes what happens during a physical change?
    A) composition changes
    B) composition stays the same
    C) form stays the same
    D) mass is lost
14. Which is an example of a chemical change?
    A) water freezes
    B) wood is carved
    C) bread is baked
    D) wire is bent
15. Which is NOT a clue that could indicate a chemical change?
    A) change in color
    B) change in shape
    C) change in energy
    D) change in odor
16. What property stays the same during physical and chemical changes?
    A) density
    B) shape
    C) mass
    D) arrangement of particles

Use the illustration below to answer question 17.

A.

B.

17. Which is an example of a physical change and which is a chemical change?

 Science Online bookk.msscience.com/vocabulary_puzzlemaker

Use the Exam*View*® Pro Testmaker CD-ROM to:
- create multiple versions of tests
- create modified tests with one mouse click for inclusion students
- edit existing questions and add your own questions
- build tests aligned with state standards using built-in State Curriculum Tags
- change English tests to Spanish with one mouse click and vice versa

Thinking Critically

18. Draw Conclusions When asked to give the physical properties of a painting, your friend says the painting is beautiful. Why isn't this description a true scientific property?

19. Draw Conclusions You are told that a sample of matter gives off energy as it changes. Can you conclude which type of change occurred? Why or why not?

20. Describe what happens to mass during chemical and physical changes. Explain.

21. Classify Decide whether the following properties are physical or chemical.
 a. Sugar can change into alcohol.
 b. Iron can rust.
 c. Alcohol can vaporize.
 d. Paper can burn.
 e. Sugar can dissolve.

Use the table below to answer question 22 and 23.

Physical Properties

Substance	Melting Point (°C)	Density (g/cm³)
Benzoic acid	122.1	1.075
Sucrose	185.0	1.581
Methane	−182.0	0.466
Urea	135.0	1.323

22. Determine A scientist has a sample of a substance with a mass of 1.4 g and a volume of 3.0 mL. According to the table above, which substance might it be?

23. Conclude Using the table above, which substance would take the longest time to melt? Explain your reasoning.

 bookk.msscience.com/chapter_review

24. Determine A jeweler bends gold into a beautiful ring. What type of change is this? Explain.

25. Compare and Contrast Relate such human characteristics as hair and eye color and height and weight to physical properties of matter. Relate human behavior to chemical properties. Think about how you observe these properties.

Performance Activities

26. Write a Story Write a story describing an event that you have experienced. Then go back through the story and circle any physical or chemical properties you mentioned. Underline any physical or chemical changes you included.

Applying Math

27. Brick Volume What is the volume of a brick that is 20 cm long, 10 cm wide, and 3 cm high?

28. Density of an Object What is the density of an object with a mass of 50 g and a volume of 5 cm³?

Use the table below to answer question 29.

Mineral Samples

Sample	Mass	Volume
A	96.5 g	5 cm³
B	38.6 g	4 cm³

29. Density of Gold The density of gold is 19.3 g/cm³. Which sample is the gold?

30. Ammonia Solubility 89.9 g of ammonia will dissolve in 100 mL of cold water. How much ammonia is needed to dissolve in 1.5 L of water?

CHAPTER REVIEW K ◆ 93

Thinking Critically

18. Beautiful is an opinion; it cannot be measured.

19. No; some physical changes, such as changing from a liquid to a solid, involve the release of energy, and some chemical changes, such as burning wood, involve the release of energy.

20. During a change of matter, either the form or the composition of matter changes. However, the particles within the matter are not destroyed nor are new particles created. As a result, the total mass of the matter is the same before and after a physical or chemical change.

21. a. chemical, b. chemical, c. physical, d. chemical, e. physical

22. methane

23. Sucrose; it has the highest boiling point.

24. Bending is a physical change because it does not change the composition of the gold.

25. Human characteristics can be observed without interacting with a person. For example, you can observe hair and eye color from a distance. Human behavior can be observed only by observing that person's interactions.

Performance Activities

26. Use **Performance Assessment in the Science Classroom**, p. 157.

Applying Math

National Math Standards
1, 2, 3, 4, 5, 9

27. 600 cm³

28. 10 g/cm³

29. Dividing the sample's mass by its volume will result in its density. Sample A is the gold.

30. 1,348.5 grams

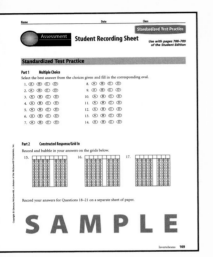

FAST FILE

Answer Sheet A practice
answer sheet can be found
at bookk.msscience.com/answer_sheet.

SAMPLE

Part 1 | Multiple Choice

1. D	4. C	7. C
2. A	5. D	8. D
3. C	6. B	9. A

Part 1 | Multiple Choice

*Record your answers on the answer sheet
provided by your teacher or on a sheet of paper.*

Use the photograph below to answer questions 1 and 2.

1. Which of the following could you do to the
   ball in the photograph above to cause a
   chemical change?
   A. cut in half   **C.** flatten
   B. paint   **D.** burn

2. Which of the following physical properties
   of the ball is size independent?
   A. density   **C.** volume
   B. mass   **D.** weight

3. Each of the following procedures results in
   the formation of bubbles. Which of these is
   a physical change?
   A. pouring an acid onto calcium carbonate
   B. dropping an antacid tablet into water
   C. heating water to its boiling point
   D. pouring vinegar onto baking soda

4. Which of the following occurs as you heat a
   liquid to its boiling point?
   A. condensation   **C.** vaporization
   B. melting   **D.** freezing

Test-Taking Tip

Essay Questions Spend a few minutes listing and organizing
the main points that you plan to discuss. Make sure to do all of
this work on your scratch paper, not on the answer sheet.

5. During an experiment, you find that you
   can dissolve 4.2 g of a substance in 250 mL
   of water at 25°C. How much of the substance would you predict that you could
   dissolve in 500 mL of water at the same
   temperature?
   A. 2.1 g   **C.** 6.3 g
   B. 4.2 g   **D.** 8.4 g

6. Which of the following is a chemical
   reaction?
   A. making ice cubes
   B. toasting bread
   C. slicing a carrot
   D. boiling water

7. When you make and eat scrambled eggs,
   many changes occur to the eggs. Which of
   the following best describes a chemical
   change?
   A. crack the eggs
   B. scramble the eggs
   C. cook the eggs
   D. chew the eggs

Use the table below to answer questions 8 and 9.

Physical Properties of Bromide	
Density	3.12 g/cm^3
Boiling point	59°C
Melting point	−7°C

8. According to the table above, what is the
   mass of 4.34 cm^3 of bromine?
   A. 0.719 g   **C.** 7.46 g
   B. 1.39 g   **D.** 13.5 g

9. At which of the following temperatures is
   bromine a solid?
   A. −10°C   **C.** 40°C
   B. 10°C   **D.** 80°C

94 STANDARDIZED TEST PRACTICE

Part 2 | Short Response/Grid In

10. A precipitate is a solid that sepa-
    rates when two solutions are com-
    bined and react chemically.

11. Rusting is a chemical change.
    When the iron in steel is exposed
    to oxygen and water in air, the iron
    and oxygen atoms combine and
    rust is formed.

12. You can see that the chain is solid. It
    is in the shape of oval links that have
    a reddish-brown color. Some physi-
    cal properties that you can't see are
    the density, melting point, and boil-
    ing point of the metal.

13. 2.72 g/cm^3

14. No, it doesn't violate the law of
    conservation of mass. The missing
    mass was probably a gas that
    formed during the chemical reac-
    tion of the two chemicals.

15. 11.3 g/mL

Part 2 | Short Response/Grid In

Record your answers on the answer sheet provided by your teacher or on a sheet of paper.

10. A precipitate is one clue that a chemical change has occurred. What is a precipitate and when is it observed?

Use the photo below to answer questions 11 and 12.

11. The photograph above shows a rusted chain. Explain why rusting is a physical or a chemical change.

12. What are some physical properties of the rusty chain that you can see? What are some physical properties that you can't see?

13. You measure the density of a 12.3-g sample of limestone as 2.72 g/cm³. What is the density of a 36.9 g sample?

14. A scientist measures the masses of two chemicals. He then combines the chemicals and measures their total mass. The total mass is less than the sum of each individual mass. Has this violated the law of conservation of mass? Explain what might have happened when the chemicals were combined.

15. A scientist measures 275 mL of water into a beaker. She then adds 51.0 g of lead into the beaker. After the addition of the lead, the volume of water in the beaker increases by 4.50 mL. What is the density of the lead?

 Science Online bookk.msscience.com/standardized_test

Part 3 | Open Ended

Record your answers on a sheet of paper.

16. Suppose you have a gas in a closed container. Explain what would happen to the mass and density of the gas if you compressed it into half the volume.

17. Color change is an indication that a chemical change may have occurred. Mixing yellow and blue modeling clay makes green modeling clay. Is this a chemical reaction? Explain why or why not.

18. At a temperature of 40°C, you find that 40 g of ammonium chloride easily dissolves in 100 mL of water. When you stir 40 g of potassium chloride into a beaker containing 100 mL of water at 40°C, you find that some of the potassium chloride remains in the bottom of the beaker. Explain why this occurs and how to make to make the remaining potassium chloride dissolve.

Use the photo below to answer questions 19 and 20.

19. What would happen if you left the glass of cold water shown in the photograph above in the hot Sun for several hours? Describe how some physical properties of the water would change.

20. What properties of the water would not change? Explain why the density of the water would or would not change.

Rubrics

The following rubrics are sample scoring devices for short response and open-ended questions.

Short Response

Points	Description
2	The student demonstrates a thorough understanding of the science of the task. The response may contain minor flaws that do not detract from the demonstration of a thorough understanding.
1	The student has provided a response that is only partially correct.
0	The student has provided a completely incorrect solution or no response at all.

Open Ended

Points	Description
4	The student demonstrates a thorough understanding of the science of the task. The response may contain minor flaws that do not detract from the demonstration of a thorough understanding.
3	The student demonstrates an understanding of the science of the task. The response is essentially correct and demonstrates an essential but less than thorough understanding of the science.
2	The student demonstrates only a partial understanding of the science of the task. Although the student may have used the correct approach to a solution or may have provided a correct solution, the work lacks an essential understanding of the underlying science concepts.
1	The student demonstrates a very limited understanding of the science of the task. The response is incomplete and exhibits many flaws.
0	The student provides a completely incorrect solution or no response at all.

Part 3 | Open Ended

16. The mass of the gas would remain the same because you haven't added or removed any of it from the container. If you decreased the volume by half, the density would be twice the original value.

17. No, it is a physical change because the substances haven't changed. Because they are mixed well, your eyes can't differentiate the colors.

18. The solubility of ammonium chloride at 40°C is higher than 40 g in 100 ml of water. The solubility of potassium chloride at 40°C is lower than 40 g in 100 ml of water. You could dissolve the remaining potassium chloride by either adding more water or by heating the solution.

19. The temperature of the water would increase. Part of the water would evaporate, changing from a liquid to a gas.

20. The melting point, boiling point, density and solubility of the water are independent of sample size and will not change. The density of the water remaining in the glass will not change.

chapter 4 Organizer

Section/Objectives	Standards		Labs/Features
Chapter Opener	National	State/Local	**Launch Lab:** Make a Model of a Periodic Pattern, p. 97 **Foldables,** p. 97
	See pp. 9T–10T for a Key to Standards.		
Section 1 Introduction to the Periodic Table ⏱ 3 sessions 📦 1.5 blocks 1. **Describe** the history of the periodic table. 2. **Interpret** an element key. 3. **Explain** how the periodic table is organized.	National Content Standards: UCP.1, UCP.2, UCP.3, UCP.5, A.1, A.2, B.1, B.3, G.3		**MiniLAB:** Designing a Periodic Table, p. 99 **Science Online,** p. 102 **Applying Science,** p. 103
Section 2 Representative Elements ⏱ 2 sessions 📦 1 block 4. **Recognize** the properties of representative elements. 5. **Identify** uses for the representative elements. 6. **Classify** elements into groups based on similar properties.	National Content Standards: UCP.1, UCP.2, UCP.3, UCP.5, A.1, A.2, B.1, B.3		**Integrate Career,** p. 108 **Integrate Life Science,** p. 109
Section 3 Transition Elements ⏱ 4 sessions 📦 2 blocks 7. **Identify** properties of some transition elements. 8. **Distinguish** lanthanides from actinides.	National Content Standards: UCP.1, UCP.2, UCP.3, UCP.5, A.1, A.2, B.1, F.1		**Integrate Physics,** p. 114 **Visualizing Synthetic Elements,** p. 115 **Science Online,** p. 116 **Lab:** Metals and Nonmetals, p. 117 **Lab:** Health Risks from Heavy Metals, p. 118 **Science and Language Arts:** Anansi Tries to Steal All Wisdom in the World, p. 120

96A ◆ **K CHAPTER 4** The Periodic Table

Glencoe Exclusive!
TeacherWorks™
All-In-One Planner and Resource Center

Lab Materials	Reproducible Resources	Section Assessment	Technology
Launch Lab: sheet of paper, pencil, set of precut shapes (4 of each shape in 4 different colors for each group)	**Chapter** *FAST FILE* **Resources** Foldables Worksheet, p. 13 Note-taking Worksheets, pp. 29–30 Directed Reading Overview, p. 15	GLENCOE'S **ASSESSMENT** ADVANTAGE	Teacher**Works** includes: • Interactive Teacher Edition • Lesson Planner with calendar • Access to all program blacklines • Correlations to standards • Web links
MiniLAB: pens, pencils	**Chapter** *FAST FILE* **Resources** Transparency Activity, p. 40 MiniLAB, p. 3 Enrichment, p. 26 Reinforcement, p. 23 Directed Reading, p. 16 Lab Activity, pp. 9–10, 11–12 Transparency Activity, pp. 43–44 **Home and Community Involvement,** p. 25	**Portfolio** Science Journal, p. 102 **Performance** MiniLAB, p. 99 Applying Science, p. 103 Applying Math, p. 104 **Content** Section Review, p. 104	Section Focus Transparency Teaching Transparency Virtual Labs CD-ROM Guided Reading Audio Program Interactive Chalkboard CD-ROM Video Lab
Need materials? Contact Science Kit at 1-800-828-7777 or www.sciencekit.com on the Internet.	**Chapter** *FAST FILE* **Resources** Transparency Activity, p. 41 Enrichment, p. 27 Reinforcement, p. 24 Directed Reading, p. 17 **Cultural Diversity,** p. 37 **Physical Science Critical Thinking/Problem Solving,** p. 9	**Portfolio** Assessment, p. 111 **Performance** Applying Skills, p. 111 **Content** Section Review, p. 111	Section Focus Transparency Virtual Labs CD-ROM Guided Reading Audio Program Interactive Chalkboard CD-ROM
Lab: test tubes and racks, test-tube brushes, 10-mL graduated cylinder, forceps or tweezers, marking pencil, mallet or hammer, $0.5M$ HCl, $0.1M$ $CuCl_2$, carbon, silicon, tin, sulfur, iron **Lab:** no materials needed	**Chapter** *FAST FILE* **Resources** Transparency Activity, p. 42 Enrichment, p. 28 Reinforcement, p. 25 Directed Reading, pp. 17, 18 Lab Worksheets, pp. 5–6, 7–8 **Lab Management and Safety,** p. 50 **Physical Science Critical Thinking/Problem Solving,** p. 13	**Portfolio** Activity, p. 114 Assessment, p. 119 **Performance** Applying Skills, p. 116 **Content** Section Review, p. 116	Section Focus Transparency Virtual Labs CD-ROM Guided Reading Audio Program Interactive Chalkboard CD-ROM

GLENCOE'S **ASSESSMENT** ADVANTAGE

End of Chapter Assessment		
Blackline Masters	**Technology**	**Professional Series**
Chapter *FAST FILE* **Resources** Chapter Review, pp. 33–34 Chapter Tests, pp. 35–38 **Standardized Test Practice,** pp. 19–22	MindJogger Videoquiz Virtual Labs CD-ROM Exam*View*® Pro Testmaker TeacherWorks CD-ROM Interactive Chalkboard CD-ROM	**Performance Assessment in the Science Classroom (PASC)**

Transparencies

Section Focus

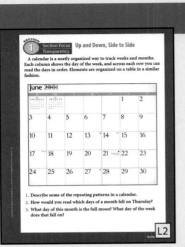

Section 1 — Section Focus Transparency: Up and Down, Side to Side

A calendar is a neatly organized way to track weeks and months. Each column shows the day of the week, and across each row you can read the days in order. Elements are organized in a table in a similar fashion.

June 2001

1. Describe some of the repeating patterns in a calendar.
2. How would you read which days of a month fell on Thursday?
3. What day of this month is the full moon? What day of the week does that fall on?

L2

Section 2 — Section Focus Transparency: Strong Reactions

Sodium and potassium belong to the same group of elements, and they share many similar properties. For example, both form important compounds with the element chlorine. Below you see each element reacting with water.

Sodium   Potassium

1. How are the pictured reactions similar? How are they different?
2. Lithium is also from the same group. Would you expect lithium to react with chlorine? What might lithium do if it were placed in water?

L2

Section 3 — Section Focus Transparency: A Touch on the Warm Side

That's liquid iron being poured at roughly 1,500°C (2,800°F). Iron is used as both a pure element and as a mixture. Steel, iron combined with other elements, is a common example of an iron mixture. There are many different iron mixtures, including cast iron, carbon steel, and stainless steel.

1. Name some properties of iron.
2. Name some items made of iron or iron mixtures. Why is iron a good choice for making these things?

L2

This is a representation of key blackline masters available in the Teacher Classroom Resources. See Resource Manager boxes within the chapter for additional information.

Assessment

Assessment Transparency: The Periodic Table

Directions: *Carefully review the table and answer the following questions.*

Metal	Symbol	Atomic number	Atomic mass	Density (g/mL)
Lithium	Li	3	7	0.53
Sodium	Na	11	23	0.97
Potassium	K	19	39	0.86
Rubidium	Rb	37	85	1.53

1. According to the table above, which of these alkali metals has a density greater than 1.00 g/mL?
   A Lithium
   B Sodium
   C Potassium
   D Rubidium
2. A scientist examined a metal and found that it had an atomic mass of 39. What was the identity of the metal?
   F Lithium
   G Rubidium
   H Sodium
   J Potassium
3. All of the following are properties of the metals listed above EXCEPT for the ability to ___.
   A be bent into different shapes
   B conduct heat and electricity
   C be gases at room temperature
   D reflect light and shine

L2

Teaching

Section 1 — Teaching Transparency: Parts of the Periodic Table

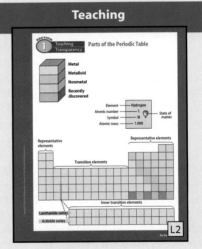

Metal
Metalloid
Nonmetal
Recently discovered

Element — Hydrogen
Atomic number
Symbol — H — State of matter
Atomic mass — 1.008

Representative elements   Representative elements
Transition elements
Inner transition elements
Lanthanide series
Actinide series

L2

Key to Teaching Strategies

The following designations will help you decide which activities are appropriate for your students.

L1 Level 1 activities should be appropriate for students with learning difficulties.

L2 Level 2 activities should be within the ability range of all students.

L3 Level 3 activities are designed for above-average students.

ELL ELL activities should be within the ability range of English Language Learners.

COOP LEARN Cooperative Learning activities are designed for small group work.

LS Multiple Learning Styles logos, as described on page 6T, are used throughout to indicate strategies that address different learning styles.

P These strategies represent student products that can be placed into a best-work portfolio.

PBL Problem-Based Learning activities apply real-world situations to learning.

Hands-on Activities

Student Text Lab Worksheet

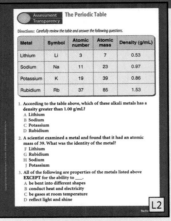

Activity — Preparing a Mixture

Lab Preview

Directions: *Answer these questions before you begin the Activity.*

1. In this activity, you will be treating metals with heat and acids. Explain the safety precautions related to this experiment.

2. Why do you use tongs to hold the penny?

Many of the most important materials in the world are mixtures of elements.

What You'll Investigate
How can two metals form an alloy?

Materials
copper penny   dilute nitric acid   tongs
*copper wire   dilute sodium hydroxide   beaker of cold tap water
30-mesh zinc   evaporating dishes (2)   teaspoon
hot plate   *250-mL beakers (2)   *Alternate materials

Goals
• Observe the changes that occur during the preparation of an alloy.
• Compare the plating of a metal to the formation of an alloy.

Safety Precautions
CAUTION: Nitric and sodium hydroxide can cause burns. Wear your eye protection and lab apron while in the lab. Thoroughly wash any spilled material.

Procedure
1. Carefully pour dilute nitric acid into one evaporating dish until the dish is half full. Using tongs, hold the penny in the nitric acid for about 20 s.
2. Still using the tongs, remove the penny from the acid. Rinse it in the beaker of cold tap water.
3. Place one teaspoonful of 30-mesh zinc in the second evaporating dish.
4. Slowly pour dilute sodium hydroxide into the dish to a depth of about 2 cm above the zinc.
5. Using tongs, gently place the penny on top of the zinc. Rinse the tongs in cold water.
6. Gently heat the contents of the evaporating dish on a hot plate until the penny turns a silver color.
7. Set the control on the hot plate to medium high. Using tongs, remove the penny from the dish and rinse it in the cold tap water.
8. Dry the penny and place it directly on the hot plate until the penny turns a golden color.
9. Your teacher will dispose of the contents of the two evaporating dishes.

L2

Laboratory Activities

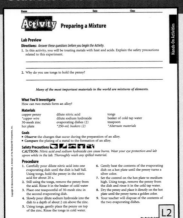

Laboratory Activity 1 — Relationships Among Elements

The periodic table is a wonderful source of information about all of the elements scientists have discovered. In this activity, you will investigate the relationship among the elements' atomic numbers, radii, and positions in the periodic table.

An atom's atomic radius is the distance from the center of the nucleus to the edge of the atom. The radii for elements with atomic numbers from 3 through 30 are given in Table 1. The radii are so small that a very small metric unit called a picometer is used. A picometer (pm) is one trillionth of a meter.

Strategy
You will plot the atomic radii of elements with atomic numbers 3 through 30.
You will examine the graph for repeated patterns.

Materials
copy of the periodic table   graph paper   pencil

Table 1

Name and symbol		Atomic number	Atomic radius (picometers)	Name and symbol		Atomic number	Atomic radius (picometers)
Aluminum	Al	13	143	Magnesium	Mg	12	160
Argon	Ar	18	191	Manganese	Mn	25	127
Arsenic	As	33	121	Neon	Ne	10	71
Beryllium	Be	4	112	Nickel	Ni	28	124
Boron	B	5	85	Nitrogen	N	7	71
Bromine	Br	35	117	Oxygen	O	8	60
Calcium	Ca	20	197	Phosphorus	P	15	109
Carbon	C	6	77	Potassium	K	19	231
Chlorine	Cl	17	91	Rubidium	Rb	37	248
Chromium	Cr	24	128	Scandium	Sc	21	162
Cobalt	Co	27	125	Selenium	Se	34	119
Copper	Cu	29	128	Silicon	Si	14	118
Fluorine	F	9	69	Sodium	Na	11	186
Gallium	Ga	31	134	Strontium	Sr	38	215
Germanium	Ge	32	123	Sulfur	S	16	103
Iron	Fe	26	126	Titanium	Ti	22	147
Krypton	Kr	36	201	Vanadium	V	23	134
Lithium	Li	3	156	Zinc	Zn	30	134

L2

Meeting Different Ability Levels

Content Outline

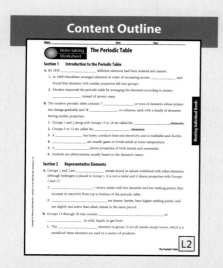

L2

Reinforcement

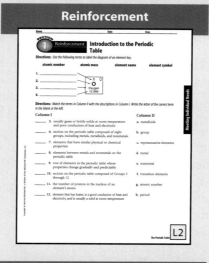

L2

Enrichment

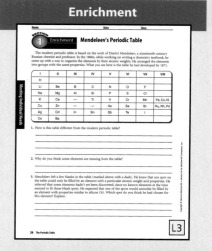

L3

Directed Reading (English/Spanish)

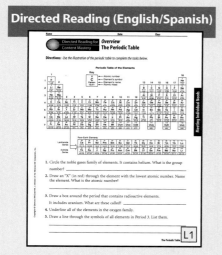

L1

Study Guide

Study Guide

Features
- Contains a study guide page for each section of the chapter
- Reviews key concepts
- Includes answer pages

L2

Reading Essentials

Reading Essentials for Glencoe Science
An Interactive Student Workbook

Features
- Condensed core content
- Actively involves students in reading
- Reinforces key vocabulary

L1

Assessment

Test Practice Workbook

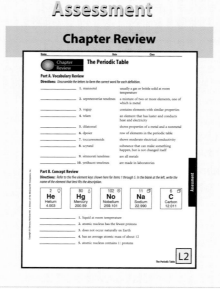

GO ON L2

Chapter Review

L2

Chapter Tests

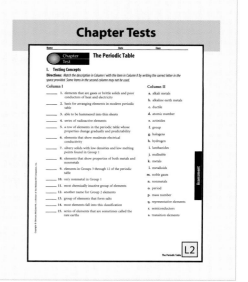

L2

Science Content Background

 Introduction to the Periodic Table
Development of the Periodic Table

As the science of chemistry grew during the nineteenth century, scientists amassed a great deal of information about known elements and their chemistry. Such information helped in the search for an organizing principle for the elements. In 1817, the German chemist Johann Dobereiner found that he could arrange many elements into groups that he called triads. For example, he noticed that lithium, sodium, and potassium all react vigorously with water. When these elements are arranged in order of atomic mass, the mass of the middle element, sodium, is almost the same as the average of the lightest and heaviest elements. Similar regularities were uncovered for calcium, strontium, and barium, and for fluorine, chlorine, and bromine.

Dobereiner's early work laid the groundwork for other chemists in the search for an organizing principle based upon the similarities in chemical properties and trends in atomic mass. In 1864 English chemist John Newlands proposed that when the known elements were arranged according to atomic mass, similarities in chemical properties occurred with every eighth element. He called this regularity the law of octaves.

1 H 1.01																	2 He 4.00
3 Li 6.94	4 Be 9.01											5 B 10.8	6 C 12.0	7 N 14.0	8 O 16.0	9 F 19.0	10 Ne 20.2
11 Na 23.0	12 Mg 24.3											13 Al 27.0	14 Si 28.1	15 P 31.0	16 S 32.1	17 Cl 35.5	18 Ar 40.0
19 K 39.1	20 Ca 40.1	21 Sc 45.0	22 Ti 47.9	23 V 50.9	24 Cr 52.0	25 Mn 54.9	26 Fe 55.8	27 Co 58.9	28 Ni 58.7	29 Cu 63.5	30 Zn 65.4	31 Ga 69.7	32 Ge 72.6	33 As 74.9	34 Se 79.0	35 Br 79.9	36 Kr 83.8
37 Rb 85.5	38 Sr 87.6	39 Y 88.9	40 Zr 91.2	41 Nb 92.9	42 Mo 95.9	43 Tc 98	44 Ru 101	45 Rh 103	46 Pd 106	47 Ag 108	48 Cd 112	49 In 115	50 Sn 119	51 Sb 122	52 Te 128	53 I 127	54 Xe 131
55 Cs 133	56 Ba 137	57 La 139	72 Hf 178	73 Ta 181	74 W 184	75 Re 186	76 Os 190	77 Ir 192	78 Pt 195	79 Au 197	80 Hg 201	81 Tl 204	82 Pb 207	83 Bi 209	84 Po 210	85 At 210	86 Rn 222
87 Fr 223	88 Ra 226	89 Ac 227	104 Rf 227	105 Db 262	106 Sg 263	107 Bh 264	108 Hs 265	109 Mt 268	110 Ds 281	111 Uuu 272	112 Uub 285	113	114 Uuq 289	115	116	117	118

58 Ce 140	59 Pr 141	60 Nd 144	61 Pm 147	62 Sm 150	63 Eu 152	64 Gd 157	65 Tb 159	66 Dy 163	67 Ho 165	68 Er 167	69 Tm 169	70 Yb 173	71 Lu 175
90 Th 232	91 Pa 231	92 U 238	93 Np 237	94 Pu 244	95 Am 243	96 Cm 247	97 Bk 247	98 Cf 251	99 Es 254	100 Fm 257	101 Md 258	102 No 255	103 Lr 256

color code = light metals -brittle metals -ductile metals -low melting metals -non-metals -noble gases -lanthanides -actinides

chapter content resources

Internet Resources
For additional content background, visit
bookk.msscience.com to:
- access your book online
- find references to related articles in popular science magazines
- access Web links with related content background
- access current events with science journal topics

Print Resources
Chemistry; The Molecular Nature of Matter and Change, by Martin S. Silberberg, McGraw-Hill, 2003
Mendeleyev's Dream: The Quest for the Elements, by Paul Strathern, St. Martin's Press, 2001
Nature's Building Blocks: An A–Z Guide to the Elements, by John Emsley, Oxford University Press, 2002

Russian chemist Dmitri Ivanovich Mendeleev created the first periodic table of elements in 1869. The modern periodic table didn't come into being until a Dutch physicist, Anton van den Broek, proposed that the elements should be arranged according to nuclear charge rather than atomic mass. Henry Moseley confirmed this hypothesis through studies of the X-ray spectra of a series of elements that had consecutive positions on the table. The change to ordering by atomic number resulted in the reversal of the positions of some elements.

Representative Elements
Sections of the Periodic Table

The periodic table divides into sections of representative elements, transition elements, and inner transition elements. The sections of the table reflect the electron configurations of the elements and the sublevels occupied by the electrons. It is the electron configuration of the atom that determines its chemical reactivity. For every principle quantum number (period or horizontal row), there are sublevels designated by letters, such as s, p, d, and f.

Teacher to Teacher
Kerry O'Brien
Dan River Middle School
Ringgold, Virginia

"Give students two blank copies of the periodic table. Have them label one blank table 'Number of Valence Electrons', the other 'Number of Energy Levels'. Have students research in books or on the internet to find out how many valence electrons and how many energy levels each element has. Write that number in the appropriate box. At the end they will see a pattern form and will understand why the elements are placed where they are in the table."

Kerry O'Brien

In the sublevels, electrons pairs are found in orbitals. There is one s orbital, three p orbitals, five d orbitals, and seven f orbitals within their respective sublevels. As you move across any period of the table, Groups 1 and 2 are filling s orbitals with two electrons. Groups 13–18 are filling p orbitals with six electrons. In periods 4 through 7, the transition elements, Groups 3–12, are filling five d orbitals with ten electrons. The inner transition elements, located below the periodic table, are filling the $4f$ and $5f$ orbitals with 14 electrons.

Transition Elements
From Metals to Nonmetals

The alkali metals have one electron in an outer s orbital. This single electron is in a higher energy level than any inner level of electrons, and the inner electrons shield it from the full attractive force of the nucleus. As a result, relatively little energy is needed to remove the electron, and thus ionize the atom to a 1+ state. As you move down the alkali metal group, the outermost s electron is farther and farther from the nucleus and ionization becomes successively easier. As a result, the reactivity of the alkali metals increases down the family.

The alkaline earth metals have two electrons in an outer s orbital. The energy needed to remove the outer electrons is low enough to make this group of elements almost as active as the alkali metals. Their chemistry is the chemistry of the 2+ ion. The trend in reactivity for the oxygen group and the halogens is opposite that of Groups 1 and 2. Fluorine is the most active of the halogens, and activity decreases down the group.

Chapter Vocabulary

period, p. 99
group, p. 99
representative element, p. 99
transition element, p. 99
metal, p. 102
nonmetal, p. 102
metalloid, p. 102
alkali metal, p. 105
alkaline earth metals, p. 106
semiconductor, p. 107
halogen, p. 110
noble gas, p. 110
catalyst, p. 113
lanthanide, p. 114
actinide, p. 114
synthetic elements, p. 114

Science Journal Answers
will vary. Look for depth and
quality of information.

INTERACTIVE CHALKBOARD with Image Bank

PowerPoint® Presentations

This CD-ROM is an editable
Microsoft® PowerPoint®
presentation that includes:
* a pre-made presentation for
  every chapter
* interactive graphics
* animations
* audio clips
* image bank
* all new section and chapter
  questions
* Standardized Test Practice
* transparencies
* pre-lab questions for all labs
* Foldables directions
* links to bookk.msscience.com

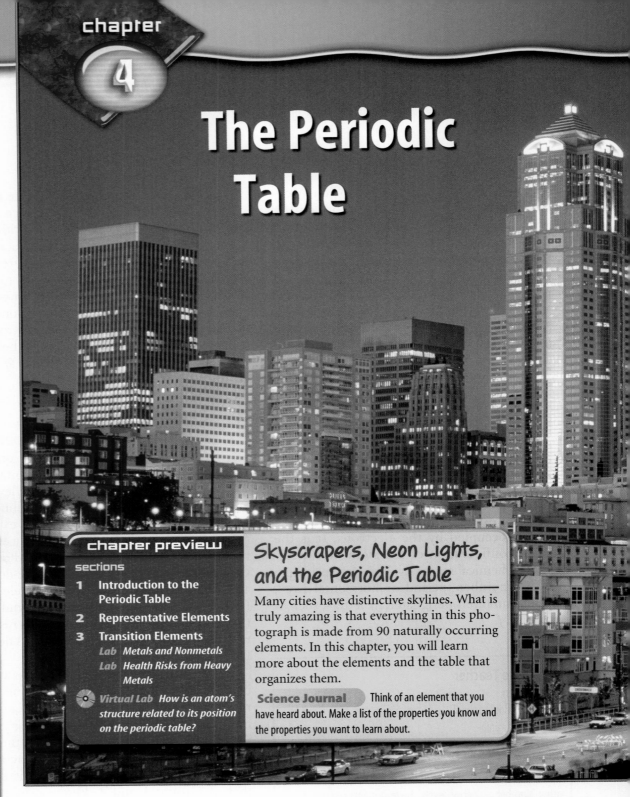

chapter 4

The Periodic Table

chapter preview

sections

1 Introduction to the Periodic Table

2 Representative Elements

3 Transition Elements
   Lab Metals and Nonmetals
   Lab Health Risks from Heavy Metals

Virtual Lab How is an atom's structure related to its position on the periodic table?

Skyscrapers, Neon Lights, and the Periodic Table

Many cities have distinctive skylines. What is truly amazing is that everything in this photograph is made from 90 naturally occurring elements. In this chapter, you will learn more about the elements and the table that organizes them.

Science Journal Think of an element that you have heard about. Make a list of the properties you know and the properties you want to learn about.

Theme Connection

Stability and Change Many characteristics of an element can be known from its position in the periodic table. Among these are the element's stability and the ways in which it combines with other elements.

About the Photo

Elements Everywhere The Dallas, Texas skyline holds many elements. The buildings, plants, lights, people, and air are all composed of elements. The periodic table organizes elements based on similar properties and helps predict an element's behavior.

Start-Up Activities

Make a Model of a Periodic Pattern

Every 29.5 days, the Moon begins to cycle through its phases from full moon to new moon and back again to full moon. Events that follow a predictable pattern are called periodic events. What other periodic events can you think of?

1. On a blank sheet of paper, make a grid with four squares across and four squares down.

2. Your teacher will give you 16 pieces of paper with different shapes and colors. Identify properties you can use to distinguish one piece of paper from another.

3. Place a piece of paper in each square on your grid. Arrange the pieces on the grid so that each column contains pieces that are similar.

4. Within each column, arrange the pieces to show a gradual change in their appearance.

5. **Think Critically** In your Science Journal, describe how the properties change in the rows across the grid and in the columns down the grid.

Preview this chapter's content and activities at
bookk.msscience.com

FOLDABLES
Study Organizer

Periodic Table Make the following Foldable to help you classify the elements in the periodic table as metals, nonmetals, and metalloids.

STEP 1 Fold a vertical sheet of paper from side to side. Make the front edge about 1.25 cm shorter than the back edge.

STEP 2 Turn lengthwise and **fold** into thirds.

STEP 3 Unfold and cut only the top layer along both folds to make three tabs. **Label** each tab as shown.

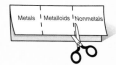

| Metals | Metalloids | Nonmetals |

Find Main Ideas As you read the chapter, write information about the three types of elements under the appropriate tabs. Use the information in your Foldable to explain how metalloids have properties between those of metals and nonmetals.

Purpose Use the Launch Lab to help students classify items according to properties. L2
ELL **IS** **Visual-Spatial**

Preparation Cut four circles of different diameters from each of four colors of paper. Leave the circles of one color whole. Remove a wedge-shaped quarter of each circle of another color. Cut another color of circles in half. For the last color, cut circles into quarters.

Materials sheet of paper, pencil, set of precut shapes (4 of each shape in 4 different colors for each group)

Teaching Strategy Allow students to arrange the pieces in any patterns they can justify.

Think Critically
Answers will vary depending on student patterns. Check to see that descriptions and grids match.

Assessment
Process Ask students to find another reasonable arrangement of the pieces of paper.

 Dinah Zike
Study Organizer **Study Fold**

Student preparation materials for this Foldable are available in the **Chapter *FAST FILE* Resources.**

Introduction to the Periodic Table

1 Motivate

Bellringer

Section Focus Transparencies also are available on the Interactive Chalkboard CD-ROM.

L2 ELL

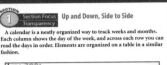

Tie to Prior Knowledge

Periodic Table Display for the class a periodic table of the elements. If you do not have one large enough to display, have students turn to the one in this chapter. Ask students to find elements they know, and have volunteers tell what they know about the element and describe its location on the periodic table.

Fun Fact

In his final version of the periodic table in 1871, Mendeleev left gaps, foretelling they would be filled by elements not yet known to scientists. He correctly predicted the properties of three of those elements.

---

as you read

What **You'll Learn**

- **Describe** the history of the periodic table.
- **Interpret** an element key.
- **Explain** how the periodic table is organized.

Why **It's Important**

The periodic table makes it easier for you to find information that you need about the elements.

Review Vocabulary
element: a substance that cannot be broken down into simpler substances

New Vocabulary
- period
- group
- representative element
- transition element
- metal
- nonmetal
- metalloid

Development of the Periodic Table

Early civilizations were familiar with a few of the substances now called elements. They made coins and jewelry from gold and silver. They also made tools and weapons from copper, tin, and iron. In the nineteenth century, chemists began to search for new elements. By 1830, they had isolated and named 55 different elements. The list continues to grow today.

Mendeleev's Table of Element A Russian chemist, Dmitri Mendeleev (men duh LAY uhf), published the first version of his periodic table in the *Journal of the Russian Chemical Society* in 1869. His table is shown in **Figure 1.** When Mendeleev arranged the elements in order of increasing atomic mass, he began to see a pattern. Elements with similar properties fell into groups on the table. At that time, not all the elements were known. To make his table work, Mendeleev had to leave three gaps for missing elements. Based on the groupings in his table, he predicted the properties for the missing elements. Mendeleev's predictions spurred other chemists to look for the missing elements. Within 15 years, all three elements—gallium, scandium, and germanium—were discovered.

Figure 1 Mendeleev published his first periodic table in 1869. This postage stamp, with his table and photo, was issued in 1969 to commemorate the event. Notice the question marks that he used to mark his prediction of yet-undiscovered elements.

98 ◆ **K CHAPTER 4** The Periodic Table

Section 1 Resource Manager

Chapter *FAST FILE* Resources
Transparency Activity, pp. 40, 43–44
Directed Reading for Content Mastery, pp. 15, 16
MiniLAB, p. 3
Enrichment, p. 26

Lab Activity, pp. 9–10, 11–12
Note-taking Worksheets, pp. 29–30
Reinforcement, p. 23
Home and Community Development, p. 25

Moseley's Contribution Although Mendeleev's table correctly organized most of the elements, a few elements seemed out of place. In the early twentieth century, the English physicist Henry Moseley, before age 27, realized that Mendeleev's table could be improved by arranging the elements according to atomic number rather than atomic mass. Moseley revised the periodic table by arranging the elements in order of increasing number of protons in the nucleus. With Moseley's table, it was clear how many elements still were undiscovered.

Today's Periodic Table

In the modern periodic table on the next page, the elements still are organized by increasing atomic number. The rows or periods are labeled 1–7. A **period** is a row of elements in the periodic table whose properties change gradually and predictably. The periodic table has 18 columns of elements. Each column contains a group, or family, of elements. A **group** contains elements that have similar physical or chemical properties.

Zones on the Periodic Table The periodic table can be divided into sections, as you can see in **Figure 2.** One section consists of the first two groups, Groups 1 and 2, and the elements in Groups 13–18. These eight groups are the **representative elements.** They include metals, metalloids, and nonmetals. The elements in Groups 3–12 are **transition elements.** They are all metals. Some transition elements, called the inner transition elements, are placed below the main table. These elements are called the lanthanide and actinide series because one series follows the element lanthanum, element 57, and the other series follows actinium, element 89.

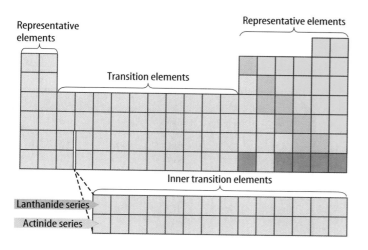

Representative elements

Transition elements

Representative elements

Inner transition elements

Lanthanide series

Actinide series

Mini LAB

Designing a Periodic Table

Procedure
1. Collect **pens** and **pencils** from everyone in your class.
2. Decide which properties of the pens and pencils you will use to organize them into a periodic table. Consider properties such as color, mass, or length. Then create your table.

Analysis
1. Explain how your periodic table is similar to the periodic table of the elements.
2. If your classmates brought different pens or pencils to class tomorrow, how would you organize them on your periodic table?

Figure 2 The periodic table is divided into sections. Traditionally, the lanthanides and actinides are placed below the table so that the table will not be as wide. These elements have similar properties.

2 Teach

Mini LAB

Purpose Students arrange pens and pencils into a model of the periodic table. [L2] **ELL**

COOP LEARN **IS** Kinesthetic

Materials students' pens and pencils

Teaching Strategy Ask students to bring to school extra pens or pencils.

Analysis
1. Student tables could show that the writing utensils in a column have similar properties, such as color, length, and shape. The properties in a row change gradually.
2. Student answers will vary based on their tables but could include that items would be placed in a column with similar utensils and in a row in which their properties were intermediate between the utensils to the right and left.

Assessment

Performance Have each student make a calendar for the present month and write on it any events he or she has scheduled, such as soccer practice or music lessons. Have the student look for periodic events. Use **Performance Assessment in the Science Classroom,** p. 165.

Differentiated Instruction

Visually Impaired The MiniLAB can be revised to use a collection of small hardware pieces of various sizes, such as screws, nuts, washers, and bolts, that can be sorted by touch instead of sight. Make sure you do not use sharp pieces, which might puncture skin. [L2] **ELL** **IS** Kinesthetic

Increasing Numbers As you move from one element to the next across the periods in the periodic table, atomic number increases by one. What else, therefore, also increases by one? the number of protons in each atom of the element
L2

Virtual Labs

Atomic Structure *How is an atom's structure related to its position on the periodic table?*

PERIODIC TABLE OF THE ELEMENTS

Columns of elements are called groups. Elements in the same group have similar chemical properties.

- Element — Hydrogen
- Atomic number — 1
- Symbol — H
- Atomic mass — 1.008

State of matter

Gas
Liquid
Solid
Synthetic

The first three symbols tell you the state of matter of the element at room temperature. The fourth symbol identifies elements that are not present in significant amounts on Earth. Useful amounts are made synthetically.

Group	1	2	3	4	5	6	7	8	9
1	Hydrogen 1 H 1.008								
2	Lithium 3 Li 6.941	Beryllium 4 Be 9.012							
3	Sodium 11 Na 22.990	Magnesium 12 Mg 24.305							
4	Potassium 19 K 39.098	Calcium 20 Ca 40.078	Scandium 21 Sc 44.956	Titanium 22 Ti 47.867	Vanadium 23 V 50.942	Chromium 24 Cr 51.996	Manganese 25 Mn 54.938	Iron 26 Fe 55.845	Cobalt 27 Co 58.933
5	Rubidium 37 Rb 85.468	Strontium 38 Sr 87.62	Yttrium 39 Y 88.906	Zirconium 40 Zr 91.224	Niobium 41 Nb 92.906	Molybdenum 42 Mo 95.94	Technetium 43 Tc (98)	Ruthenium 44 Ru 101.07	Rhodium 45 Rh 102.906
6	Cesium 55 Cs 132.905	Barium 56 Ba 137.327	Lanthanum 57 La 138.906	Hafnium 72 Hf 178.49	Tantalum 73 Ta 180.948	Tungsten 74 W 183.84	Rhenium 75 Re 186.207	Osmium 76 Os 190.23	Iridium 77 Ir 192.217
7	Francium 87 Fr (223)	Radium 88 Ra (226)	Actinium 89 Ac (227)	Rutherfordium 104 Rf (261)	Dubnium 105 Db (262)	Seaborgium 106 Sg (266)	Bohrium 107 Bh (264)	Hassium 108 Hs (277)	Meitnerium 109 Mt (268)

The number in parentheses is the mass number of the longest-lived isotope for that element.

Rows of elements are called periods. Atomic number increases across a period.

The arrow shows where these elements would fit into the periodic table. They are moved to the bottom of the table to save space.

Lanthanide series

Cerium 58 Ce 140.116	Praseodymium 59 Pr 140.908	Neodymium 60 Nd 144.24	Promethium 61 Pm (145)	Samarium 62 Sm 150.36

Actinide series

Thorium 90 Th 232.038	Protactinium 91 Pa 231.036	Uranium 92 U 238.029	Neptunium 93 Np (237)	Plutonium 94 Pu (244)

100 ◆ K CHAPTER 4 The Periodic Table

Teacher FYI

Isotope Mass Different isotopes of an element have different atomic masses. The atomic mass given for an element in the periodic table is calculated by taking the relative abundance of each isotope, multiplying it by the mass of that isotope, and then adding these numbers together.

Curriculum Connection

History The German scientist Lothar Meyer published a periodic table that was almost identical to Mendeleev's table. Have students find out why Meyer was not given equal credit for the periodic table. Because of a delay in the submission of Meyer's article, Mendeleev's work was published one year earlier. L2

Metal
Metalloid
Nonmetal

The color of an element's block tells you if the element is a metal, nonmetal, or metalloid.

Science Online
Visit bookk.msscience.com for updates to the periodic table.

	13	14	15	16	17	18
						Helium 2 **He** 4.003
	Boron 5 **B** 10.811	Carbon 6 **C** 12.011	Nitrogen 7 **N** 14.007	Oxygen 8 **O** 15.999	Fluorine 9 **F** 18.998	Neon 10 **Ne** 20.180
	Aluminum 13 **Al** 26.982	Silicon 14 **Si** 28.086	Phosphorus 15 **P** 30.974	Sulfur 16 **S** 32.065	Chlorine 17 **Cl** 35.453	Argon 18 **Ar** 39.948

10	11	12						
Nickel 28 **Ni** 58.693	Copper 29 **Cu** 63.546	Zinc 30 **Zn** 65.409	Gallium 31 **Ga** 69.723	Germanium 32 **Ge** 72.64	Arsenic 33 **As** 74.922	Selenium 34 **Se** 78.96	Bromine 35 **Br** 79.904	Krypton 36 **Kr** 83.798
Palladium 46 **Pd** 106.42	Silver 47 **Ag** 107.868	Cadmium 48 **Cd** 112.411	Indium 49 **In** 114.818	Tin 50 **Sn** 118.710	Antimony 51 **Sb** 121.760	Tellurium 52 **Te** 127.60	Iodine 53 **I** 126.904	Xenon 54 **Xe** 131.293
Platinum 78 **Pt** 195.078	Gold 79 **Au** 196.967	Mercury 80 **Hg** 200.59	Thallium 81 **Tl** 204.383	Lead 82 **Pb** 207.2	Bismuth 83 **Bi** 208.980	Polonium 84 **Po** (209)	Astatine 85 **At** (210)	Radon 86 **Rn** (222)
Darmstadtium 110 **Ds** (281)	Unununium * 111 **Uuu** (272)	Ununbium * 112 **Uub** (285)		Ununquadium * 114 **Uuq** (289)		** 116		** 118

* The names and symbols for elements 111–114 are temporary. Final names will be selected when the elements' discoveries are verified.

** Elements 116 and 118 were thought to have been created. The claim was retracted because the experimental results could not be repeated.

Europium 63 **Eu** 151.964	Gadolinium 64 **Gd** 157.25	Terbium 65 **Tb** 158.925	Dysprosium 66 **Dy** 162.500	Holmium 67 **Ho** 164.930	Erbium 68 **Er** 167.259	Thulium 69 **Tm** 168.934	Ytterbium 70 **Yb** 173.04	Lutetium 71 **Lu** 174.967
Americium 95 **Am** (243)	Curium 96 **Cm** (247)	Berkelium 97 **Bk** (247)	Californium 98 **Cf** (251)	Einsteinium 99 **Es** (252)	Fermium 100 **Fm** (257)	Mendelevium 101 **Md** (258)	Nobelium 102 **No** (259)	Lawrencium 103 **Lr** (262)

Use Science Words

Word Usage Have students explain why using *period* and *family* to describe parts of the periodic table corresponds to common usage of these terms. Period refers to something occurring in a repeating pattern; properties repeat in a pattern on the periodic table. Family refers to individuals with similar characteristics; elements in a family have similar properties. L2 LS
Linguistic

Use an Analogy

Element Families Ask students to brainstorm similar characteristics of human family members. Include those characteristics that can be seen, such as hair color and ear shape, and those that can't be seen, such as artistic talent or disposition. Have them suggest ways in which groups of elements might also have similar properties that can and cannot be observed with the eyes. For example, chlorine and bromine exist in different states at room temperature, but their chemical properties are similar.

Activity

Handling Elements To help students appreciate the different properties of the elements, allow them to handle as many samples of safe-to-handle elements (metals and nonmetals) as you have available. If possible, give them metals in the form of wire or sheets, such as aluminum foil. L1
ELL LS **Kinesthetic**

Science Journal

Periodic Table Call attention to the color-coding of metals, nonmetals, and metalloids. Ask students to locate elements they already know about and classify them in their Science Journals. Have them locate the liquid elements and list all the gaseous elements that they already know. L2 LS
Visual-Spatial

Visual Learning

Figure 3 Are the transition elements metals, nonmetals, or metalloids? metals L1

Text Question Answer

Answers might include door knobs, wire, automobile engines and bodies, toasters, and so on.

Quick Demo

Alkaline Earth Metals

Materials magnesium strip, empty can

Estimated Time 10 minutes

Procedure Darken the room. Burn the strip of magnesium inside the empty can. Students will observe the reflected white light.

Science Journal

Metalloids Ask each student to choose one of the metalloids and to find out how it is similar to a metal and how it is similar to a nonmetal. Have students write their findings in their Science Journals. Metalloids include boron, silicon, germanium, arsenic, antimony, tellurium, polonium, and astatine. L3 LS **Linguistic** P

Reading Check

Answer seventeen elements

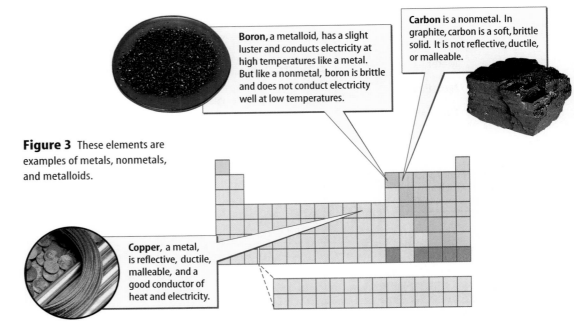

Boron, a metalloid, has a slight luster and conducts electricity at high temperatures like a metal. But like a nonmetal, boron is brittle and does not conduct electricity well at low temperatures.

Carbon is a nonmetal. In graphite, carbon is a soft, brittle solid. It is not reflective, ductile, or malleable.

Figure 3 These elements are examples of metals, nonmetals, and metalloids.

Copper, a metal, is reflective, ductile, malleable, and a good conductor of heat and electricity.

Science Online

Topic: Elements
Visit bookk.msscience.com for Web links to information about how the periodic table was developed.

Activity Select an element and write about how, when, and by whom it was discovered.

Metals If you look at the periodic table, you will notice it is color coded. The colors represent elements that are metals, nonmetals, or metalloids. Examples of a metal, a nonmental, and a metalloid are illustrated in **Figure 3.** With the exception of mercury, all the metals are solids, most with high melting points. A **metal** is an element that has luster, is a good conductor of heat and electricity, is malleable, and is ductile. The ability to reflect light is a property of metals called luster. Many metals can be pressed or pounded into thin sheets or shaped into objects because they are malleable (MAL yuh bul). Metals are also ductile (DUK tul), which means that they can be drawn out into wires. Can you think of any items that are made of metals?

Nonmetals and Metalloids **Nonmetals** are usually gases or brittle solids at room temperature and poor conductors of heat and electricity. There are only 17 nonmetals, but they include many elements that are essential for life—carbon, sulfur, nitrogen, oxygen, phosphorus, and iodine.

The elements between metals and nonmetals on the periodic table are called metalloids (ME tuh loydz). As you might expect from the name, a **metalloid** is an element that shares some properties with metals and some with nonmetals. These elements also are called semimetals.

Reading Check *How many elements are nonmetals?*

Differentiated Instruction

Challenge As you move from left to right across the groups of representative elements in the periodic table, the number of electrons in each atom's outer energy level increases by one. Elements in Group 1 each have one electron in the outer energy level, the elements in Group 2 have two electrons, elements in Group 13 have three, and so on. Most complete outer energy levels hold eight electrons. Have students find out what effect this has on the elements' behavior. When atoms react with one another, they try to complete their outer energy levels. Groups 1, 2, and 13 generally complete their outer energy levels by losing electrons. Elements in Group 14 can either gain or lose electrons. Elements in Groups 15, 16, and 17 generally gain electrons, while elements in Group 18 have full outer electron energy levels, which is why they are so unreactive. L3 LS **Logical-Mathematical**

The Element Keys Each element is represented on the periodic table by a box called the element key. An enlarged key for hydrogen is shown in **Figure 4.** An element key shows you the name of the element, its atomic number, its symbol, and its average atomic mass. Element keys for elements that occur naturally on Earth include a logo that tells whether the element is a solid, a liquid, or a gas at room temperature. All the gases except hydrogen are on the right side of the table. They are marked with a balloon logo. Most of the other elements are solids at room temperature and are marked with a cube. Two elements on the periodic table are liquids at room temperature. Their logo is a drop. Elements that do not occur naturally on Earth are marked with a bull's-eye logo. These are synthetic elements.

Element —— Hydrogen
Atomic number —— 1
Symbol —— **H** —— State of matter
Atomic mass —— 1.008

Figure 4 As you can see from the element key, a lot of information about an element is given on the periodic table.
Identify the two elements that are liquids at room temperature.

Applying Science

What does *periodic* mean in the periodic table?

Elements often combine with oxygen to form oxides and chlorine to form chlorides. For example, two hydrogen atoms combine with one oxygen atom to form oxide, H_2O or water. One sodium atom combines with one chlorine atom to form sodium chloride, NaCl or table salt. The location of an element on the periodic table is an indication of how it combines with other elements.

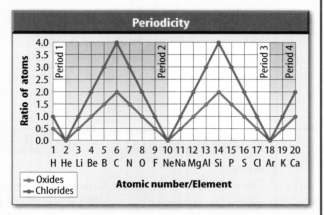

Periodicity

Identifying the Problem
    The graph shows the number of oxygen atoms (red) and chlorine atoms (green) that will combine with the first 20 elements. What pattern do you see?

Solving the Problem
1. Find all of the elements in Group 1 on the graph. Do the same with the elements in Groups 14 and 18. What do you notice about their positions on the graph?
2. This relationship demonstrates one of the properties of a group of elements. Follow the elements in order on the periodic table and on the graph. Write a statement using the word *periodic* that describes what occurs with the elements and their properties.

LAB DEMONSTRATION

Purpose to help students visualize the properties of nonmetals using carbon
Materials charcoal, cloth, hammer, conductivity tester
Procedure Show students a piece of charcoal. Have them note its appearance. Cover the charcoal with a cloth, and use a hammer to break off some pieces. Test a piece of the charcoal with the conductivity tester.

Expected Outcome Carbon is dull in appearance, brittle, and charcoal is a nonconductor.

Assessment
Why aren't nonmetals used for wiring? They are brittle and would break, and they are nonconductors. Why wouldn't a nonmetal be used to make jewelry? Nonmetals are too brittle and dull.

Check for Understanding

Visual-Spatial Give each student a copy of a blank periodic table. Ask students to write the names of as many elements as they can in the correct spaces. L3 LS

Reteach

Periodic Table Zones Give each student a copy of a blank periodic table. Ask students to identify the areas of the table occupied by the representative elements, the transition elements, and the inner transition elements. Ask them to color code the metals, nonmetals, and metalloids. Ask them to label the 18 groups and the 7 periods. L1 LS **Visual-Spatial**

✔ Assessment

Content Have students make up written questions about the periodic table and give them to you. Sort the questions, and use them to give a rapid-fire oral quiz. Use **Performance Assessment in the Science Classroom**, p. 91.

Table 1 Chemical Symbols and Their Origins

Name	Symbol	Origin of Name
Mendelevium	Md	For Dimitri Mendeleev
Lead	Pb	The Latin name for lead is *plumbum*.
Thorium	Th	The Norse god of thunder is Thor.
Polonium	Po	For Poland, where Marie Curie, a famous scientist, was born
Hydrogen	H	From Greek words meaning "water former."
Mercury	Hg	*Hydrargyrum* means "liquid silver" in Greek.
Gold	Au	*Aurum* means "shining dawn" in Latin.
Unununium	Uuu	Named using the IUPAC naming system.

Symbols for the Elements The symbols for the elements are either one- or two-letter abbreviations, often based on the element name. For example, V is the symbol for vanadium, and Sc is the symbol for scandium. Sometimes the symbols don't match the names. Examples are Ag for silver and Na for sodium. In those cases, the symbol might come from Greek or Latin names for the elements. Some elements are named for scientists such as Lise Meitner (meitnerium, Mt). Some are named for geographic locations such as France (francium, Fr).

Newly synthesized elements are given a temporary name and 3-letter symbol that is related to the element's atomic number. The International Union of Pure and Applied Chemistry (IUPAC) adopted this system in 1978. Once the discovery of the element is verified, the discoverers can choose a permanent name. **Table 1** shows the origin of some element names and symbols.

---

section 1 review

Summary

Development of the Periodic Table
- Dmitri Mendeleev published the first version of the periodic table in 1869.
- Mendeleev left three gaps on the periodic table for missing elements.
- Moseley arranged Mendeleev's table according to atomic number, not by atomic mass.

Today's Periodic Table
- The periodic table is divided into sections.
- A period is a row of elements whose properties change gradually and predictably.
- Groups 1 and 2 along with Groups 13–18 are called representative elements.
- Groups 3–12 are called transition elements.

Self Check

1. **Evaluate** the elements in period 4 to show how the physical state changes as the atomic number increases.
2. **Describe** where the metals, nonmetals, and metalloids are located in the periodic table.
3. **Classify** each of the following elements as metal, nonmetal, or metalloid: Fe, Li, B, Cl, Si, Na, and Ni.
4. **Define** what an element key contains.
5. **Think Critically** How would the modern periodic table be different if elements were arranged by average atomic mass instead of by atomic number?

Applying Math

6. **Solve One-Step Equations** What is the difference in atomic mass of iodine and magnesium?

 Science Online bookk.msscience.com/self_check_quiz

---

section 1 review

1. Elements are solid through Group 16, liquid in Group 17, and gaseous in Group 18.
2. Metals are on the left side; nonmetals are on the right side; metalloids are on a slanting line between metals and nonmetals.
3. Fe, Li, Na, and Ni are metals. Cl is a nonmetal. B and Si are metalloids.
4. the name of the element, its atomic number, its symbol, its average atomic mass, its state at room temperature, and whether it occurs naturally
5. Some pairs of elements, such as K and Ar, and Ni and Co, would exchange places and elements that have similar properties would no longer appear in the correct group.
6. 126.9 (iodine) − 24.3 (magnesium) = 102.6

Representative Elements

Groups 1 and 2

Groups 1 and 2 are always found in nature combined with other elements. They're called active metals because of their readiness to form new substances with other elements. They are all metals except hydrogen, the first element in Group 1. Although hydrogen is placed in Group 1, it shares properties with the elements in Group 1 and Group 17.

Alkali Metals The Group 1 elements have a specific family name—**alkali metals.** All the alkali metals are silvery solids with low densities and low melting points. These elements increase in their reactivity, or tendency to combine with other substances, as you move from top to bottom on the periodic table. Some uses of the alkali metals are shown in **Figure 5.**

Alkali metals are found in many items. Lithium batteries are used in cameras. Sodium chloride is common table salt. Sodium and potassium, dietary requirements, are found in small quantities in potatoes and bananas.

as you read

What You'll Learn

■ **Recognize** the properties of representative elements.
■ **Identify** uses for the representative elements.
■ **Classify** elements into groups based on similar properties.

Why It's Important

Many representative elements play key roles in your body, your environment, and in the things you use every day.

Review Vocabulary
atomic number: the number of protons in the nucleus of a given element

New Vocabulary
● alkali metal
● alkaline earth metal
● semiconductor
● halogen
● noble gas

Bellringer

Section Focus Transparencies also are available on the Interactive Chalkboard CD-ROM.

L2 ELL

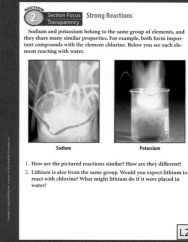

Figure 5 These items contain alkali metals.

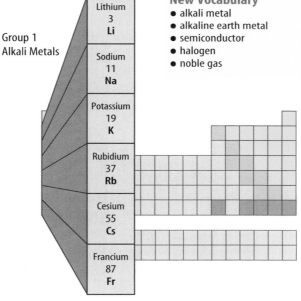

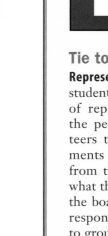

Group 1
Alkali Metals

| Lithium 3 **Li** |
| Sodium 11 **Na** |
| Potassium 19 **K** |
| Rubidium 37 **Rb** |
| Cesium 55 **Cs** |
| Francium 87 **Fr** |

Tie to Prior Knowledge

Representative Elements Have students look at the eight groups of representative elements on the periodic table. Ask volunteers to name any of the elements they are familiar with from these groups and explain what they know about them. On the board, keep a list of student responses organized according to group.

SECTION 2 Representative Elements **K** ◆ **105**

Section 2 Resource Manager

Chapter *FAST FILE* Resources
  Transparency Activity, p. 41
  Directed Reading for Content Mastery, p. 17
  Enrichment, p. 27
  Reinforcement, p. 24

Life Science Critical Thinking/Problem Solving, p. 15
Cultural Diversity, p. 37
Physical Science Critical Thinking/Problem Solving, p. 9
Earth Science Critical Thinking/Problem Solving, p. 13

Storing Metals Tell students that alkali metals are stored under mineral oil or kerosene. Why? because they react so readily with both oxygen and water vapor in the air [L2]
[IS] **Logical-Mathematical**

☑ Reading Check

Answer beryllium, magnesium, calcium, strontium, barium, radium

Teacher FYI

Boron Elemental boron has two forms, an amorphous black or brown powder and a brittle, black or silver crystalline form with the high luster of metals. Because the bonds in crystalline boron are not the same as those of metals, it is not malleable or ductile. Boron carbide is one of the hardest substances known and is used to make bulletproof armor.

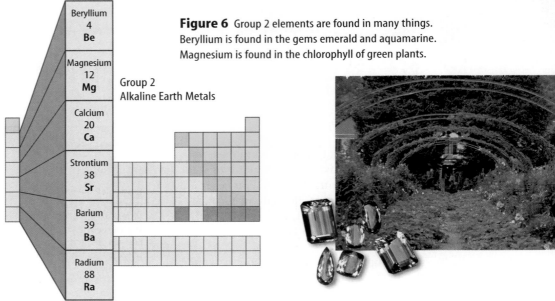

Group 2
Alkaline Earth Metals

Figure 6 Group 2 elements are found in many things. Beryllium is found in the gems emerald and aquamarine. Magnesium is found in the chlorophyll of green plants.

Alkaline Earth Metals Next door to the alkali metals' family are their Group 2 neighbors, the **alkaline earth metals.** Each alkaline earth metal is denser and harder and has a higher melting point than the alkali metal in the same period. Alkaline earth metals are reactive, but not as reactive as the alkali metals. Some uses of the alkaline earth elements are shown in **Figure 6.**

☑ Reading Check *What are the names of the elements that are alkaline earth metals?*

Groups 13 through 18

Notice on the periodic table that the elements in Groups 13–18 are not all solid metals like the elements of Groups 1 and 2. In fact, a single group can contain metals, nonmetals, and metalloids and have members that are solids, liquids, and gases.

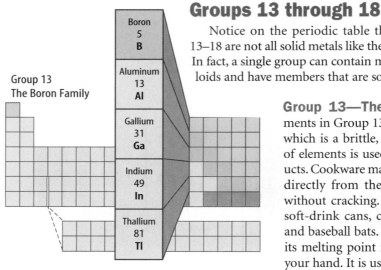

Group 13
The Boron Family

Group 13—The Boron Family The elements in Group 13 are all metals except boron, which is a brittle, black metalloid. This family of elements is used to make a variety of products. Cookware made with boron can be moved directly from the refrigerator into the oven without cracking. Aluminum is used to make soft-drink cans, cookware, siding for homes, and baseball bats. Gallium is a solid metal, but its melting point is so low that it will melt in your hand. It is used to make computer chips.

Science Journal

Calcium Have students research how the alkaline earth metal calcium is found in Earth's crust and write their findings in their Science Journals. Most calcium is found as calcium carbonate in marble and limestone rocks. Most limestone was formed from the skeletons of marine invertebrates, who take calcium from the sea and use it to make their shells. When the animals die, their shells fall to the sea floor, where the shells are compressed into the sedimentary rock limestone. When limestone is subjected to heat and pressure, it becomes the metamorphic rock marble. [L2]
[IS] **Linguistic**

Group 14—The Carbon Group If you look at Group 14, you can see that carbon is a nonmetal, silicon and germanium are metalloids, and tin and lead are metals. The nonmetal carbon exists as an element in several forms. You're familiar with two of them—diamond and graphite. Carbon also is found in all living things. Carbon is followed by the metalloid silicon, an abundant element contained in sand. Sand contains ground-up particles of minerals such as quartz, which is composed of silicon and oxygen. Glass is an important product made from sand.

Silicon and its Group 14 neighbor, germanium, are metalloids. They are used in electronics as semiconductors. A **semiconductor** doesn't conduct electricity as well as a metal, but does conduct electricity better than a nonmetal. Silicon and small amounts of other elements are used for computer chips as shown in **Figure 7.**

Tin and lead are the two heaviest elements in Group 14. Lead is used in the apron, shown in **Figure 7,** to protect your torso during dental X rays. It also is used in car batteries, low-melting alloys, protective shielding around nuclear reactors, particle accelerators, X-ray equipment, and containers used for storing and transporting radioactive materials. Tin is used in pewter, toothpaste, and the coating on steel cans used for food.

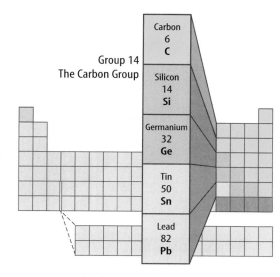

Group 14
The Carbon Group

| Carbon 6 C |
| Silicon 14 Si |
| Germanium 32 Ge |
| Tin 50 Sn |
| Lead 82 Pb |

Figure 7 Members of Group 14 include one nonmetal, two metalloids, and two metals.

Lead is used to shield your body from unwanted X-ray exposure.

All living things contain carbon compounds.

Silicon crystals are used to make computer chips.

Make a Model

Connecting Carbon Have students use a model kit or toothpicks and gumdrops to model how carbon atoms are connected to each other in diamond and graphite. In diamond, each carbon atom bonds with four other carbon atoms in a rigid, tetrahedral, three-dimensional array. In graphite, the carbon atoms form planar sheets of connecting hexagons. The sheets are not connected by carbon-to-carbon bonds, so one sheet can slide easily past another. This property makes graphite a good lubricant for the moving parts of machinery and explains the use of graphite in pencils. [L3] [LS] **Kinesthetic**

IDENTIFYING Misconceptions

Semiconductors Not all metalloids are semiconductors, and not all semiconductors are metalloids. Some semiconductors, such as gallium arsenide, indium antimonide, and aluminum phosphide, are compounds. Gray tin has also been used as a semiconductor.

Cultural Diversity

Women and Semiconductors Today scientists from all over the world make contributions to our knowledge of the behavior of matter. A few of the women making contributions to the field of semiconductors are Dr. Tineke Thio, Dr. Gertrude Neumark, Prof. Jingyu Lin, Dr. Hilda Kanber, Dr. Shirley A. Jackson, and Dr. Elsa Garmire. Have students report on the contributions of at least two of these women. [L2]

Differentiated Instruction

Physically Challenged The Make a Model activity above can be revised to use larger items that are easier to pick-up and handle. Substitute marshmallows and straws for the gum drops and toothpicks. [L3] [LS] **Kinesthetic**

Figure 8 Ammonia is used to make
nylon, a tough, light fiber capable of
replacing silk in many applications,
including parachutes.

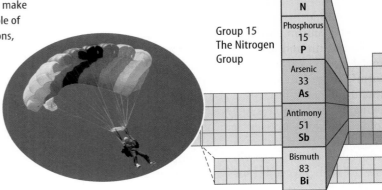

Group 15
The Nitrogen
Group

Nitrogen
7
N

Phosphorus
15
P

Arsenic
33
As

Antimony
51
Sb

Bismuth
83
Bi

Quick Demo

The Nitrogen Group

Materials cloth dampened with household cleaning solution containing ammonia

Estimated Time 15 minutes

Procedure Let students smell sharp odor as it diffuses through the air. **WARNING:** *Do not let students smell the ammonia directly.*

Activity

Feeling Fabric Allow students to feel a piece of nylon cloth and a piece of silk. Discuss with them the similarities and differences between the two fabrics. L1 IS
Kinesthetic

✔ Reading Check

Answer No. Nitrogen is obtained by eating plants. Bacteria in the soil changes nitrogen gas into substances that plants absorb.

INTEGRATE Career

Farmers Too many nutrients are non-beneficial to the farmer. Not only can crops be adversely affected, but the excess nutrients can leach into the water table and pollute streams, rivers, and lakes. Many government agencies provide guidelines on safely using nutrients.

Fun Fact

Nitrogen is relatively unreactive. Sometimes it is used inside a sealed case to protect valuable documents that might react with oxygen or other gases in air.

INTEGRATE Career

Farmers Each year farmers test their soil to determine the level of nutrients, the matter needed for plants to grow. The results of the test help the farmer decide how much nitrogen, phosphorus, and potassium to add to the fields. The additional nutrients increase the chance of having a successful crop.

Figure 9 Nitrogen and phosphorus are required for healthy green plants. This synthetic fertilizer label shows the nitrogen and phosphorous compounds that provide these.

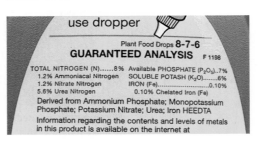

use dropper

Plant Food Drops **8-7-6**
GUARANTEED ANALYSIS F 1198

TOTAL NITROGEN (N)......8%   Available PHOSPHATE (P₂O₅)..7%
1.2% Ammoniacal Nitrogen   SOLUBLE POTASH (K₂O).......6%
1.2% Nitrate Nitrogen   IRON (Fe)........................0.10%
5.6% Urea Nitrogen   0.10% Chelated Iron (Fe)

Derived from Ammonium Phosphate; Monopotassium Phosphate; Potassium Nitrate; Urea; Iron HEEDTA

Information regarding the contents and levels of metals in this product is available on the internet at

Group 15—The Nitrogen Group At the top of Group 15 are the two nonmetals—nitrogen and phosphorus. Nitrogen and phosphorus are required by living things and are used to manufacture various items. These elements also are parts of the biological materials that store genetic information and energy in living organisms. Although almost 80 percent of the air you breathe is nitrogen, you can't get the nitrogen your body needs by breathing nitrogen gas. Bacteria in the soil must first change nitrogen gas into substances that can be absorbed through the roots of plants. Then, by eating the plants, nitrogen becomes available to your body.

✔ Reading Check
Can your body obtain nitrogen by breathing air? Explain.

Ammonia is a gas that contains nitrogen and hydrogen. When ammonia is dissolved in water, it can be used as a cleaner and disinfectant. Liquid ammonia is sometimes applied directly to soil as a fertilizer. Ammonia also can be converted into solid fertilizers. It also is used to freeze-dry food and as a refrigerant. Ammonia also is used to make nylon for parachutes, as shown in **Figure 8.**

The element phosphorus comes in two forms—white and red. White phosphorus is so active it can't be exposed to oxygen in the air or it will burst into flames. The heads of matches contain the less active red phosphorus, which ignites from the heat produced by friction when the match is struck. Phosphorous compounds are essential ingredients for healthy teeth and bones. Plants also need phosphorus, so it is one of the nutrients in most fertilizers. The fertilizer label in **Figure 9** shows the compounds of nitrogen and phosphorus that are used to give plants a synthetic supply of these elements.

Curriculum Connection

History The age of polymers and plastics began with the synthesis of celluloid in 1869. Ask students to find more about the first synthetic plastic material and the other new polymers that followed. John Wesley Hyatt, an American, made celluloid from cellulose nitrate and camphor. Celluloid was soon replaced by Bakelite, a registered trademark of Union Carbide. Many new synthetic materials were available after WW II. L2

Differentiated Instruction

Challenge In addition to red phosphorus and white phosphorus, a third form of elemental phosphorus, called black phosphorus, exists. Have students find out the differences in the structures of these three types of phosphorus. White phosphorus exists as tetrahedral P_4 molecules. In black phosphorus, the P_4 molecules form layers. Red phosphorus consists of P_4 molecules bonded in an amorphous structure that some believe to be polymeric. L3 IS **Linguistic**

Group 16—The Oxygen Family The first two members of Group 16, oxygen and sulfur, are essential for life. The heavier members of the group, tellurium and polonium, are both metalloids.

About 20 percent of Earth's atmosphere is the oxygen you breathe. Your body needs oxygen to release the energy from the foods you eat. Oxygen is abundant in Earth's rocks and minerals because it readily combines with other elements. Oxygen also is required for combustion to occur. Foam is used in fire fighting to keep oxygen away from the burning item, as shown in **Figure 10.** Ozone, a less common form of oxygen, is formed in the upper atmosphere through the action of electricity during thunderstorms. The presence of ozone is important because it shields living organisms from some harmful radiation from the Sun.

Sulfur is a solid, yellow nonmetal. Large amounts of sulfur are used to manufacture sulfuric acid, one of the most commonly used chemicals in the world. Sulfuric acid is a combination of sulfur, hydrogen, and oxygen. It is used in the manufacture of paints, fertilizers, detergents, synthetic fibers, and rubber.

Selenium conducts electricity when exposed to light, so it is used in solar cells, light meters, and photographic materials. Its most important use is as the light-sensitive component in photocopy machines. Traces of selenium are also necessary for good health.

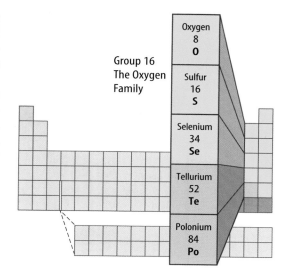

Group 16
The Oxygen Family

| Oxygen 8 O |
| Sulfur 16 S |
| Selenium 34 Se |
| Tellurium 52 Te |
| Polonium 84 Po |

Poison Buildup Arsenic disrupts the normal function of an organism by disrupting cellular metabolism. Because arsenic builds up in hair, forensic scientists can test hair samples to confirm or disprove a case of arsenic poisoning. Tests of Napoleon's hair suggest that he was poisoned with arsenic. Use reference books to find out who Napoleon I was and why someone might have wanted to poison him.

Figure 10 The foam used in aircraft fires forms a film of water over the burning fuel which suffocates the fire.

Poison Buildup Napoleon I (1769–1821) led the French in wars against Italy, Austria, England, Russia, Germany, and the Ottoman Empire. He ruled France as a dictator from 1799 to 1814, and was finally defeated at the Battle of Waterloo in 1815. Sulfur is a part of almost all enzymes, catalysts in the body that carry out cell functions. Replacement of sulfur in the enzyme by arsenic can seriously affect the healthy functioning of cells and lead to death.

Research Have students research the effects of other poisonous elements such as mercury, lead, or radon on the functioning of healthy cells. What systems do the poisonous elements affect? Have students write a newspaper article including the two-letter chemical symbol and a health warning. L2 IS **Linguistic**

Fun Fact

About 46 percent of Earth's crust is oxygen, nearly all of it in the form of silicates, oxides, or water.

Active Reading

Jigsaw In this collaborative learning technique, individuals become experts on a portion of a text and share their expertise with a small group, called their home group. Everyone shares responsibility for learning the assigned reading. Assign each person in each home group an expert number (1 through 5, for example). Have students gather into the expert groups that correspond to the number they were assigned. Have them read, discuss, and master chapter concepts and determine how best to teach them to their home groups. Have students return to their home groups and share the content they learned in their expert groups. Have students use the Jigsaw strategy with the groups of elements in the periodic table discussed in this section. L2

Quick Demo

Halogens

Materials household chlorine bleach in unmarked container

Estimated Time 15 minutes

Procedure Without telling students what is in the container, open it and give them the opportunity to smell it. Be sure they use the waft method. Ask whether they can identify the odor.

Answer salts

Identifying Periodic Properties

Purpose To increase knowledge of periodic properties by studying one group in detail and by hearing and viewing classmates' presentations L2 IS **Auditory-Musical**

Possible Materials research materials, poster materials, computers

Estimated Time 2 class sessions (1 for research, 1 for presentations)

Teaching Strategies

• Have students research one group of the periodic table and make a presentation.

• The presentation may take the form of a poster, web page, poem, song, or report.

• Research topics may include occurrence in nature, uses in industry and households, appearance, chemical reactivity, and historical discovery.

• Encourage students to brainstorm questions they have before beginning the research.

For additional inquiry activities, see *Science Inquiry Labs.*

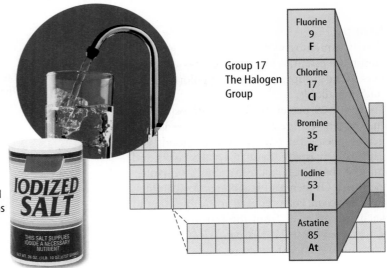

Figure 11 The halogens are a group of elements that are important to us in a variety of ways. Chlorine is added to drinking water to kill bacteria.

Iodine is needed by many systems in your body.

Group 17 The Halogen Group

Group 17—The Halogen Group All the elements in Group 17 are nonmetals except for astatine, which is a radioactive metalloid. These elements are called **halogens,** which means "salt-former." Table salt, sodium chloride, is a substance made from sodium and chlorine. All of the halogens form similar salts with sodium and with the other alkali metals.

The halogen fluorine is the most reactive of the halogens in combining with other elements. Chlorine is less reactive than fluorine, and bromine is less reactive than chlorine. Iodine is the least reactive of the four nonmetals. **Figure 11** shows some uses of halogens.

Reading Check *What do halogens form with the alkali metals?*

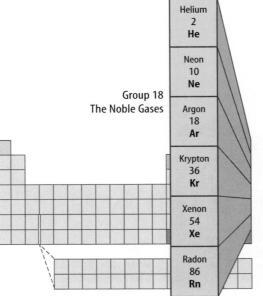

Group 18 The Noble Gases

Group 18—The Noble Gases The Group 18 elements are called the **noble gases.** This is because they rarely combine with other elements and are found only as uncombined elements in nature. Their reactivity is very low.

Helium is less dense than air, so it's great for all kinds of balloons, from party balloons to blimps that carry television cameras high above sporting events. Helium balloons, such as the one in **Figure 12,** lift instruments into the upper atmosphere to measure atmospheric conditions. Even though hydrogen is lighter than helium, helium is preferred for these purposes because helium will not burn.

110 ◆ **K** CHAPTER 4 Periodic Table

Differentiated Instruction

Challenge Have students use dictionaries to find the origins of the names of the halogens and the noble gases and explain why the names are appropriate. (all Greek except F) Cl, *chloros -*, greenish yellow; F, Latin, *fluere-*, flow; Br, *bromos-*, bad smell; I, *ioeides-*, violet-colored; As, *astatos -*, unsteady; Ar, *argos-*, lazy; Ne, *neos-*, new; Kr, *kryptos-*, hidden; Xe, *xenos-*, stranger; He, *helios-*, god of the Sun L3 IS **Linguistic**

Visual Learning

Figure 12 What properties of helium make it desirable for use in this balloon? Helium is relatively unreactive and has a lower density than air, allowing it to float upward in the air. L2 IS **Logical-Mathematical**

Uses for the Noble Gases The "neon" lights you see in advertising signs, like the one in **Figure 12,** can contain any of the noble gases, not just neon. Electricity is passed through the glass tubes that make up the sign. These tubes contain the noble gas, and the electricity causes the gas to glow. Each noble gas produces a unique color. Helium glows yellow, neon glows red-orange, and argon produces a bluish-violet color.

Argon, the most abundant of the noble gases on Earth, was first found in 1894. Krypton is used with nitrogen in ordinary lightbulbs because these gases keep the glowing filament from burning out. When a mixture of argon, krypton, and xenon is used, a bulb can last longer than bulbs that do not contain this mixture. Krypton lights are used to illuminate landing strips at airports, and xenon is used in strobe lights and was once used in photographic flash cubes.

At the bottom of the group is radon, a radioactive gas produced naturally as uranium decays in rocks and soil. If radon seeps into a home, the gas can be harmful because it continues to emit radiation. When people breathe the gas over a period of time, it can cause lung cancer.

Figure 12 Noble gases are used in many applications. Scientists use helium balloons to measure atmospheric conditions.

Each noble gas glows a different color when an electric current is passed through it.

✔ **Reading Check** *Why are noble gases used in lights?*

Teacher FYI

Radon Radon is formed from the radioactive decay of uranium and radium. Small amounts of uranium and radium exist in most rocks and soil but are most often found in granite, shale, and phosphate. The half-life of radon is about three days.

✔ **Reading Check**

Answer They glow in bright colors and they are relatively unreactive.

3 Assess

DAILY INTERVENTION

Check for Understanding

Interpersonal Have teams of students make charts on the board with a column for each family of the representative elements. Challenge the groups to list in each column as many of the uses of the elements in that family as they know. L2 COOP LEARN LS

Reteach

Periodic Groups Give students a blank periodic table, and have them fill in the symbols and group numbers for the elements studied in this section. Have them identify by color or shading the metals, nonmetals, and metalloids. L1 LS **Visual-Spatial**

✔ **Assessment**

Content Have groups of students make posters of photos and drawings that illustrate the importance of carbon, oxygen, and nitrogen in their lives. Use **Performance Assessment in the Science Classroom,** p. 145. P

section 2 review

Summary

Groups 1 and 2

- Groups 1 and 2 elements are always combined with other elements.
- The elements in Groups 1 and 2 are all metals except for hydrogen.
- Alkaline earth metals are not as active as the alkali metals.

Groups 13–18

- With Groups 13–18, a single group can contain metals, nonmetals, and metalloids.
- Nitrogen and phosphorus are required by living things.
- The halogen group will form salts with alkali metals.

Self Check

1. **Compare and contrast** the elements in Group 1 and the elements in Group 17.
2. **Describe** two uses for a member of each representative group.
3. **Identify** the group of elements that does not readily combine with other elements.
4. **Think Critically** Francium is a rare radioactive alkali metal at the bottom of Group 1. Its properties have not been studied carefully. Would you predict that francium would combine with water more or less readily than cesium?

Applying Skills

5. **Predict** how readily astatine would form a salt compared to the other elements in Group 17. Is there a trend for reactivity in this group?

section 2 review

1. Group 1 and Group 17 elements readily combine with other elements. Group 1 elements are alkali metals while Group 17 elements are halogens.
2. Answer will vary.
3. Group 18
4. More readily, because the reactivity of alkali metals increases down the group.
5. It would combine less readily than other halogens because the reactivity decreases down the group.

Transition Elements

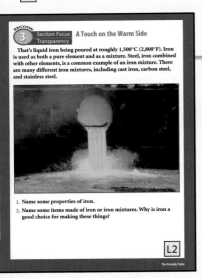
as you read

What You'll Learn
- **Identify** properties of some transition elements.
- **Distinguish** lanthanides from actinides.

Why It's Important
Transition elements provide the materials for many things including electricity in your home and steel for construction.

🔍 Review Vocabulary
mass number: the sum of neutrons and protons in the nucleus of an atom

New Vocabulary
- catalyst
- lanthanide
- actinide
- synthetic element

Figure 13 These buildings and bridges have steel in their structure. **Explain** why you think steel is used in their construction.

The Iron Triad

Iron 26 Fe	Cobalt 27 Co	Nickel 28 Ni

The Metals in the Middle

Groups 3–12 are called the transition elements and all of them are metals. Across any period from Group 3 through 12, the properties of the elements change less noticeably than they do across a period of representative elements.

Most transition elements are found combined with other elements in ores. A few transition elements such as gold and silver are found as pure elements.

The Iron Triad Three elements in period 4—iron, cobalt, and nickel—have such similar properties that they are known as the iron triad. These elements, among others, have magnetic properties. Industrial magnets are made from an alloy of nickel, cobalt, and aluminum. Nickel is used in batteries along with cadmium. Iron is a necessary part of hemoglobin, the substance that transports oxygen in the blood.

Iron also is mixed with other metals and with carbon to create a variety of steels with different properties. Structures such as bridges and skyscrapers, shown in **Figure 13,** depend upon steel for their strength.

✔ Reading Check *Which metals make up the iron triad?*

Section 3 Resource Manager

Chapter *FAST FILE* Resources
Transparency Activity, p. 42
Directed Reading for Content Mastery, pp. 17, 18
Reinforcement, p. 25
Enrichment, p. 28
Lab Worksheets, pp. 5–6, 7–8

Physical Science Critical Thinking/Problem Solving, p. 13
Earth Science Critical Thinking/Problem Solving, p. 2

Uses of Transition Elements Most transition metals have higher melting points than the representative elements. The filaments of lightbulbs, like the one in **Figure 14,** are made of tungsten, element 74. Tungsten has the highest melting point of any metal (3,410°C) and will not melt when a current passes through it.

Mercury, which has the lowest melting point of any metal (−39°C), is used in thermometers and in barometers. Mercury is the only metal that is a liquid at room temperatures. Like many of the heavy metals, mercury is poisonous to living beings. Therefore, mercury must be handled with care.

Chromium's name comes from the Greek word for color, *chroma,* and the element lives up to its name. Two substances containing chromium are shown in **Figure 15.** Many other transition elements combine to form substances with equally brilliant colors.

Ruthenium, rhodium, palladium, osmium, iridium, and platinum are sometimes called the platinum group because they have similar properties. They do not combine easily with other elements. As a result, they can be used as catalysts. A **catalyst** is a substance that can make something happen faster but is not changed itself. Other transition elements, such as nickel, zinc, and cobalt, can be used as catalysts. As catalysts, the transition elements are used to produce electronic and consumer goods, plastics, and medicines.

Figure 14 The transition metal tungsten is used in lightbulbs because of its high melting point.

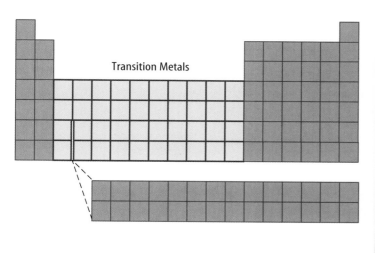

Transition Metals

Figure 15 Transition metals are used in a variety of products.

Visual Learning

Figure 14 Point out the tungsten filament. Describe what happens in the tungsten when the light is turned on. Electricity flows through the tungsten. The tungsten has enough resistance to the electricity that it heats up and glows as the electricity passes through it. L2 LS **Visual-Spatial**

Discussion

Poisonous Mercury Why are mercury thermometers not recommended for school laboratory work? Mercury liquid and vapors are poisonous. If a thermometer breaks, the mercury is difficult to pick up. Some of it might be absorbed through the skin or remain in the classroom and contaminate the air with its vapors. L2 LS **Logical-Mathematical**

Teacher FYI

Transition Elements In the transition elements, as you move from left to right along a period of the periodic table, the electrons that are added fill the next-to-outer energy level, the *d* energy level, of the atom. The outer energy level, the *s* energy level is already filled. The differences between the energies of the *d* energy level electrons and the energies of the electrons of the outer *s* energy level are very small. Therefore, each of these elements is capable of forming several different oxidation states.

Differentiated Instruction

English-Language Learners Have students make 40 cards approximately five cm by five cm. Write one element name per card for the first 20 elements in the student's native language. Write the English element name on the other 20 cards. Turn all the cards face down and mix them together. Have the students match the native language element card with the English language element card. Only turn over two cards at once. If a match is made, remove the set. If no match is made, return the cards to the face down position. Continue until all cards are matched. L2 ELL

Bright Lights A color television picture uses three electron guns to produce each of the three primary colors. These electron guns stimulate color phosphor dots on the color monitor. More than 1 million tiny dots are arranged in clusters. Each cluster contains a red, green, and blue phosphor. The stream of electrons from each gun falls only on its appropriate color phosphor.

Activity

Synthetic Actinides Ask each student to choose one of the synthetic actinides and prepare a poster illustrating its structure, telling when and where it was first synthesized, and giving the half-life of its most stable isotope. Example: Neptunium was first synthesized in 1940 at the University of California at Berkeley. It has 93 protons and electrons, and its most stable isotope, neptunium-237, has 144 neutrons and a half-life of about 2 million years. L3 **Visual-Spatial** P

Fun Fact

Molecules containing transition elements are important to the life processes of many organisms. Perhaps the most familiar example of this is found in the iron-containing heme complex of hemoglobin, which is responsible for oxygen transport in the blood of all vertebrates and some invertebrates.

Bright Lights Yttrium oxide (Y_2O_3) and europium oxide (Eu_2O_3) are used in color television screens to give a bright, natural color red. This blend of lanthanide elements will give off a red light when it's hit with a beam of electrons. Other compounds are used to make the additional colors required for a natural-looking picture.

Figure 16 The flint in this lighter is called misch metal, which is about 50% cerium, 25% lanthanum, 15% neodymium, and 10% other rare earth metals and iron.

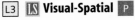

Inner Transition Elements

There are two series of inner transition elements. The first series, from cerium to lutetium, is called the **lanthanides.** The lanthanides also are called the rare earths because at one time they were thought to be scarce. The lanthanides are usually found combined with oxygen in Earth's crust. The second series of elements, from thorium to lawrencium, is called the **actinides.**

✔ Reading Check *What other name is used to refer to the lanthanides?*

The Lanthanides The lanthanides are soft metals that can be cut with a knife. The elements are so similar that they are hard to separate when they occur in the same ore, which they often do. Despite the name rare earth, the lanthanides are not as rare as originally thought. Earth's crust contains more cerium than lead. Cerium makes up 50 percent of an alloy called misch (MIHSH) metal. Flints in lighters, like the one in **Figure 16,** are made from misch metal. The other ingredients in flint are lanthanum, neodymium, and iron.

The Actinides All the actinides are radioactive. The nuclei of atoms of radioactive elements are unstable and decay to form other elements. Thorium, protactinium, and uranium are the only actinides that now are found naturally on Earth. Uranium is found in Earth's crust because its half-life is long—4.5 billion years. All other actinides are synthetic elements. **Synthetic elements** are made in laboratories and nuclear reactors. **Figure 17** shows how synthetic elements are made. The synthetic elements have many uses. Plutonium is used as a fuel in nuclear power plants. Americium is used in some home smoke detectors. Californium-252 is used to kill cancer cells.

✔ Reading Check *What property do all actinides share?*

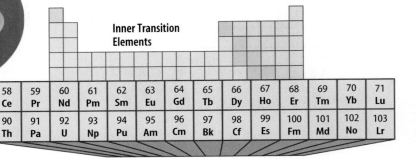

Inner Transition Elements

Lanthanide Series

58 Ce	59 Pr	60 Nd	61 Pm	62 Sm	63 Eu	64 Gd	65 Tb	66 Dy	67 Ho	68 Er	69 Tm	70 Yb	71 Lu

Actinide Series

90 Th	91 Pa	92 U	93 Np	94 Pu	95 Am	96 Cm	97 Bk	98 Cf	99 Es	100 Fm	101 Md	102 No	103 Lr

Curriculum Connection

History The term *misch metal* comes from the German word *mischen,* which means "to mix." Have students find out more about misch metal. Misch metal was developed by the Austrian chemist Carl Auer von Welsbach, who lived from 1858 to 1929. Misch metal is also used in miners' lamps and in carbon arc lamps, and to remove sulfur, gases, and oxides from other alloys. L3

Linguistic

Teacher FYI

Inner Transition Elements Like that of the transition metals, the outer energy level of the inner transition elements is filled, and as you move from left to right across each period, the added electrons fill the next-to-last energy level. Unlike the transition metals, the inner transition elements mostly form +3 oxidation states.

Figure 17

No element heavier than uranium, with 92 protons and 146 neutrons, is typically found in nature. But by using a device called a particle accelerator, scientists can make synthetic elements with atomic numbers greater than that of uranium. Within the accelerator, atomic nuclei are made to collide at high speeds in the hope that some will fuse together to form new, heavier elements. These "heavy" synthetic elements are radioactive isotopes, some of which are so unstable that they survive only a fraction of a second before emitting radioactive particles and decaying into other, lighter elements.

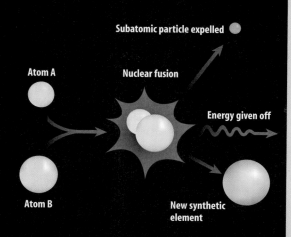

▲ When atoms collide in an accelerator, their nuclei may undergo a fusion reaction to form a new—and often short-lived—synthetic element. Energy and one or more subatomic particles typically are given off in the process.

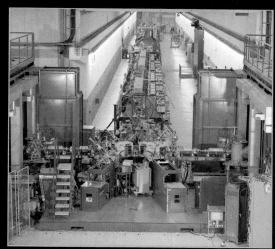

▲ Inside the airless vacuum chamber of a particle accelerator, such as this one in Hesse, Germany, streams of atoms move at incredibly high speeds.

▶ Recently, the IUPAC (International Union of Pure and Applied Chemistry) General Assembly confirmed the official name and symbol of element 110. Element 110 was previously known as Ununnilium and its symbol was Uun. The new name is darmstadtium and its symbol is Ds. Element 111 is expected to receive its official name and symbol in the near future.

SECTION 3 Transition Elements **K** ◆ **115**

Visualizing Synthetic Elements

Have students examine the pictures and read the captions. Then ask the following questions.

• Why do you think that elements above atomic number 92 are not typically found in nature? because they are structurally unstable and decay quickly into less complex particles

• Why do you think it is important for the particle accelerator to have an airless vacuum chamber? Answers may vary, but may be similar to the following. Scientists are interested in fusing two specific nuclei together in the chamber. If the chamber contains air, there is a multitude of molecules inside the chamber, in addition to the ones that the scientists are interested in. This would create too many variables for the scientists to try to control.

Activity

Element Reports Challenge the students to research uses for the elements above atomic number 92. Students should report the information that they find to the class. L2 LS **Linguistic**

Differentiated Instruction

Challenge Have each student choose a synthetic element and research how it was made. Students should prepare a diagram detailing the reaction sequence that took place. Subatomic particle information should be included whenever possible, throughout the reaction sequence. L3 LS **Visual-Spatial**

Reading Check

Answer The new materials do not contain mercury, a potential health hazard, like amalgam does.

3 Assess

Science Online

Topic: Health Risks
Visit bookk.msscience.com for Web links to information about health risks due to mercury.

Activity Write a paragraph on how mercury can affect your health.

INTEGRATE Health

Dentistry and Dental Materials

Dentists have been using amalgam for over 150 years to fill cavities in decayed teeth. Amalgam, a mixture of silver, copper, tin, and mercury, is the familiar "silver filling." Because amalgam contains mercury, some people are concerned that the use of this type of filling may unnecessarily expose a person to mercury vapor. Today dentists have alternatives to amalgam. New composites, resins, and porcelains are being used to repair decayed, broken, or missing teeth. These new materials are strong, chemically resistant to body fluids, and can be altered to have the natural color of the tooth. Some of the new resins also contain fluoride that will protect the tooth from further decay. Many of these new materials would be useless without the development of new bonding agents. The new "glues" or bonding agents adhere the new materials to the natural tooth. These bonding agents must be strong and chemically resistant to body fluids.

Reading Check *Why are these new dental materials desirable for repairing teeth?*

Orthodontists are using new nickel and titanium alloys for the wires on braces. These wires have shape memory. The wires undergo a special heat treatment process to lock in their shapes. If the wires are forced out of their heat-treated shape, the wires will try to return to their original shape. Orthodontists have found these wires useful in straightening crooked teeth. How do you think these wires help to straighten crooked teeth?

section 3 review

Summary

Transition Elements
- Groups 3–12, which are transition elements, are all metals.
- Their properties change less than the representative elements.
- The elements in the iron triad are iron, cobalt, and nickel.

Inner Transition Elements
- The lanthanide series contains elements from cerium to lutetium.
- The lanthanides also are known as the rare earth elements.
- The actinide series contains elements from thorium to lawrencium.

Self Check

1. **State** how the elements in the iron triad differ from other transition metals.
2. **Explain** the major difference between the lanthanides and actinides.
3. **Explain** how mercury is used.
4. **Describe** how synthetic elements are made.
5. **Think Critically** Iridium and cadmium are both transition elements. Predict which element is toxic and which element is more likely to be a catalyst. Explain.

Applying Skills

6. **Form Hypotheses** How does the appearance of a burned-out lightbulb compare to a new lightbulb? What could explain the difference?

 Science Online bookk.msscience.com/self_check_quiz

section 3 review

1. They have magnetic properties.
2. All of the actinides are radioactive while the lanthanides are not. Also, many of the actinides are synthetic elements not found naturally on Earth.
3. thermometers, barometers, and some dental materials
4. Answer will vary. Synthetic elements are made by fusing two smaller nuclei together in a particle accelerator.
5. Cadmium, like mercury, is a member of group 12 and is toxic in certain quantities. Iridium is more likely to be a catalyst because it is part of the platinum group.
6. A burned-out lightbulb is darker than a new lightbulb from deposits of tungsten caused by the constant heating of the metal.

Metals and Nonmetals

Real-World Question

Metals on asteroids appear attractive for mining to space programs because the metals are essential for space travel. An asteroid could be processed to provide very pure iron and nickel. Valuable by-products would include cobalt, platinum, and gold. How can miners determine if an element is a metal or a nonmetal?

Goals

■ **Describe** the appearance of metals and nonmetals.

■ **Evaluate** the malleability or brittleness of metals and nonmetals

■ **Observe** chemical reactions of metals and nonmetals with an acid and a base.

Materials (per group of 2–3 students)

10 test tubes with rack
10-mL graduated cylinder
forceps or tweezers
small hammer or mallet
dropper bottle of 0.5*M* HCl
dropper bottle of 0.1*M* CuCl₂
test-tube brush

marking pencil
25 g carbon
25 g silicon
25 g tin
25 g sulfur
25 g iron

Safety Precautions

Procedure

1. Copy data table into your Science Journal. Fill in data table as you complete the lab.

2. Describe in as much detail as possible the appearance of the sample, including color, luster, and state of matter.

3. Use the hammer or mallet to determine malleability or brittleness.

4. Label 5 test tubes #1–5. Place a 1-g sample of each element in separate test tubes. Add 5 mL of HCl to each tube. If bubbles form, this indicates a chemical reaction.

5. Repeat step 4, substituting HCl with CuCl₂. Do not discard the solutions immediately. Continue to observe for five minutes. Some of the changes may be slow. A chemical reaction is indicated by a change in appearance of the element.

Analyze Your Data

1. **Analyze Results** What characteristics distinguish metals from nonmetals?

2. **List** which elements you discovered to be metals.

3. **Describe** a metalloid. Are any of the elements tested a metalloid? If so, name them.

Conclude and Apply

1. **Explain** how the future might increase or decrease the need for selected elements.

2. **Infer** why discovering and mining metals on asteroids might be an important find.

Metal and Nonmetal Data

Element	Appearance	Malleable or Brittle	Reaction wth HCl	Reaction with CuCl₂
carbon	gray, dull	brittle	no	no
silicon	gray, shiny	brittle	no	no
tin	silver, shiny	malleable	bubbles	darkens
sulfur	yellow, dull	brittle	no	no
iron	gray, shiny	malleable	bubbles	darkens

Real-World Question

Purpose Students will learn how to distinguish metallic from nonmetallic elements by examining their physical and chemical properties. L2 ELL LS **Kinesthetic**

Process Skills observe, describe, and classify elements, compare and contrast, make and use tables, record observations

Time Required 45 minutes

Procedure

Teaching Strategies The chemical change that students are looking for in step 5 is a change in color.

Analyze Your Data

1. Metals are shiny, react with acid, and malleable. Nonmetals are dull, brittle, and do not react with acid.
2. Metals are iron and tin.
3. Elements that exhibit properties of a metal and nonmetal. silicon

Conclude and Apply

1. Answers will vary.
2. They are a possible source of metals for use on Earth and are necessary for space travel.

Real-World Question

Purpose L2 **IS Linguistic**

Internet Students will gather data from the Internet that can be accessed at bookk.msscience. com/internet_lab. Students can post their findings and acquire information from other schools around the country.

Non-Internet Sources Contact libraries, and gather data from newspapers and local television news broadcasts. Possible references:

• Kusinitz, Mark. *Poisons and Toxins (Encyclopedia of Health, Medical Disorders and Their Treatment)*. Chelsea House Pub., 1992
• W. Salomons, U. Forstner, P. Mader. *Heavy Metals: Problems and Solutions*. Springer Verlag, 1995

Time Required one to two weeks

Make a Plan

Preparation

Internet Visit the website bookk. msscience.com/internet_lab to run through the steps that students will follow.

Non-Internet Sources Scan the local newspaper for articles that connect health to chemical use.

Use the Internet

Health Risks fr☠m Heavy Metals

Goals
■ **Organize** and synthesize information on a chemical or heavy metal thought to cause health problems in the area where you live.
■ **Communicate** your findings to others in your class.

Data Source
Science☉nline
Visit bookk.msscience.com/ internet_lab for more information about health risks from heavy metals, hints on health risks, and data from other students.

Real-World Question

Many heavy metals are found naturally on the planet. People and animals are exposed to these metals every day. One way to reduce the exposure is to know as much as possible about the effects of chemicals on you and the environment. Do heavy metals and other chemicals pose a threat to the health of humans? Could health problems be caused by exposure to heavy metals such as lead, or a radioactive chemical element, such as radon? Is the incidence of these problems higher in one area than another?

Make a Plan

1. Read general information concerning heavy metals and other potentially hazardous chemicals.
2. Use the sites listed at the link to the left to research possible health problems in your area caused by exposure to chemicals or heavy metals. Do you see a pattern in the type of health risks that you found in your research?
3. Check the link to the left to see what others have learned.

Health Risk Data Table				
Location	Chemical or Heavy Metal	How People Come in Contact with Chemical	Potential Health Problem	Who Is Affected
		Answers will vary.		

118 ◆ K CHAPTER 4 The Periodic Table

Alternative Inquiry Lab

Further Research To extend this Lab into an Inquiry Lab, have students brainstorm further research in related areas that interest them, and present their findings. Some sample areas of interest could be: problems with lead in urban areas leftover from decades of leaded gasoline use; effects of urban pollution on wildlife around the world; clean-up and restoration of contaminated areas; government pollution regulations for industry; government and environmental organization initiatives in the area of heavy metal contamination and clean-up; a comparison of the persistence of heavy metal pollutants compared to other pollutants, which may break down safely in the environment.

▶ Follow Your Plan

1. Make sure your teacher approves your plan before you start.
2. **Research information** that can help you find out about health risks in your area.
3. **Organize** your information in a data table like the one shown.
4. **Write** a report in your Science Journal using the results of your research on heavy metals.
5. Post your data in the table provided at the link below.

▶ Analyze Your Data

1. **Evaluate** Did all your sources agree on the health risk of the chemical or heavy metal?
2. **Analyze** all your sources for possible bias. Are some sources more reliable than others?
3. **Explain** how the health risk differs for adults and children.
4. **Identify** the sources of the heavy metals in your area. Are the heavy metals still being deposited in your area?

▶ Conclude and Apply

1. **Analyze Results** Were the same substances found to be health risks in other parts of the country? From the data at the link below, try to predict what chemicals or heavy metals are health risks in different parts of the country.
2. **Determine** what information you think is the most important for the public to be aware of.
3. **Explain** what could be done to decrease the risk of the health problems you identified.

Communicating Your Data

Find this lab using the link below. **Post** your data in the table provided. **Compare** your data to those of other students. **Analyze** and look for patterns in the data.

Science Online

bookk.msscience.com/internet_lab

▶ Follow Your Plan

Teaching Strategies

- Motivate students to start their investigations by brainstorming ways that chemicals benefit society. Then, present a few examples of severe health or environmental problems that have resulted from lack of information about chemicals such as dioxin, DDT, or CFCs.
- Present examples of initial research questions, such as: Are heavy metals present in fertilizer? How harmful is antimony to humans? Where in the human body does mercury accumulate?
- Go over some of the unfamiliar words that students may encounter, such as *carcinogenic, soluble,* and *toxic.*

▶ Analyze Your Data

Answers will be subjective and based on the students' individual research.

▶ Conclude and Apply

Answers will be individualized and often based on the students' own opinion of their research. Look for depth and quality of research performed.

☑ Assessment

Portfolio Have students design and produce an informational pamphlet. The pamphlet should be geared to the general population and should include information found by all of the students in the class. It could provide facts and figures that explain the potential health risks posed by chemicals for the local environment and/or population. Use **Performance Assessment in the Science Classroom,** p. 129. P

Communicating Your Data

Students might choose different criteria for patterns. For example, students might choose to make generalizations based on location. They might find that certain types of chemicals and heavy metals are found in urban areas only.

Science and Language Arts

Understanding Literature

Folktales Fairy tales are usually set in fantasy lands, while tall tales generally portray historical characters who perform super-human deeds.

Respond to the Reading

1. Students' answers may vary, but should indicate that Anansi was not as clever as his youngest son.
2. because all the wisdom in the world did not help him solve a simple problem
3. **Linking Science and Writing** Students could describe what behavior they have observed that makes an animal seem smart.

 Elements

A nineteenth century Russian chemist, Dmitri Ivanovich Mendeleev, drew up the first satisfactory periodic table. He found that certain natural patterns reveal an underlying regularity in the variation of properties among the elements. This happens because the electrons in atoms are arranged in energy levels, and each energy level holds a certain number of electrons. All the elements with the same number of electrons in the outermost energy level act in similar ways.

The table of elements is arranged in order of increasing proton number to show similarities in chemical behavior between elements. Horizontal rows of elements are called periods. Across a period there is a general trend from metallic to non-metallic behavior. Vertical columns of related elements are called groups. There is an increase in atomic size and in electro-positive behavior down a group.

Anansi Tries to Steal All the Wisdom in the World
A folktale, adapted by Matt Evans

The following African folktale about a spider named Anansi (or Anancy) is from the Ashanti people in Western Africa.

Anansi the spider knew that he was not wise… "I know… if I can get all of the wisdom in the village and put it in a hollow gourd… I would be the wisest of all!" So he set out to find a suitable gourd and then began his journey to collect the village's wisdom… He looked around and spotted a tall, tall tree. "Ah," he said to himself, "if I could hide my wisdom high in that tree, I would never have to worry about someone stealing it from me!"… He first took a cloth band and tied it around his waist. Then he tied the heavy gourd to the front of his belly where it would be safe. As he began to climb, however, the gourd full of wisdom kept getting in the way…

Soon Anansi's youngest son walked by… "But Father," said the son, "wouldn't it be much easier if you tied the gourd behind you instead of in front?"… Anansi moved the gourd so that it was behind him and proceeded up the tree with no problems at all. When he had reached the top, he cried out, "I walked all over and collected so much wisdom I am the wisest person ever, but still my baby son is wiser than me. Take back your wisdom!" He lifted the gourd high over his head and spilled its contents into the wind. The wisdom blew far and wide and settled across the land. And this is how wisdom came to the world.

Understanding Literature

Folktales The African folktale you have just read is called an animal-trickster tale. Trickster tales come from Africa, the Caribbean, and Latin American countries. Trickster tales portray a wily and cunning animal or human who at times bewilders the more powerful and at other times becomes a victim of his or her own schemes. Describe other kinds of folktales, such as fairy tales and tall tales

Respond to the Reading

1. Is Anansi a clever spider?
2. Why did Anansi scatter the wisdom he had collected?
3. **Linking Science and Writing** Write a folktale featuring an animal as a trickster.

Elements are classified in relation to one another in a periodic table. They also are classified in groups of elements that share similar characteristics. Thus, there is a group of elements known as the alkali metals, another called the halogens, and so on. This way of classifying elements is similar to the way in which folktales are classified. Trickster tales have similar characteristics such as a character that has certain traits, like cleverness, wit, cunning, and an ability to survive.

Resources for Teachers and Students

A Dictionary of African Mythology: The Mythmaker as Storyteller, by Harold Scheub, Oxford University Press, 2000

The Hero with an African Face: Mythic Wisdom of Traditional Africa, by Clyde W. Ford, Bantam Books, 1999

The Center for Folklife and Cultural Heritage, 750 Ninth Street NW, Suite 4100, Smithsonian Institution, Washington, D.C. 20560-0953, (202) 275-1150

Reviewing Main Ideas

Section 1 **Introduction to the Periodic Table**

1. When organized according to atomic number in a table, elements with similar properties occupy the same column and are called a group or family.

2. On the periodic table, the properties of the elements change gradually across a horizontal row called a period.

3. The periodic table can be divided into representative elements and transition elements.

Section 2 **Representative Elements**

1. The groups on the periodic table are known also by other names. For instance, Group 17 is known as halogens.

2. Atoms of elements in Groups 1 and 2 readily combine with atoms of other elements.

3. Each element in Group 2 combines less readily than its neighbor in Group 1. Each alkaline earth metal is denser and has a higher melting point than the alkali metal in its period.

4. Sodium, potassium, magnesium, and calcium have important biological roles.

Section 3 **Transition Elements**

1. The metals in the iron triad are found in a variety of places. Iron is found in blood and in the structure of skyscrapers.

2. Copper, silver, and gold are fairly unreactive, malleable elements.

3. The lanthanides are naturally occurring elements with similar properties.

4. The actinides are radioactive elements. All actinides except thorium, proactinium, and uranium are synthetic.

Reviewing Main Ideas

Summary statements can be used by students to review the major concepts of the chapter.

Visualizing Main Ideas

See student page.

Visit bookk.msscience.com
/self_check_quiz
/interactive_tutor
/vocabulary_puzzlemaker
/chapter_review
/standardized_test

Assessment Transparency

For additional assessment questions, use the *Assessment Transparency* located in the transparency book.

Visualizing Main Ideas

Copy and complete the following concept map on the periodic table.

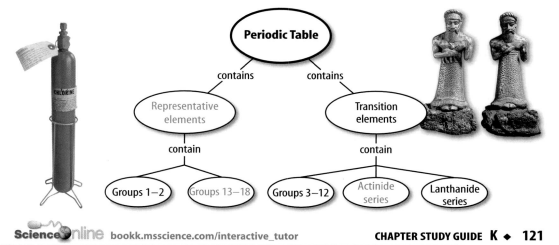

Using Vocabulary

1. A group is a column on the periodic table, and a period is a row on the periodic table.

2. Metalloids are elements that share properties with both metals and nonmetals. Semiconductors are materials that conduct electricity better than nonmetals but not as well as metals. Some semiconductors are metalloids.

3. A catalyst is a substance that can make something happen faster but is not changed itself.

4. The terms nonmetal, metalloid, and metal are in order of increasing ability to conduct heat and electricity.

5. Both conduct electricity, but a metal conducts better. A metalloid has some other properties of metals.

6. Synthetic elements are elements that don't occur in nature but that have been made by scientists.

7. In general, transition elements are metals that are malleable, ductile, and lustrous; conduct heat and electricity; and have high boiling points.

8. Some gases are considered to be noble because they do not combine readily with other elements.

Checking Concepts

9. C
10. B
11. B
12. B
13. D
14. A
15. A
16. C
17. D

Using Vocabulary

actinides p. 114
alkali metals p. 105
alkaline earth
   metals p. 106
catalyst p. 113
group p. 99
halogens p. 110
lanthanides p. 114
metal p. 102

metalloid p. 102
noble gases p. 110
nonmetal p. 102
period p. 99
representative
   element p. 99
semiconductor p. 107
synthetic elements p. 114
transition elements p. 99

Answer the following questions using complete sentences.

1. What is the difference between a group and a period?

2. What is the connection between a metalloid and a semiconductor?

3. What is a catalyst?

4. Arrange the terms *nonmetal, metal,* and *metalloid* according to increasing heat and electrical conductivity.

5. How is a metalloid like a metal? How is it different from a metal?

6. What are synthetic elements?

7. How are transition elements alike?

8. Why are some gases considered to be noble?

Checking Concepts

Choose the word or phrase that best answers the question.

9. Which of the following groups from the periodic table combines most readily with other elements to form compounds?
   A) transition metals
   B) alkaline earth metals
   C) alkali metals
   D) iron triad

 Science Online bookk.msscience.com/vocabulary_puzzlemaker

---

10. Which element is NOT a part of the iron triad?
    A) nickel
    B) copper
    C) cobalt
    D) iron

11. Which element is located in Group 6, period 4?
    A) tungsten   **C)** titanium
    B) chromium   **D)** hafnium

12. Which element below is NOT a transition element?
    A) gold   **C)** silver
    B) calcium   **D)** copper

13. Several groups contain only metals. Which group contains only nonmetals?
    A) Group 1   **C)** Group 2
    B) Group 12   **D)** Group 18

14. Which of the following elements is likely to be contained in a substance with a brilliant yellow color?
    A) chromium   **C)** iron
    B) carbon   **D)** tin

15. Which halogen is radioactive?
    A) astatine   **C)** bromine
    B) chlorine   **D)** iodine

16. Which of the following describes the element tellurium?
    A) alkali metal
    B) transition metal
    C) metalloid
    D) lanthanide

17. A brittle, non-conducting, solid might belong to which of the following groups?
    A) alkali metals
    B) alkaline earth metals
    C) actinide series
    D) oxygen group

Use the Exam*View*® Pro Testmaker CD-ROM to:
- create multiple versions of tests
- create modified tests with one mouse click for inclusion students
- edit existing questions and add your own questions
- build tests aligned with state standards using built-in State Curriculum Tags
- change English tests to Spanish with one mouse click and vice versa

Thinking Critically

18. Explain why it is important that mercury be kept out of streams and waterways.

19. Determine If you were going to try to get the noble gas argon to combine with another element, would fluorine be a good choice for the other element? Explain.

Use the figure below to answer question 20.

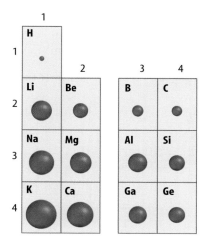

20. Interpret Data The periodic table shows trends across the rows and down the columns. In this portion of the periodic table, the relative size of the atom is represented by a ball. What trend can you see in this part of the table for relative size?

21. Evaluate It is theorized that some of the actinides beyond uranium were once present in Earth's crust. If this theory is true, how would their half-lives compare with the half-life of uranium, which is 4.5 billion years?

22. Recognize Cause and Effect Why do photographers work in low light when they work with materials containing selenium?

 Science online bookk.msscience.com/chapter_review

23. Predict How would life on Earth be different if the atmosphere were 80 percent oxygen and 20 percent nitrogen instead of the other way around?

24. Compare and contrast Na and Mg, which are in the same period, with F and Cl, which are in the same group.

Performance Activities

25. Ask Questions Research the contribution that Henry G. J. Moseley made to the development of the modern periodic table. Research the background and work of this scientist. Write your findings in the form of an interview.

Applying Math

26. Elements at Room Temperature Make a bar graph of the representative elements that shows how many of the elements are solids, liquids, and gases at room temperature.

27. Calculate Using the information that you collected in question 26, calculate the percentage of solids, liquids, and gases within the representative elements.

Use the figure below to answer question 28.

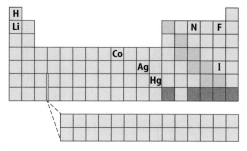

28. Element Details For each element shown, give the element's period and group number; whether the element is a metal or a nonmetal; and whether it is a solid, liquid, or gas at room temperature.

CHAPTER REVIEW K ◆ 123

Thinking Critically

18. Mercury is poisonous and can kill organisms that live in waterways.

19. Yes, fluorine is the most reactive nonmetal.

20. The relative size increases down a group and decreases moving left to right across a period.

21. They would be shorter.

22. Selenium is light-sensitive. Too much light might interfere with imaging.

23. Answers should include recognition of oxygen's ability to react with other elements while nitrogen won't.

24. Na, Mg, F, and Cl are all representative elements. Na and Mg are solid metals while F and Cl are gaseous nonmetals. F and Cl have more similar properties to each other than Na and Mg, because they are in the same group.

Performance Activities

25. Answers will vary but should include that he discovered a method for determining the number of protons in the nucleus of an atom. Use **PASC**, p. 141.

Applying Math

National Math Standards
1, 2, 5, 9

26. Graphs should show that 32 are solid, 1 is liquid, and 11 are gaseous.

27. 73% solids, 2% liquids, 25% gases

28. H: 1, 1, nonmetal, gas
Li: 2, 1, metal, solid
N: 2, 15, nonmetal, gas
F: 2, 17, nonmetal, gas
Co: 4, 9, metal, solid
Ag: 5, 11, metal, solid
I: 5, 17, nonmetal, solid
Hg: 6, 12, metal, liquid

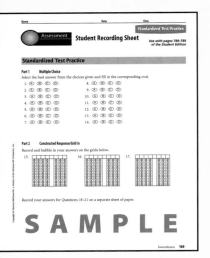

FAST FILE

Answer Sheet A practice answer sheet can be found at bookk.msscience.com/answer_sheet.

S A M P L E

Part 1 | Multiple Choice

1. C
2. D
3. D
4. B
5. A
6. A
7. D
8. A

 Part 1 | Multiple Choice

Record your answers on the answer sheet provided by your teacher or on a sheet of paper.

1. Which statement about the periodic table is TRUE?
   A. Elements all occur naturally on Earth.
   B. Elements occur in the order in which they were discovered.
   C. Elements with similar properties occupy the same group.
   D. Elements are arranged in the order Mendeleev chose.

2. Which of these is NOT a property of metals?
   A. malleability
   B. luster
   C. ductility
   D. poor conductor of heat and electricity

Use the illustration below to answer questions 3 and 4.

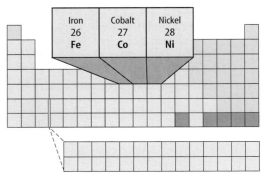

3. What name is given to these three elements which are used in processes that create steel and other metal mixtures?
   A. lanthanides   **C.** actinides
   B. the coin metals   **D.** the iron triad

Test-Taking Tip

The Best Answer Read all choices before answering the questions.

4. To which category do these elements belong?
   A. nonmetals
   B. transition elements
   C. noble gases
   D. representative metals

5. Which member of the boron family is used to make soft-drink cans, baseball bats, and siding for homes?
   A. aluminum   **C.** indium
   B. boron   **D.** gallium

Use the table below to answer questions 6 and 7.

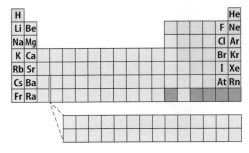

6. Halogens are highly reactive nonmetals. Which group combines most readily with them?
   A. Group 1, alkali metals
   B. Group 2, alkaline earth metals
   C. Group 17, halogens
   D. Group 18, noble gases

7. Which alkali metal element is most reactive?
   A. Li   **C.** K
   B. Na   **D.** Cs

8. Many elements that are essential for life, including nitrogen, oxygen, and carbon, are part of what classification?
   A. nonmetals   **C.** metalloids
   B. metals   **D.** noble gases

124 ◆ **K** STANDARDIZED TEST PRACTICE

Part 2 | Short Response

9. Both gold and silver are metals which are solid at room temperature. Both are group 11 elements, while silver is found in period 5 and gold in period 6. The atomic mass of gold is nearly twice that of silver.

10. Some symbols come from Greek or Latin names. Examples include

gold, whose symbol Au comes from the Latin word Aurum, which means "shining dawn," and Mercury's symbol Hg, which comes from the Greek word Hydrargyrum, which means "liquid silver."

11. Periodic properties show a trend when elements are arranged in

order of increasing atomic number.

12. Moving to the right across the periodic table, the boiling point increases, peaking with the carbon group, and then becoming low again towards the noble gases.

13. Amalgam is a mixture of silver, copper, tin, and mercury. Increas-

Part 2 | Short Response/Grid In

Record your answers on the answer sheet provided by your teacher or on a sheet of paper.

9. Based on the information found in the periodic table, compare and contrast properties of the elements gold and silver.

10. Why don't the element symbols always match the name? Give two examples and describe the origin of each symbol.

Use the graph below to answer questions 11 and 12.

Boiling Points of Period 1, 2, and 3 Elements

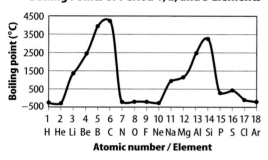

11. The data shows that boiling point is a periodic property. Explain what the term *periodic property* means.

12. Describe patterns evident in this data.

13. Describe the mixture used by dentists for the past 150 years to fill cavities in decayed teeth. Why do many dentists today use other materials to repair teeth?

14. Compare and contrast the periodic table that Mendeleev developed to the periodic table that Mosley organized.

15. Choose a representative element group and list the elements in that group. Then list three to four uses for those elements.

 bookk.msscience.com/standardized_test

Part 3 | Open Ended

Record your answers on a sheet of paper.

16. What role does nitrogen play in the human body? Explain the importance of bacteria in the soil which change the form in which nitrogen naturally occurs.

17. Much of the wiring in houses is made from copper. What properties of copper make it ideal for this purpose?

18. Why do some homeowners check for the presence of the noble gas radon in their homes?

Use the graph below to answer questions 19 and 20.

Elements in the Human Body

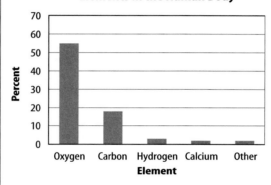

19. The graph above shows elements present in the greatest amounts in the human body. Use information from the periodic table to create a chart which shows properties of each element, including its symbol, atomic number, the group to which it belongs, and whether it is a metal, nonmetal, or metalloid.

20. One element shown here is an alkaline earth metal. Compare the properties of the elements in this family to those of the elements found in Group 1.

125

Part 3 | Open Ended

16. Nitrogen is part of the cellular structures that contain genetic information and store energy in the human body. Humans cannot use nitrogen in the form in which it is found in nature. Certain soil bacteria change nitrogen into a form which is absorbed by plants and can be used by humans.

17. Copper is a metallic solid with a high melting point. It is a good electrical conductor, bends easily, and can be drawn out into wire of various thicknesses.

18. Radon, a radioactive gas found in rocks and soil in some geographic locations, can seep into a home. Radon emits radiation which can cause lung cancer.

19. Oxygen: O, 8, 16, nonmetal
Carbon: C, 6, 14, nonmetal
Hydrogen: H, 1, 1, nonmetal
Nitrogen: N, 7, 15, nonmetal
Calcium: Ca, 20, 2, metal

20. Calcium is an alkaline earth metal (Group 2). Alkaline earth metals are more dense and harder and have higher melting points than the alkali metal in the same period. Alkaline earth metals are not as reactive as alkali metals.

Rubrics

For more help evaluating open-ended assessment questions, see the rubric on p. 10T. Wrap the extra questions around the bottom to the side.

---

ing concern about the toxicity of mercury is leading many dentists to use new materials which do not contain mercury.

14. Mendeleev arranged the periodic table in order of increasing atomic mass. Mendeleev's table had gaps for elements not then discovered.

Mosley arranged the periodic table according to atomic number. Mosley's table also had gaps, but it was clear how many elements were still undiscovered.

15. Answers may vary. One answer could be the carbon group. Carbon, silicon, germanium, tin, and lead.

Some uses include diamond, graphite—carbon; semiconductors—silicon and germanium; pewter, coating on steel cans—tin; X-ray shielding aprons—lead.

Student Resources

CONTENTS

Science Skill Handbook 128
Scientific Methods 128
Identify a Question 128
Gather and Organize
   Information 128
Form a Hypothesis 131
Test the Hypothesis 132
Collect Data 132
Analyze the Data 135
Draw Conclusions 136
Communicate 136
Safety Symbols 137
Safety in the Science Laboratory 138
General Safety Rules 138
Prevent Accidents 138
Laboratory Work 138
Laboratory 139
Emergencies 139

Extra Try at Home Labs 140
Comparing Particles 140
Microscopic Crystals 140
Good and Bad Apples 141
Research Race 141

Technology Skill Handbook ...142
Computer Skills 142
Use a Word Processing Program ...142
Use a Database 143
Use the Internet 143
Use a Spreadsheet 144
Use Graphics Software 144
Presentation Skills 145
Develop Multimedia
   Presentations 145
Computer Presentations 145

Math Skill Handbook 146
Math Review 146
Use Fractions 146
Use Ratios 149
Use Decimals 150
Use Proportions 150
Use Percentages 151
Solve One-Step Equations 151
Use Statistics 152
Use Geometry 153
Science Applications 156
Measure in SI 156
Dimensional Analysis 156
Precision and Significant Digits ...158
Scientific Notation 158
Make and Use Graphs 159

Reference Handbooks 161
Physical Science Reference Tables 161
Periodic Table of the Elements 162
Physical Science References 164

English/Spanish Glossary 165

Index 170

Credits 174

Scientific Methods

Scientists use an orderly approach called scientific methods to solve problems. These include organizing and recording data so others can understand them. Scientists use many variations in these methods when they solve problems.

Identify a Question

The first step in a scientific investigation or experiment is to identify a question to be answered or a problem to be solved. For example, you might ask which gasoline is the most efficient.

Gather and Organize Information

After you have identified your question, begin gathering and organizing information. There are many ways to gather information, such as researching in a library, interviewing those knowledgeable about the subject, testing and working in the laboratory and field. Fieldwork is investigations and observations done outside of a laboratory.

Researching Information Before moving in a new direction, it is important to gather the information that already is known about the subject. Start by asking yourself questions to determine exactly what you need to know. Then you will look for the information in various reference sources, like the student is doing in **Figure 1.** Some sources may include textbooks, encyclopedias, government documents, professional journals, science magazines, and the Internet. Always list the sources of your information.

Figure 1 The Internet can be a valuable research tool.

Evaluate Sources of Information Not all sources of information are reliable. You should evaluate all of your sources of information, and use only those you know to be dependable. For example, if you are researching ways to make homes more energy efficient, a site written by the U.S. Department of Energy would be more reliable than a site written by a company that is trying to sell a new type of weatherproofing material. Also, remember that research always is changing. Consult the most current resources available to you. For example, a 1985 resource about saving energy would not reflect the most recent findings.

Sometimes scientists use data that they did not collect themselves, or conclusions drawn by other researchers. This data must be evaluated carefully. Ask questions about how the data were obtained, if the investigation was carried out properly, and if it has been duplicated exactly with the same results. Would you reach the same conclusion from the data? Only when you have confidence in the data can you believe it is true and feel comfortable using it.

Interpret Scientific Illustrations As you research a topic in science, you will see drawings, diagrams, and photographs to help you understand what you read. Some illustrations are included to help you understand an idea that you can't see easily by yourself, like the tiny particles in an atom in **Figure 2.** A drawing helps many people to remember details more easily and provides examples that clarify difficult concepts or give additional information about the topic you are studying. Most illustrations have labels or a caption to identify or to provide more information.

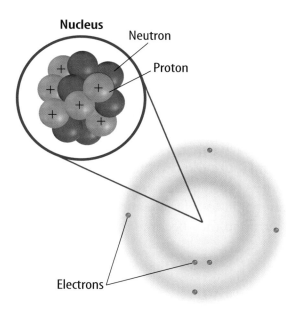

Figure 2 This drawing shows an atom of carbon with its six protons, six neutrons, and six electrons.

Concept Maps One way to organize data is to draw a diagram that shows relationships among ideas (or concepts). A concept map can help make the meanings of ideas and terms more clear, and help you understand and remember what you are studying. Concept maps are useful for breaking large concepts down into smaller parts, making learning easier.

Network Tree A type of concept map that not only shows a relationship, but how the concepts are related is a network tree, shown in **Figure 3.** In a network tree, the words are written in the ovals, while the description of the type of relationship is written across the connecting lines.

When constructing a network tree, write down the topic and all major topics on separate pieces of paper or notecards. Then arrange them in order from general to specific. Branch the related concepts from the major concept and describe the relationship on the connecting line. Continue to more specific concepts until finished.

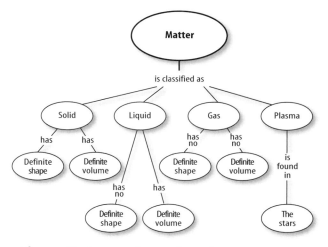

Figure 3 A network tree shows how concepts or objects are related.

Events Chain Another type of concept map is an events chain. Sometimes called a flow chart, it models the order or sequence of items. An events chain can be used to describe a sequence of events, the steps in a procedure, or the stages of a process.

When making an events chain, first find the one event that starts the chain. This event is called the initiating event. Then, find the next event and continue until the outcome is reached, as shown in **Figure 4.**

Science Skill Handbook

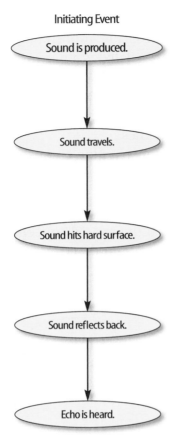

Initiating Event

Figure 4 Events-chain concept maps show the order of steps in a process or event. This concept map shows how a sound makes an echo.

Cycle Map A specific type of events chain is a cycle map. It is used when the series of events do not produce a final outcome, but instead relate back to the beginning event, such as in **Figure 5.** Therefore, the cycle repeats itself.

To make a cycle map, first decide what event is the beginning event. This is also called the initiating event. Then list the next events in the order that they occur, with the last event relating back to the initiating event. Words can be written between the events that describe what happens from one event to the next. The number of events in a cycle map can vary, but usually contain three or more events.

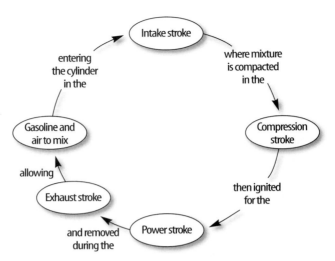

Figure 5 A cycle map shows events that occur in a cycle.

Spider Map A type of concept map that you can use for brainstorming is the spider map. When you have a central idea, you might find that you have a jumble of ideas that relate to it but are not necessarily clearly related to each other. The spider map on sound in **Figure 6** shows that if you write these ideas outside the main concept, then you can begin to separate and group unrelated terms so they become more useful.

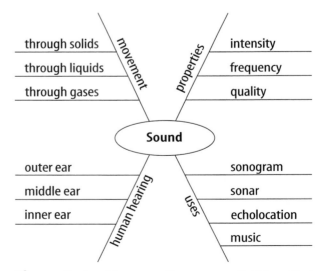

Figure 6 A spider map allows you to list ideas that relate to a central topic but not necessarily to one another.

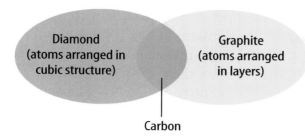

Figure 7 This Venn diagram compares and contrasts two substances made from carbon.

Venn Diagram To illustrate how two subjects compare and contrast you can use a Venn diagram. You can see the characteristics that the subjects have in common and those that they do not, shown in **Figure 7.**

To create a Venn diagram, draw two overlapping ovals that that are big enough to write in. List the characteristics unique to one subject in one oval, and the characteristics of the other subject in the other oval. The characteristics in common are listed in the overlapping section.

Make and Use Tables One way to organize information so it is easier to understand is to use a table. Tables can contain numbers, words, or both.

To make a table, list the items to be compared in the first column and the characteristics to be compared in the first row. The title should clearly indicate the content of the table, and the column or row heads should be clear. Notice that in **Table 1** the units are included.

Table 1 Recyclables Collected During Week			
Day of Week	Paper (kg)	Aluminum (kg)	Glass (kg)
Monday	5.0	4.0	12.0
Wednesday	4.0	1.0	10.0
Friday	2.5	2.0	10.0

Make a Model One way to help you better understand the parts of a structure, the way a process works, or to show things too large or small for viewing is to make a model. For example, an atomic model made of a plastic-ball nucleus and pipe-cleaner electron shells can help you visualize how the parts of an atom relate to each other. Other types of models can by devised on a computer or represented by equations.

Form a Hypothesis

A possible explanation based on previous knowledge and observations is called a hypothesis. After researching gasoline types and recalling previous experiences in your family's car you form a hypothesis—our car runs more efficiently because we use premium gasoline. To be valid, a hypothesis has to be something you can test by using an investigation.

Predict When you apply a hypothesis to a specific situation, you predict something about that situation. A prediction makes a statement in advance, based on prior observation, experience, or scientific reasoning. People use predictions to make everyday decisions. Scientists test predictions by performing investigations. Based on previous observations and experiences, you might form a prediction that cars are more efficient with premium gasoline. The prediction can be tested in an investigation.

Design an Experiment A scientist needs to make many decisions before beginning an investigation. Some of these include: how to carry out the investigation, what steps to follow, how to record the data, and how the investigation will answer the question. It also is important to address any safety concerns.

Test the Hypothesis

Now that you have formed your hypothesis, you need to test it. Using an investigation, you will make observations and collect data, or information. This data might either support or not support your hypothesis. Scientists collect and organize data as numbers and descriptions.

Follow a Procedure In order to know what materials to use, as well as how and in what order to use them, you must follow a procedure. **Figure 8** shows a procedure you might follow to test your hypothesis.

Procedure
1. Use regular gasoline for two weeks.
2. Record the number of kilometers between fill-ups and the amount of gasoline used.
3. Switch to premium gasoline for two weeks.
4. Record the number of kilometers between fill-ups and the amount of gasoline used.

Figure 8 A procedure tells you what to do step by step.

Identify and Manipulate Variables and Controls In any experiment, it is important to keep everything the same except for the item you are testing. The one factor you change is called the independent variable. The change that results is the dependent variable. Make sure you have only one independent variable, to assure yourself of the cause of the changes you observe in the dependent variable. For example, in your gasoline experiment the type of fuel is the independent variable. The dependent variable is the efficiency.

Many experiments also have a control—an individual instance or experimental subject for which the independent variable is not changed. You can then compare the test results to the control results. To design a control you can have two cars of the same type. The control car uses regular gasoline for four weeks. After you are done with the test, you can compare the experimental results to the control results.

Collect Data

Whether you are carrying out an investigation or a short observational experiment, you will collect data, as shown in **Figure 9.** Scientists collect data as numbers and descriptions and organize it in specific ways.

Observe Scientists observe items and events, then record what they see. When they use only words to describe an observation, it is called qualitative data. Scientists' observations also can describe how much there is of something. These observations use numbers, as well as words, in the description and are called quantitative data. For example, if a sample of the element gold is described as being "shiny and very dense" the data are qualitative. Quantitative data on this sample of gold might include "a mass of 30 g and a density of 19.3 g/cm^3."

Figure 9 Collecting data is one way to gather information directly.

Figure 10 Record data neatly and clearly so it is easy to understand.

When you make observations you should examine the entire object or situation first, and then look carefully for details. It is important to record observations accurately and completely. Always record your notes immediately as you make them, so you do not miss details or make a mistake when recording results from memory. Never put unidentified observations on scraps of paper. Instead they should be recorded in a note-book, like the one in **Figure 10.** Write your data neatly so you can easily read it later. At each point in the experiment, record your observations and label them. That way, you will not have to determine what the figures mean when you look at your notes later. Set up any tables that you will need to use ahead of time, so you can record any observations right away. Remember to avoid bias when collecting data by not including personal thoughts when you record observations. Record only what you observe.

Estimate Scientific work also involves esti-mating. To estimate is to make a judgment about the size or the number of something without measuring or counting. This is important when the number or size of an object or population is too large or too dif-ficult to accurately count or measure.

Sample Scientists may use a sample or a portion of the total number as a type of estimation. To sample is to take a small, rep-resentative portion of the objects or organ-isms of a population for research. By making careful observations or manipulat-ing variables within that portion of the group, information is discovered and con-clusions are drawn that might apply to the whole population. A poorly chosen sample can be unrepresentative of the whole. If you were trying to determine the rainfall in an area, it would not be best to take a rainfall sample from under a tree.

Measure You use measurements everyday. Scientists also take measurements when col-lecting data. When taking measurements, it is important to know how to use measuring tools properly. Accuracy also is important.

Length To measure length, the distance between two points, scientists use meters. Smaller measurements might be measured in centimeters or millimeters.

Length is measured using a metric ruler or meter stick. When using a metric ruler, line up the 0-cm mark with the end of the object being measured and read the number of the unit where the object ends. Look at the metric ruler shown in **Figure 11.** The cen-timeter lines are the long, numbered lines, and the shorter lines are millimeter lines. In this instance, the length would be 4.50 cm.

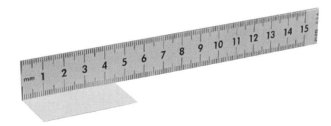

Figure 11 This metric ruler has centimeter and millimeter divisions.

Mass The SI unit for mass is the kilogram (kg). Scientists can measure mass using units formed by adding metric prefixes to the unit gram (g), such as milligram (mg). To measure mass, you might use a triple-beam balance similar to the one shown in **Figure 12.** The balance has a pan on one side and a set of beams on the other side. Each beam has a rider that slides on the beam.

When using a triple-beam balance, place an object on the pan. Slide the largest rider along its beam until the pointer drops below zero. Then move it back one notch. Repeat the process for each rider proceeding from the larger to smaller until the pointer swings an equal distance above and below the zero point. Sum the masses on each beam to find the mass of the object. Move all riders back to zero when finished.

Instead of putting materials directly on the balance, scientists often take a tare of a container. A tare is the mass of a container into which objects or substances are placed for measuring their masses. To mass objects or substances, find the mass of a clean container. Remove the container from the pan, and place the object or substances in the container. Find the mass of the container with the materials in it. Subtract the mass of the empty container from the mass of the filled container to find the mass of the materials you are using.

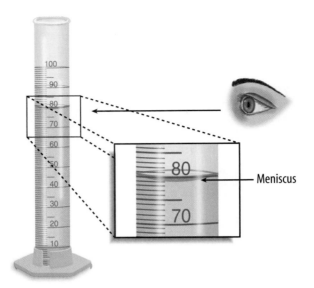

Figure 13 Graduated cylinders measure liquid volume.

Liquid Volume To measure liquids, the unit used is the liter. When a smaller unit is needed, scientists might use a milliliter. Because a milliliter takes up the volume of a cube measuring 1 cm on each side it also can be called a cubic centimeter ($cm^3 = cm \times cm \times cm$).

You can use beakers and graduated cylinders to measure liquid volume. A graduated cylinder, shown in **Figure 13,** is marked from bottom to top in milliliters. In lab, you might use a 10-mL graduated cylinder or a 100-mL graduated cylinder. When measuring liquids, notice that the liquid has a curved surface. Look at the surface at eye level, and measure the bottom of the curve. This is called the meniscus. The graduated cylinder in **Figure 13** contains 79.0 mL, or 79.0 cm^3, of a liquid.

Temperature Scientists often measure temperature using the Celsius scale. Pure water has a freezing point of 0°C and boiling point of 100°C. The unit of measurement is degrees Celsius. Two other scales often used are the Fahrenheit and Kelvin scales.

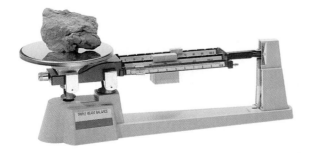

Figure 12 A triple-beam balance is used to determine the mass of an object.

Figure 14 A thermometer measures the temperature of an object.

Scientists use a thermometer to measure temperature. Most thermometers in a laboratory are glass tubes with a bulb at the bottom end containing a liquid such as colored alcohol. The liquid rises or falls with a change in temperature. To read a glass thermometer like the thermometer in **Figure 14,** rotate it slowly until a red line appears. Read the temperature where the red line ends.

Form Operational Definitions An operational definition defines an object by how it functions, works, or behaves. For example, when you are playing hide and seek and a tree is home base, you have created an operational definition for a tree.

Objects can have more than one operational definition. For example, a ruler can be defined as a tool that measures the length of an object (how it is used). It can also be a tool with a series of marks used as a standard when measuring (how it works).

Analyze the Data

To determine the meaning of your observations and investigation results, you will need to look for patterns in the data. Then you must think critically to determine what the data mean. Scientists use several approaches when they analyze the data they have collected and recorded. Each approach is useful for identifying specific patterns.

Interpret Data The word *interpret* means "to explain the meaning of something." When analyzing data from an experiment, try to find out what the data show. Identify the control group and the test group to see whether or not changes in the independent variable have had an effect. Look for differences in the dependent variable between the control and test groups.

Classify Sorting objects or events into groups based on common features is called classifying. When classifying, first observe the objects or events to be classified. Then select one feature that is shared by some members in the group, but not by all. Place those members that share that feature in a subgroup. You can classify members into smaller and smaller subgroups based on characteristics. Remember that when you classify, you are grouping objects or events for a purpose. Keep your purpose in mind as you select the features to form groups and subgroups.

Compare and Contrast Observations can be analyzed by noting the similarities and differences between two more objects or events that you observe. When you look at objects or events to see how they are similar, you are comparing them. Contrasting is looking for differences in objects or events.

Recognize Cause and Effect A cause is a reason for an action or condition. The effect is that action or condition. When two events happen together, it is not necessarily true that one event caused the other. Scientists must design a controlled investigation to recognize the exact cause and effect.

Draw Conclusions

When scientists have analyzed the data they collected, they proceed to draw conclusions about the data. These conclusions are sometimes stated in words similar to the hypothesis that you formed earlier. They may confirm a hypothesis, or lead you to a new hypothesis.

Infer Scientists often make inferences based on their observations. An inference is an attempt to explain observations or to indicate a cause. An inference is not a fact, but a logical conclusion that needs further investigation. For example, you may infer that a fire has caused smoke. Until you investigate, however, you do not know for sure.

Apply When you draw a conclusion, you must apply those conclusions to determine whether the data supports the hypothesis. If your data do not support your hypothesis, it does not mean that the hypothesis is wrong. It means only that the result of the investigation did not support the hypothesis. Maybe the experiment needs to be redesigned, or some of the initial observations on which the hypothesis was based were incomplete or biased. Perhaps more observation or research is needed to refine your hypothesis. A successful investigation does not always come out the way you originally predicted.

Avoid Bias Sometimes a scientific investigation involves making judgments. When you make a judgment, you form an opinion. It is important to be honest and not to allow any expectations of results to bias your judgments. This is important throughout the entire investigation, from researching to collecting data to drawing conclusions.

Communicate

The communication of ideas is an important part of the work of scientists. A discovery that is not reported will not advance the scientific community's understanding or knowledge. Communication among scientists also is important as a way of improving their investigations.

Scientists communicate in many ways, from writing articles in journals and magazines that explain their investigations and experiments, to announcing important discoveries on television and radio. Scientists also share ideas with colleagues on the Internet or present them as lectures, like the student is doing in **Figure 15.**

Figure 15 A student communicates to his peers about his investigation.

SAFETY SYMBOLS

	HAZARD	EXAMPLES	PRECAUTION	REMEDY
DISPOSAL	Special disposal procedures need to be followed.	certain chemicals, living organisms	Do not dispose of these materials in the sink or trash can.	Dispose of wastes as directed by your teacher.
BIOLOGICAL	Organisms or other biological materials that might be harmful to humans	bacteria, fungi, blood, unpreserved tissues, plant materials	Avoid skin contact with these materials. Wear mask or gloves.	Notify your teacher if you suspect contact with material. Wash hands thoroughly.
EXTREME TEMPERATURE	Objects that can burn skin by being too cold or too hot	boiling liquids, hot plates, dry ice, liquid nitrogen	Use proper protection when handling.	Go to your teacher for first aid.
SHARP OBJECT	Use of tools or glassware that can easily puncture or slice skin	razor blades, pins, scalpels, pointed tools, dissecting probes, broken glass	Practice common-sense behavior and follow guidelines for use of the tool.	Go to your teacher for first aid.
FUME	Possible danger to respiratory tract from fumes	ammonia, acetone, nail polish remover, heated sulfur, moth balls	Make sure there is good ventilation. Never smell fumes directly. Wear a mask.	Leave foul area and notify your teacher immediately.
ELECTRICAL	Possible danger from electrical shock or burn	improper grounding, liquid spills, short circuits, exposed wires	Double-check setup with teacher. Check condition of wires and apparatus.	Do not attempt to fix electrical problems. Notify your teacher immediately.
IRRITANT	Substances that can irritate the skin or mucous membranes of the respiratory tract	pollen, moth balls, steel wool, fiberglass, potassium permanganate	Wear dust mask and gloves. Practice extra care when handling these materials.	Go to your teacher for first aid.
CHEMICAL	Chemicals can react with and destroy tissue and other materials	bleaches such as hydrogen peroxide; acids such as sulfuric acid, hydrochloric acid; bases such as ammonia, sodium hydroxide	Wear goggles, gloves, and an apron.	Immediately flush the affected area with water and notify your teacher.
TOXIC	Substance may be poisonous if touched, inhaled, or swallowed.	mercury, many metal compounds, iodine, poinsettia plant parts	Follow your teacher's instructions.	Always wash hands thoroughly after use. Go to your teacher for first aid.
FLAMMABLE	Flammable chemicals may be ignited by open flame, spark, or exposed heat.	alcohol, kerosene, potassium permanganate	Avoid open flames and heat when using flammable chemicals.	Notify your teacher immediately. Use fire safety equipment if applicable.
OPEN FLAME	Open flame in use, may cause fire.	hair, clothing, paper, synthetic materials	Tie back hair and loose clothing. Follow teacher's instruction on lighting and extinguishing flames.	Notify your teacher immediately. Use fire safety equipment if applicable.

 Eye Safety Proper eye protection should be worn at all times by anyone performing or observing science activities.

 Clothing Protection This symbol appears when substances could stain or burn clothing.

 Animal Safety This symbol appears when safety of animals and students must be ensured.

 Handwashing After the lab, wash hands with soap and water before removing goggles.

Safety in the Science Laboratory

The science laboratory is a safe place to work if you follow standard safety procedures. Being responsible for your own safety helps to make the entire laboratory a safer place for everyone. When performing any lab, read and apply the caution statements and safety symbol listed at the beginning of the lab.

General Safety Rules

1. Obtain your teacher's permission to begin all investigations and use laboratory equipment.

2. Study the procedure. Ask your teacher any questions. Be sure you understand safety symbols shown on the page.

3. Notify your teacher about allergies or other health conditions which can affect your participation in a lab.

4. Learn and follow use and safety procedures for your equipment. If unsure, ask your teacher.

5. Never eat, drink, chew gum, apply cosmetics, or do any personal grooming in the lab. Never use lab glassware as food or drink containers. Keep your hands away from your face and mouth.

6. Know the location and proper use of the safety shower, eye wash, fire blanket, and fire alarm.

Prevent Accidents

1. Use the safety equipment provided to you. Goggles and a safety apron should be worn during investigations.

2. Do NOT use hair spray, mousse, or other flammable hair products. Tie back long hair and tie down loose clothing.

3. Do NOT wear sandals or other open-toed shoes in the lab.

4. Remove jewelry on hands and wrists. Loose jewelry, such as chains and long necklaces, should be removed to prevent them from getting caught in equipment.

5. Do not taste any substances or draw any material into a tube with your mouth.

6. Proper behavior is expected in the lab. Practical jokes and fooling around can lead to accidents and injury.

7. Keep your work area uncluttered.

Laboratory Work

1. Collect and carry all equipment and materials to your work area before beginning a lab.

2. Remain in your own work area unless given permission by your teacher to leave it.

3. Always slant test tubes away from yourself and others when heating them, adding substances to them, or rinsing them.

4. If instructed to smell a substance in a container, hold the container a short distance away and fan vapors towards your nose.

5. Do NOT substitute other chemicals/substances for those in the materials list unless instructed to do so by your teacher.

6. Do NOT take any materials or chemicals outside of the laboratory.

7. Stay out of storage areas unless instructed to be there and supervised by your teacher.

Laboratory Cleanup

1. Turn off all burners, water, and gas, and disconnect all electrical devices.

2. Clean all pieces of equipment and return all materials to their proper places.

3. Dispose of chemicals and other materials as directed by your teacher. Place broken glass and solid substances in the proper containers. Never discard materials in the sink.

4. Clean your work area.

5. Wash your hands with soap and water thoroughly BEFORE removing your goggles.

Emergencies

1. Report any fire, electrical shock, glassware breakage, spill, or injury, no matter how small, to your teacher immediately. Follow his or her instructions.

2. If your clothing should catch fire, STOP, DROP, and ROLL. If possible, smother it with the fire blanket or get under a safety shower. NEVER RUN.

3. If a fire should occur, turn off all gas and leave the room according to established procedures.

4. In most instances, your teacher will clean up spills. Do NOT attempt to clean up spills unless you are given permission and instructions to do so.

5. If chemicals come into contact with your eyes or skin, notify your teacher immediately. Use the eyewash or flush your skin or eyes with large quantities of water.

6. The fire extinguisher and first-aid kit should only be used by your teacher unless it is an extreme emergency and you have been given permission.

7. If someone is injured or becomes ill, only a professional medical provider or someone certified in first aid should perform first-aid procedures.

1 Comparing Particles

Time Required 30 minutes

Materials If 2-L bags are not available, use two 1-L bags. Milk cartons could also be used, but these are not see-through so the visual effect is reduced.

Safety Precautions
• Check the bags for leaks before beginning.
• Conduct this lab outside if possible.

Teaching Strategy
Explain to students that chemists often count the mass of an electron as zero to make calculations easier.

Conclude and Apply
1. They are nearly the same.
2. Electrons have little mass, and protons and neutrons are found only in the nucleus.

EXTRA (Try at Home) Labs
From Your Kitchen, Junk Drawer, or Yard

Extra Try at Home Labs

1 Comparing Particles

Real-World Question
How do the masses of an electron, neutron, and proton compare?

Possible Materials
• large, self-sealing plastic bags or clear 2-L bottles (6)
• liquid measuring cup
• marker
• large poster paper

Procedure
1. Measure exactly 1 mL of water into a plastic bag. Seal it. Write *Electron* on it. Make another bag exactly the same.
2. Measure exactly 1,837 mL into another plastic bag. Seal it. Write *Proton* on it. Make another bag exactly the same.
3. Measure exactly 1,839 mL into another plastic bag. Seal it. Write *Neutron* on it. Make another bag exactly the same.
4. Draw a large helium atom on the paper. Put the four bags representing two neutrons and the two protons in the central nucleus. Put the two electron bags at a distance from the nucleus, representing their orbit around the nucleus.

Conclude and Apply
1. Compare the mass of the proton and neutron.
2. Infer why nearly all the mass of an atom is located in its nucleus.

2 Microscopic Crystals

Real-World Question
What do crystalline and non-crystalline solids look like under a magnifying lens?

Possible Materials
• salt or sugar   • bowl
• pepper   • spoon
• magnifying lens   • measuring cup
• paper

Procedure
1. Pour 10 mL of salt into a bowl and grind the salt into small, powdery pieces with the back of the spoon.
2. Sprinkle a few grains of salt from the bowl onto a piece of paper and view the salt grains with the magnifying lens.
3. Clean out the bowl.
4. Pour 10 mL of pepper into the bowl and grind it into powder with the spoon.
5. Sprinkle a few grains of pepper from the bowl onto the paper and view the grains with the magnifying lens.

Conclude and Apply
1. Compare the difference between the salt and pepper grains under the magnifying lens.
2. Describe what a crystal is.

Adult supervision required for all labs.

These labs are available at bookk.msscience.com.

---

2 Microscopic Crystals

Time Required 20 minutes

Materials Students can also view sugar crystals under the magnifying lens. The crystals will be seen more clearly under lower powers of magnification.

Safety Precaution Caution students not to eat or drink anything in science class.

Teaching Strategy Have students view crystals of different sizes under the microscope to observe the consistency of their crystalline structure.

Conclude and Apply
1. Salt grains will be cube-shaped crystals. The pepper grains will have an irregular, non-repeating structure.
2. A crystal is a solid with its particles arranged in a repeating, three-dimensional pattern.

3 Good and Bad Apples

Real-World Question
How can the chemical reaction that turns apples brown be stopped?

Possible Materials
- apple
- concentrated lemon juice
- orange juice
- vitamin C tablet (1000 mg)
- water
- cola
- bowls (5)
- measuring cup
- kitchen knife
- paper plates (6)
- black marker

Procedure
1. Cut an apple into six equal slices.
2. Place one slice on a paper plate and label the plate *Untreated*.
3. Pour 100 mL of water into the first two bowls.
4. Dissolve a vitamin C tablet in the second bowl of water.
5. Pour 100 mL lemon juice, 100 mL of orange juice, and 100 mL of cola into the three remaining bowls.
6. Submerge an apple slice in each bowl for 10 min.
7. Label your other five plates *Water, Vitamin C Water, Lemon Juice, Orange Juice,* and *Cola.*
8. Take your apple wedges out of the bowls, place them on their correct plates. Observe the slices after one hour.

Conclude and Apply
1. Describe the results of your experiment.
2. Infer why some apple slices did not turn brown after being submerged.

4 Research Race

Real-World Question
How many secrets of the periodic table's elements can you find by research?

Possible Materials
- reference materials
- access to library

Procedure
1. Get together with a team of your friends. Look at the Race Questions and divide them between you.
2. Try to get as many answers as you can in a certain amount of time.
3. Be sure to keep a record of each resource. You get a point for each correct answer. You also get a point for each properly listed book, magazine, or Web site that you list.

Race Questions:
- List colored compounds of transition metals.
- List uses of colored transition metal compounds.
- List elements that are dangerous to human health, especially heavy metals. Where are they found in society?
- List elements that are needed for human health. What food sources are each found in?
- List any other interesting information about elements that show up as you do your research.

Conclude and Apply
1. Which resources did you find most helpful?
2. Name an interesting fact you found.

Extra Try at Home Labs

3 Good and Bad Apples

Time Required 20 minutes (five minute observation period after one hour)

Materials
- Students can test sodas with lemon-lime flavors, which will also prevent apples from browning.
- Students can use a volume other than 100 mL for the liquids, but the apple pieces must be submerged.

Safety Precautions
- Have students handle kitchen knives with care.
- Avoid using serrated knives for this lab.
- Students should never eat or drink in science class.

Teaching Strategy Be certain students rinse their measuring cup thoroughly after each use to prevent contamination of one liquid by another.

Conclude and Apply
1. When exposed to air, apple tissues undergo a chemical reaction called oxidation that turns the tissue brown.
2. The apple wedges that were soaked in vitamin C water, lemon juice, and orange juice will not turn brown, but the untreated slice and the slices soaked in water and cola will turn brown.

4 Research Race

Time Required one to two class periods

Safety Precaution An adult should accompany the student to the library.

Teaching Strategy This lab helps students learn research and recording strategies. Help students understand that the quality of their referencing is just as important as the facts they find. If they cannot find a fact again, it may be disqualified.

Conclude and Apply
1. Answers will vary.
2. Answers will vary.

Computer Skills

People who study science rely on computers, like the one in **Figure 16,** to record and store data and to analyze results from investigations. Whether you work in a laboratory or just need to write a lab report with tables, good computer skills are a necessity.

Using the computer comes with responsibility. Issues of ownership, security, and privacy can arise. Remember, if you did not author the information you are using, you must provide a source for your information. Also, anything on a computer can be accessed by others. Do not put anything on the computer that you would not want everyone to know. To add more security to your work, use a password.

Use a Word Processing Program

A computer program that allows you to type your information, change it as many times as you need to, and then print it out is called a word processing program. Word processing programs also can be used to make tables.

Figure 16 A computer will make reports neater and more professional looking.

Learn the Skill To start your word processing program, a blank document, sometimes called "Document 1," appears on the screen. To begin, start typing. To create a new document, click the *New* button on the standard tool bar. These tips will help you format the document.

- The program will automatically move to the next line; press *Enter* if you wish to start a new paragraph.
- Symbols, called non-printing characters, can be hidden by clicking the *Show/Hide* button on your toolbar.
- To insert text, move the cursor to the point where you want the insertion to go, click on the mouse once, and type the text.
- To move several lines of text, select the text and click the *Cut* button on your toolbar. Then position your cursor in the location that you want to move the cut text and click *Paste*. If you move to the wrong place, click *Undo*.
- The spell check feature does not catch words that are misspelled to look like other words, like "cold" instead of "gold." Always reread your document to catch all spelling mistakes.
- To learn about other word processing methods, read the user's manual or click on the *Help* button.
- You can integrate databases, graphics, and spreadsheets into documents by copying from another program and pasting it into your document, or by using desktop publishing (DTP). DTP software allows you to put text and graphics together to finish your document with a professional look. This software varies in how it is used and its capabilities.

Use a Database

A collection of facts stored in a computer and sorted into different fields is called a database. A database can be reorganized in any way that suits your needs.

Learn the Skill A computer program that allows you to create your own database is a database management system (DBMS). It allows you to add, delete, or change information. Take time to get to know the features of your database software.

- Determine what facts you would like to include and research to collect your information.
- Determine how you want to organize the information.
- Follow the instructions for your particular DBMS to set up fields. Then enter each item of data in the appropriate field.
- Follow the instructions to sort the information in order of importance.
- Evaluate the information in your database, and add, delete, or change as necessary.

Use the Internet

The Internet is a global network of computers where information is stored and shared. To use the Internet, like the students in **Figure 17,** you need a modem to connect your computer to a phone line and an Internet Service Provider account.

Learn the Skill To access internet sites and information, use a "Web browser," which lets you view and explore pages on the World Wide Web. Each page is its own site, and each site has its own address, called a URL. Once you have found a Web browser, follow these steps for a search (this also is how you search a database).

Figure 17 The Internet allows you to search a global network for a variety of information.

- Be as specific as possible. If you know you want to research "gold," don't type in "elements." Keep narrowing your search until you find what you want.
- Web sites that end in *.com* are commercial Web sites; *.org, .edu,* and *.gov* are nonprofit, educational, or government Web sites.
- Electronic encyclopedias, almanacs, indexes, and catalogs will help locate and select relevant information.
- Develop a "home page" with relative ease. When developing a Web site, NEVER post pictures or disclose personal information such as location, names, or phone numbers. Your school or community usually can host your Web site. A basic understanding of HTML (hypertext mark-up language), the language of Web sites, is necessary. Software that creates HTML code is called authoring software, and can be downloaded free from many Web sites. This software allows text and pictures to be arranged as the software is writing the HTML code.

Use a Spreadsheet

A spreadsheet, shown in **Figure 18,** can perform mathematical functions with any data arranged in columns and rows. By entering a simple equation into a cell, the program can perform operations in specific cells, rows, or columns.

Learn the Skill Each column (vertical) is assigned a letter, and each row (horizontal) is assigned a number. Each point where a row and column intersect is called a cell, and is labeled according to where it is located—Column A, Row 1 (A1).

- Decide how to organize the data, and enter it in the correct row or column.
- Spreadsheets can use standard formulas or formulas can be customized to calculate cells.
- To make a change, click on a cell to make it activate, and enter the edited data or formula.
- Spreadsheets also can display your results in graphs. Choose the style of graph that best represents the data.

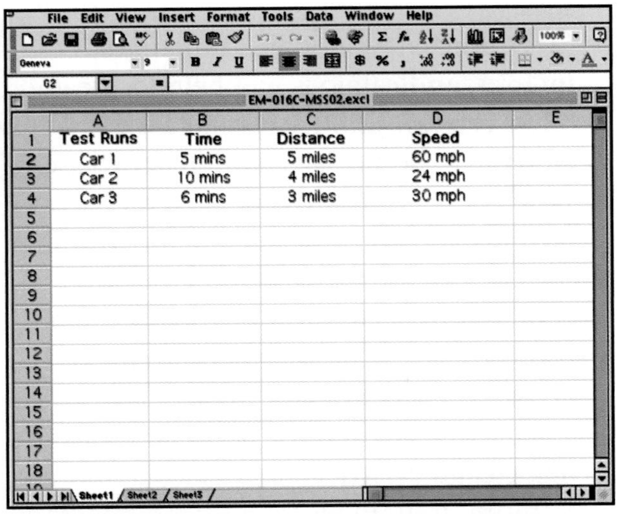

Figure 18 A spreadsheet allows you to perform mathematical operations on your data.

Use Graphics Software

Adding pictures, called graphics, to your documents is one way to make your documents more meaningful and exciting. This software adds, edits, and even constructs graphics. There is a variety of graphics software programs. The tools used for drawing can be a mouse, keyboard, or other specialized devices. Some graphics programs are simple. Others are complicated, called computer-aided design (CAD) software.

Learn the Skill It is important to have an understanding of the graphics software being used before starting. The better the software is understood, the better the results. The graphics can be placed in word-processing document.

- Clip art can be found on a variety of internet sites, and on CDs. These images can be copied and pasted into your document.
- When beginning, try editing existing drawings, then work up to creating drawings.
- The images are made of tiny rectangles of color called pixels. Each pixel can be altered.
- Digital photography is another way to add images. The photographs in the memory of a digital camera can be downloaded into a computer, then edited and added to the document.
- Graphics software also can allow animation. The software allows drawings to have the appearance of movement by connecting basic drawings automatically. This is called in-betweening, or tweening.
- Remember to save often.

Presentation Skills

Develop Multimedia Presentations

Most presentations are more dynamic if they include diagrams, photographs, videos, or sound recordings, like the one shown in **Figure 19.** A multimedia presentation involves using stereos, overhead projectors, televisions, computers, and more.

Learn the Skill Decide the main points of your presentation, and what types of media would best illustrate those points.

- Make sure you know how to use the equipment you are working with.
- Practice the presentation using the equipment several times.
- Enlist the help of a classmate to push play or turn lights out for you. Be sure to practice your presentation with him or her.
- If possible, set up all of the equipment ahead of time, and make sure everything is working properly.

Figure 19 These students are engaging the audience using a variety of tools.

Computer Presentations

There are many different interactive computer programs that you can use to enhance your presentation. Most computers have a compact disc (CD) drive that can play both CDs and digital video discs (DVDs). Also, there is hardware to connect a regular CD, DVD, or VCR. These tools will enhance your presentation.

Another method of using the computer to aid in your presentation is to develop a slide show using a computer program. This can allow movement of visuals at the presenter's pace, and can allow for visuals to build on one another.

Learn the Skill In order to create multimedia presentations on a computer, you need to have certain tools. These may include traditional graphic tools and drawing programs, animation programs, and authoring systems that tie everything together. Your computer will tell you which tools it supports. The most important step is to learn about the tools that you will be using.

- Often, color and strong images will convey a point better than words alone. Use the best methods available to convey your point.
- As with other presentations, practice many times.
- Practice your presentation with the tools you and any assistants will be using.
- Maintain eye contact with the audience. The purpose of using the computer is not to prompt the presenter, but to help the audience understand the points of the presentation.

Reduce Fractions

$$\frac{66 \div 6}{90 \div 6} = \frac{11}{15}$$

Add and Subtract Fractions

$$\frac{4}{9} + \frac{2}{9} = \frac{6}{9}$$

$$\frac{6 \div 3}{9 \div 3} = \frac{2}{3}$$

Math Review

Use Fractions

A fraction compares a part to a whole. In the fraction $\frac{2}{3}$, the 2 represents the part and is the numerator. The 3 represents the whole and is the denominator.

Reduce Fractions To reduce a fraction, you must find the largest factor that is common to both the numerator and the denominator, the greatest common factor (GCF). Divide both numbers by the GCF. The fraction has then been reduced, or it is in its simplest form.

Example Twelve of the 20 chemicals in the science lab are in powder form. What fraction of the chemicals used in the lab are in powder form?

Step 1 Write the fraction.
$$\frac{part}{whole} = \frac{12}{20}$$

Step 2 To find the GCF of the numerator and denominator, list all of the factors of each number.
Factors of 12: 1, 2, 3, 4, 6, 12 (the numbers that divide evenly into 12)
Factors of 20: 1, 2, 4, 5, 10, 20 (the numbers that divide evenly into 20)

Step 3 List the common factors.
1, 2, 4.

Step 4 Choose the greatest factor in the list.
The GCF of 12 and 20 is 4.

Step 5 Divide the numerator and denominator by the GCF.
$$\frac{12 \div 4}{20 \div 4} = \frac{3}{5}$$

In the lab, $\frac{3}{5}$ of the chemicals are in powder form.

Practice Problem At an amusement park, 66 of 90 rides have a height restriction. What fraction of the rides, in its simplest form, has a height restriction?

Add and Subtract Fractions To add or subtract fractions with the same denominator, add or subtract the numerators and write the sum or difference over the denominator. After finding the sum or difference, find the simplest form for your fraction.

Example 1 In the forest outside your house, $\frac{1}{8}$ of the animals are rabbits, $\frac{3}{8}$ are squirrels, and the remainder are birds and insects. How many are mammals?

Step 1 Add the numerators.
$$\frac{1}{8} + \frac{3}{8} = \frac{(1 + 3)}{8} = \frac{4}{8}$$

Step 2 Find the GCF.
$$\frac{4}{8} \text{ (GCF, 4)}$$

Step 3 Divide the numerator and denominator by the GCF.
$$\frac{4}{4} = 1, \; \frac{8}{4} = 2$$

$\frac{1}{2}$ of the animals are mammals.

Example 2 If $\frac{7}{16}$ of the Earth is covered by freshwater, and $\frac{1}{16}$ of that is in glaciers, how much freshwater is not frozen?

Step 1 Subtract the numerators.
$$\frac{7}{16} - \frac{1}{16} = \frac{(7 - 1)}{16} = \frac{6}{16}$$

Step 2 Find the GCF.
$$\frac{6}{16} \text{ (GCF, 2)}$$

Step 3 Divide the numerator and denominator by the GCF.
$$\frac{6}{2} = 3, \; \frac{16}{2} = 8$$

$\frac{3}{8}$ of the freshwater is not frozen.

Practice Problem A bicycle rider is going 15 km/h for $\frac{4}{9}$ of his ride, 10 km/h for $\frac{2}{9}$ of his ride, and 8 km/h for the remainder of the ride. How much of his ride is he going over 8 km/h?

Math Skill Handbook

Unlike Denominators To add or subtract fractions with unlike denominators, first find the least common denominator (LCD). This is the smallest number that is a common multiple of both denominators. Rename each fraction with the LCD, and then add or subtract. Find the simplest form if necessary.

Example 1 A chemist makes a paste that is $\frac{1}{2}$ table salt (NaCl), $\frac{1}{3}$ sugar ($C_6H_{12}O_6$), and the rest water (H_2O). How much of the paste is a solid?

Step 1 Find the LCD of the fractions.

$\frac{1}{2} + \frac{1}{3}$ (LCD, 6)

Step 2 Rename each numerator and each denominator with the LCD.

$1 \times 3 = 3, \ 2 \times 3 = 6$
$1 \times 2 = 2, \ 3 \times 2 = 6$

Step 3 Add the numerators.

$\frac{3}{6} + \frac{2}{6} = \frac{(3+2)}{6} = \frac{5}{6}$

$\frac{5}{6}$ of the paste is a solid.

Example 2 The average precipitation in Grand Junction, CO, is $\frac{7}{10}$ inch in November, and $\frac{3}{5}$ inch in December. What is the total average precipitation?

Step 1 Find the LCD of the fractions.

$\frac{7}{10} + \frac{3}{5}$ (LCD, 10)

Step 2 Rename each numerator and each denominator with the LCD.

$7 \times 1 = 7, \ 10 \times 1 = 10$
$3 \times 2 = 6, \ 5 \times 2 = 10$

Step 3 Add the numerators.

$\frac{7}{10} + \frac{6}{10} = \frac{(7+6)}{10} = \frac{13}{10}$

$\frac{13}{10}$ inches total precipitation, or $1\frac{3}{10}$ inches.

Practice Problem On an electric bill, about $\frac{1}{8}$ of the energy is from solar energy and about $\frac{1}{10}$ is from wind power. How much of the total bill is from solar energy and wind power combined?

Example 3 In your body, $\frac{7}{10}$ of your muscle contractions are involuntary (cardiac and smooth muscle tissue). Smooth muscle makes $\frac{3}{15}$ of your muscle contractions. How many of your muscle contractions are made by cardiac muscle?

Step 1 Find the LCD of the fractions.

$\frac{7}{10} - \frac{3}{15}$ (LCD, 30)

Step 2 Rename each numerator and each denominator with the LCD.

$7 \times 3 = 21, \ 10 \times 3 = 30$
$3 \times 2 = 6, \ 15 \times 2 = 30$

Step 3 Subtract the numerators.

$\frac{21}{30} - \frac{6}{30} = \frac{(21-6)}{30} = \frac{15}{30}$

Step 4 Find the GCF.

$\frac{15}{30}$ (GCF, 15)

$\frac{1}{2}$

$\frac{1}{2}$ of all muscle contractions are cardiac muscle.

Example 4 Tony wants to make cookies that call for $\frac{3}{4}$ of a cup of flour, but he only has $\frac{1}{3}$ of a cup. How much more flour does he need?

Step 1 Find the LCD of the fractions.

$\frac{3}{4} - \frac{1}{3}$ (LCD, 12)

Step 2 Rename each numerator and each denominator with the LCD.

$3 \times 3 = 9, \ 4 \times 3 = 12$
$1 \times 4 = 4, \ 3 \times 4 = 12$

Step 3 Subtract the numerators.

$\frac{9}{12} - \frac{4}{12} = \frac{(9-4)}{12} = \frac{5}{12}$

$\frac{5}{12}$ of a cup of flour.

Practice Problem Using the information provided to you in Example 3 above, determine how many muscle contractions are voluntary (skeletal muscle).

Unlike Denominators

Problem 1

$1 \times 5 = 5, 8 \times 5 = 40$
$1 \times 4 = 4, 10 \times 4 = 40$
$\frac{5}{40} + \frac{4}{40} = \frac{9}{40}$

Problem 2

If $\frac{7}{10}$ are involuntary, the remainder are voluntary.

$\frac{10}{10} - \frac{7}{10} = \frac{3}{10}$

Multiply Fractions

$$\frac{3}{14} \times \frac{5}{16} = \frac{(3 \times 5)}{(14 \times 16)} = \frac{15}{224}$$

Find a Reciprocal

$$\frac{9}{4}$$

Divide Fractions

The reciprocal of $\frac{7}{10}$ is $\frac{10}{7}$.

$$\frac{3}{11} \times \frac{10}{7} = \frac{(3 \times 10)}{(11 \times 7)} = \frac{30}{77}$$

Multiply Fractions To multiply with fractions, multiply the numerators and multiply the denominators. Find the simplest form if necessary.

Example Multiply $\frac{3}{5}$ by $\frac{1}{3}$.

Step 1 Multiply the numerators and denominators.

$$\frac{3}{5} \times \frac{1}{3} = \frac{(3 \times 1)}{(5 \times 3)} = \frac{3}{15}$$

Step 2 Find the GCF.

$$\frac{3}{15} \quad (\text{GCF, 3})$$

Step 3 Divide the numerator and denominator by the GCF.

$$\frac{3}{3} = 1, \quad \frac{15}{3} = 5$$

$$\frac{1}{5}$$

$\frac{3}{5}$ multiplied by $\frac{1}{3}$ is $\frac{1}{5}$.

Practice Problem Multiply $\frac{3}{14}$ by $\frac{5}{16}$.

Find a Reciprocal Two numbers whose product is 1 are called multiplicative inverses, or reciprocals.

Example Find the reciprocal of $\frac{3}{8}$.

Step 1 Inverse the fraction by putting the denominator on top and the numerator on the bottom.

$$\frac{8}{3}$$

The reciprocal of $\frac{3}{8}$ is $\frac{8}{3}$.

Practice Problem Find the reciprocal of $\frac{4}{9}$.

Divide Fractions To divide one fraction by another fraction, multiply the dividend by the reciprocal of the divisor. Find the simplest form if necessary.

Example 1 Divide $\frac{1}{9}$ by $\frac{1}{3}$.

Step 1 Find the reciprocal of the divisor.

The reciprocal of $\frac{1}{3}$ is $\frac{3}{1}$.

Step 2 Multiply the dividend by the reciprocal of the divisor.

$$\frac{\frac{1}{9}}{\frac{1}{3}} = \frac{1}{9} \times \frac{3}{1} = \frac{(1 \times 3)}{(9 \times 1)} = \frac{3}{9}$$

Step 3 Find the GCF.

$$\frac{3}{9} \quad (\text{GCF, 3})$$

Step 4 Divide the numerator and denominator by the GCF.

$$\frac{3}{3} = 1, \quad \frac{9}{3} = 3$$

$$\frac{1}{3}$$

$\frac{1}{9}$ divided by $\frac{1}{3}$ is $\frac{1}{3}$.

Example 2 Divide $\frac{3}{5}$ by $\frac{1}{4}$.

Step 1 Find the reciprocal of the divisor.

The reciprocal of $\frac{1}{4}$ is $\frac{4}{1}$.

Step 2 Multiply the dividend by the reciprocal of the divisor.

$$\frac{\frac{3}{5}}{\frac{1}{4}} = \frac{3}{5} \times \frac{4}{1} = \frac{(3 \times 4)}{(5 \times 1)} = \frac{12}{5}$$

$\frac{3}{5}$ divided by $\frac{1}{4}$ is $\frac{12}{5}$ or $2\frac{2}{5}$.

Practice Problem Divide $\frac{3}{11}$ by $\frac{7}{10}$.

Use Ratios

When you compare two numbers by division, you are using a ratio. Ratios can be written 3 to 5, 3:5, or $\frac{3}{5}$. Ratios, like fractions, also can be written in simplest form.

Ratios can represent probabilities, also called odds. This is a ratio that compares the number of ways a certain outcome occurs to the number of outcomes. For example, if you flip a coin 100 times, what are the odds that it will come up heads? There are two possible outcomes, heads or tails, so the odds of coming up heads are 50:100. Another way to say this is that 50 out of 100 times the coin will come up heads. In its simplest form, the ratio is 1:2.

Example 1 A chemical solution contains 40 g of salt and 64 g of baking soda. What is the ratio of salt to baking soda as a fraction in simplest form?

Step 1 Write the ratio as a fraction.
$$\frac{salt}{baking\ soda} = \frac{40}{64}$$

Step 2 Express the fraction in simplest form.
The GCF of 40 and 64 is 8.
$$\frac{40}{64} = \frac{40 \div 8}{64 \div 8} = \frac{5}{8}$$

The ratio of salt to baking soda in the sample is 5:8.

Example 2 Sean rolls a 6-sided die 6 times. What are the odds that the side with a 3 will show?

Step 1 Write the ratio as a fraction.
$$\frac{number\ of\ sides\ with\ a\ 3}{number\ of\ sides} = \frac{1}{6}$$

Step 2 Multiply by the number of attempts.
$$\frac{1}{6} \times 6\ attempts = \frac{6}{6}\ attempts = 1\ attempt$$

1 attempt out of 6 will show a 3.

Practice Problem Two metal rods measure 100 cm and 144 cm in length. What is the ratio of their lengths in simplest form?

Use Decimals

A fraction with a denominator that is a power of ten can be written as a decimal. For example, 0.27 means $\frac{27}{100}$. The decimal point separates the ones place from the tenths place.

Any fraction can be written as a decimal using division. For example, the fraction $\frac{5}{8}$ can be written as a decimal by dividing 5 by 8. Written as a decimal, it is 0.625.

Add or Subtract Decimals When adding and subtracting decimals, line up the decimal points before carrying out the operation.

Example 1 Find the sum of 47.68 and 7.80.

Step 1 Line up the decimal places when you write the numbers.
```
  47.68
+  7.80
```

Step 2 Add the decimals.
```
  47.68
+  7.80
-------
  55.48
```

The sum of 47.68 and 7.80 is 55.48.

Example 2 Find the difference of 42.17 and 15.85.

Step 1 Line up the decimal places when you write the number.
```
  42.17
- 15.85
```

Step 2 Subtract the decimals.
```
  42.17
- 15.85
-------
  26.32
```

The difference of 42.17 and 15.85 is 26.32.

Practice Problem Find the sum of 1.245 and 3.842.

Use Ratios
$$\frac{100\ cm}{144\ cm} = \frac{100 \div 4}{144 \div 4} = \frac{25}{36}$$
25:36

Add or Subtract Decimals
```
    1
  1.245
+ 3.842
-------
  5.087
```

Multiply Decimals

Multiply 4.6 and 2.2 by 10.

$46 \times 22 = 1012$

Each factor had one decimal place.

10.12

Divide Decimals

Multiply both factors by 10.

Divide 756 by 36.

$$\begin{array}{r} 21 \\ 36\overline{)756} \\ 72 \\ \hline 36 \\ 36 \\ \hline 0 \end{array}$$

Use Proportions

$\dfrac{3}{18} = \dfrac{5}{w}$

$w \times 3 = 5 \times 18$

$\dfrac{3w}{3} = \dfrac{90}{3}$

$w = 30$

Multiply Decimals To multiply decimals, multiply the numbers like any other number, ignoring the decimal point. Count the decimal places in each factor. The product will have the same number of decimal places as the sum of the decimal places in the factors.

Example Multiply 2.4 by 5.9.

Step 1 Multiply the factors like two whole numbers.
$24 \times 59 = 1416$

Step 2 Find the sum of the number of decimal places in the factors. Each factor has one decimal place, for a sum of two decimal places.

Step 3 The product will have two decimal places.
14.16

The product of 2.4 and 5.9 is 14.16.

Practice Problem Multiply 4.6 by 2.2.

Divide Decimals When dividing decimals, change the divisor to a whole number. To do this, multiply both the divisor and the dividend by the same power of ten. Then place the decimal point in the quotient directly above the decimal point in the dividend. Then divide as you do with whole numbers.

Example Divide 8.84 by 3.4.

Step 1 Multiply both factors by 10.
$3.4 \times 10 = 34, \ 8.84 \times 10 = 88.4$

Step 2 Divide 88.4 by 34.

$$\begin{array}{r} 2.6 \\ 34\overline{)88.4} \\ -68 \\ \hline 204 \\ -204 \\ \hline 0 \end{array}$$

8.84 divided by 3.4 is 2.6.

Practice Problem Divide 75.6 by 3.6.

Use Proportions

An equation that shows that two ratios are equivalent is a proportion. The ratios $\dfrac{2}{4}$ and $\dfrac{5}{10}$ are equivalent, so they can be written as $\dfrac{2}{4} = \dfrac{5}{10}$. This equation is a proportion.

When two ratios form a proportion, the cross products are equal. To find the cross products in the proportion $\dfrac{2}{4} = \dfrac{5}{10}$, multiply the 2 and the 10, and the 4 and the 5. Therefore $2 \times 10 = 4 \times 5$, or $20 = 20$.

Because you know that both proportions are equal, you can use cross products to find a missing term in a proportion. This is known as solving the proportion.

Example The heights of a tree and a pole are proportional to the lengths of their shadows. The tree casts a shadow of 24 m when a 6-m pole casts a shadow of 4 m. What is the height of the tree?

Step 1 Write a proportion.
$\dfrac{\text{height of tree}}{\text{height of pole}} = \dfrac{\text{length of tree's shadow}}{\text{length of pole's shadow}}$

Step 2 Substitute the known values into the proportion. Let h represent the unknown value, the height of the tree.
$\dfrac{h}{6} = \dfrac{24}{4}$

Step 3 Find the cross products.
$h \times 4 = 6 \times 24$

Step 4 Simplify the equation.
$4h = 144$

Step 5 Divide each side by 4.
$\dfrac{4h}{4} = \dfrac{144}{4}$
$h = 36$

The height of the tree is 36 m.

Practice Problem The ratios of the weights of two objects on the Moon and on Earth are in proportion. A rock weighing 3 N on the Moon weighs 18 N on Earth. How much would a rock that weighs 5 N on the Moon weigh on Earth?

Use Percentages

The word *percent* means "out of one hundred." It is a ratio that compares a number to 100. Suppose you read that 77 percent of the Earth's surface is covered by water. That is the same as reading that the fraction of the Earth's surface covered by water is $\frac{77}{100}$. To express a fraction as a percent, first find the equivalent decimal for the fraction. Then, multiply the decimal by 100 and add the percent symbol.

Example Express $\frac{13}{20}$ as a percent.

Step 1 Find the equivalent decimal for the fraction.

$$\begin{array}{r} 0.65 \\ 20\overline{)13.00} \\ \underline{12\ 0} \\ 1\ 00 \\ \underline{1\ 00} \\ 0 \end{array}$$

Step 2 Rewrite the fraction $\frac{13}{20}$ as 0.65.

Step 3 Multiply 0.65 by 100 and add the % sign.
$0.65 \times 100 = 65 = 65\%$

So, $\frac{13}{20} = 65\%$.

This also can be solved as a proportion.

Example Express $\frac{13}{20}$ as a percent.

Step 1 Write a proportion.
$$\frac{13}{20} = \frac{x}{100}$$

Step 2 Find the cross products.
$1300 = 20x$

Step 3 Divide each side by 20.
$$\frac{1300}{20} = \frac{20x}{20}$$
$65\% = x$

Practice Problem In one year, 73 of 365 days were rainy in one city. What percent of the days in that city were rainy?

Solve One-Step Equations

A statement that two things are equal is an equation. For example, $A = B$ is an equation that states that A is equal to B.

An equation is solved when a variable is replaced with a value that makes both sides of the equation equal. To make both sides equal the inverse operation is used. Addition and subtraction are inverses, and multiplication and division are inverses.

Example 1 Solve the equation $x - 10 = 35$.

Step 1 Find the solution by adding 10 to each side of the equation.
$x - 10 = 35$
$x - 10 + 10 = 35 + 10$
$x = 45$

Step 2 Check the solution.
$x - 10 = 35$
$45 - 10 = 35$
$35 = 35$

Both sides of the equation are equal, so $x = 45$.

Example 2 In the formula $a = bc$, find the value of c if $a = 20$ and $b = 2$.

Step 1 Rearrange the formula so the unknown value is by itself on one side of the equation by dividing both sides by b.
$a = bc$
$\frac{a}{b} = \frac{bc}{b}$
$\frac{a}{b} = c$

Step 2 Replace the variables a and b with the values that are given.
$\frac{a}{b} = c$
$\frac{20}{2} = c$
$10 = c$

Step 3 Check the solution.
$a = bc$
$20 = 2 \times 10$
$20 = 20$

Both sides of the equation are equal, so $c = 10$ is the solution when $a = 20$ and $b = 2$.

Practice Problem In the formula $h = gd$, find the value of d if $g = 12.3$ and $h = 17.4$.

Use Percentages
$$\frac{73}{365} = \frac{x}{100}$$
$$\frac{7300}{365} = \frac{365x}{365}$$
$20\% = x$

Solve One-Step Equations
$h = gd$
$$\frac{17.4}{12.3} = \frac{12.3d}{12.3}$$
$1.41 = d$

Use Statistics

mean

$8 + 4 + 12 + 8 + 11 + 14 + 16 = 73$

$73 \div 7 = 10.4$

median

4, 8, 8, <u>11</u>, 12, 14, 16

mode

4, <u>8</u>, <u>8</u>, 11, 12, 14, 16

range

<u>4</u>, 8, 8, 11, 12, 14, <u>16</u>

$16 - 4 = 12$

Use Statistics

The branch of mathematics that deals with collecting, analyzing, and presenting data is statistics. In statistics, there are three common ways to summarize data with a single number—the mean, the median, and the mode.

The **mean** of a set of data is the arithmetic average. It is found by adding the numbers in the data set and dividing by the number of items in the set.

The **median** is the middle number in a set of data when the data are arranged in numerical order. If there were an even number of data points, the median would be the mean of the two middle numbers.

The **mode** of a set of data is the number or item that appears most often.

Another number that often is used to describe a set of data is the range. The **range** is the difference between the largest number and the smallest number in a set of data.

A **frequency table** shows how many times each piece of data occurs, usually in a survey. **Table 2** below shows the results of a student survey on favorite color.

Table 2 Student Color Choice		
Color	**Tally**	**Frequency**
red	||||	4
blue	₩	5
black	||	2
green	|||	3
purple	₩ ||	7
yellow	₩ |	6

Based on the frequency table data, which color is the favorite?

Example The speeds (in m/s) for a race car during five different time trials are 39, 37, 44, 36, and 44.

To find the mean:

Step 1 Find the sum of the numbers.

$39 + 37 + 44 + 36 + 44 = 200$

Step 2 Divide the sum by the number of items, which is 5.

$200 \div 5 = 40$

The mean is 40 m/s.

To find the median:

Step 1 Arrange the measures from least to greatest.

36, 37, 39, 44, 44

Step 2 Determine the middle measure.

36, 37, <u>39</u>, 44, 44

The median is 39 m/s.

To find the mode:

Step 1 Group the numbers that are the same together.

44, 44, 36, 37, 39

Step 2 Determine the number that occurs most in the set.

<u>44, 44</u>, 36, 37, 39

The mode is 44 m/s.

To find the range:

Step 1 Arrange the measures from largest to smallest.

44, 44, 39, 37, 36

Step 2 Determine the largest and smallest measures in the set.

<u>44</u>, 44, 39, 37, <u>36</u>

Step 3 Find the difference between the largest and smallest measures.

$44 - 36 = 8$

The range is 8 m/s.

Practice Problem Find the mean, median, mode, and range for the data set 8, 4, 12, 8, 11, 14, 16.

Use Geometry

The branch of mathematics that deals with the measurement, properties, and relationships of points, lines, angles, surfaces, and solids is called geometry.

Perimeter The **perimeter** (P) is the distance around a geometric figure. To find the perimeter of a rectangle, add the length and width and multiply that sum by two, or $2(l + w)$. To find perimeters of irregular figures, add the length of the sides.

Example 1 Find the perimeter of a rectangle that is 3 m long and 5 m wide.

Step 1 You know that the perimeter is 2 times the sum of the width and length.
$P = 2(3\text{ m} + 5\text{ m})$

Step 2 Find the sum of the width and length.
$P = 2(8\text{ m})$

Step 3 Multiply by 2.
$P = 16\text{ m}$

The perimeter is 16 m.

Example 2 Find the perimeter of a shape with sides measuring 2 cm, 5 cm, 6 cm, 3 cm.

Step 1 You know that the perimeter is the sum of all the sides.
$P = 2 + 5 + 6 + 3$

Step 2 Find the sum of the sides.
$P = 2 + 5 + 6 + 3$
$P = 16$

The perimeter is 16 cm.

Practice Problem Find the perimeter of a rectangle with a length of 18 m and a width of 7 m.

Practice Problem Find the perimeter of a triangle measuring 1.6 cm by 2.4 cm by 2.4 cm.

Area of a Rectangle The **area** (A) is the number of square units needed to cover a surface. To find the area of a rectangle, multiply the length times the width, or $l \times w$. When finding area, the units also are multiplied. Area is given in square units.

Example Find the area of a rectangle with a length of 1 cm and a width of 10 cm.

Step 1 You know that the area is the length multiplied by the width.
$A = (1\text{ cm} \times 10\text{ cm})$

Step 2 Multiply the length by the width. Also multiply the units.
$A = 10\text{ cm}^2$

The area is 10 cm².

Practice Problem Find the area of a square whose sides measure 4 m.

Area of a Triangle To find the area of a triangle, use the formula:

$A = \frac{1}{2}(\text{base} \times \text{height})$

The base of a triangle can be any of its sides. The height is the perpendicular distance from a base to the opposite endpoint, or vertex.

Example Find the area of a triangle with a base of 18 m and a height of 7 m.

Step 1 You know that the area is $\frac{1}{2}$ the base times the height.
$A = \frac{1}{2}(18\text{ m} \times 7\text{ m})$

Step 2 Multiply $\frac{1}{2}$ by the product of 18×7. Multiply the units.
$A = \frac{1}{2}(126\text{ m}^2)$
$A = 63\text{ m}^2$

The area is 63 m².

Practice Problem Find the area of a triangle with a base of 27 cm and a height of 17 cm.

Perimeter
Problem 1
$P = 2(18\text{ m} + 7\text{ m})$
$P = 2(25\text{ m})$
$P = 50\text{ m}$

Problem 2
$P = 1.6\text{ cm} + 2.4\text{ cm} + 2.4\text{ cm}$
$P = 6.4\text{ cm}$

Area of a Rectangle
$A = (4\text{ m} \times 4\text{ m})$
$A = 16\text{ m}^2$

Area of a Triangle
$A = \frac{1}{2}(27\text{ cm} \times 17\text{ cm})$
$A = \frac{1}{2}(459\text{ cm}^2)$
$A = 229.5\text{ cm}^2$

Circumference of a Circle

$C = 2\pi r$

$C = 2\pi(19)$

$C = 38\pi$

$C = 119.3$

Area of a Circle

$A = \pi r^2$

$A = \pi(16\,\text{m})^2$

$A = \pi\,256\,\text{m}^2$

$A = 803.8\,\text{m}^2$

Circumference of a Circle The **diameter** (d) of a circle is the distance across the circle through its center, and the **radius** (r) is the distance from the center to any point on the circle. The radius is half of the diameter. The distance around the circle is called the **circumference** (C). The formula for finding the circumference is:

$$C = 2\pi r \ \ or \ \ C = \pi d$$

The circumference divided by the diameter is always equal to 3.1415926... This nonterminating and nonrepeating number is represented by the Greek letter π (pi). An approximation often used for π is 3.14.

Example 1 Find the circumference of a circle with a radius of 3 m.

Step 1 You know the formula for the circumference is 2 times the radius times π.
$C = 2\pi(3)$

Step 2 Multiply 2 times the radius.
$C = 6\pi$

Step 3 Multiply by π.
$C = 19\,\text{m}$

The circumference is 19 m.

Example 2 Find the circumference of a circle with a diameter of 24.0 cm.

Step 1 You know the formula for the circumference is the diameter times π.
$C = \pi(24.0)$

Step 2 Multiply the diameter by π.
$C = 75.4\,\text{cm}$

The circumference is 75.4 cm.

Practice Problem Find the circumference of a circle with a radius of 19 cm.

Area of a Circle The formula for the area of a circle is:
$A = \pi r^2$

Example 1 Find the area of a circle with a radius of 4.0 cm.

Step 1 $A = \pi(4.0)^2$

Step 2 Find the square of the radius.
$A = 16\pi$

Step 3 Multiply the square of the radius by π.
$A = 50\,\text{cm}^2$

The area of the circle is 50 cm².

Example 2 Find the area of a circle with a radius of 225 m.

Step 1 $A = \pi(225)^2$

Step 2 Find the square of the radius.
$A = 50625\pi$

Step 3 Multiply the square of the radius by π.
$A = 158962.5$

The area of the circle is 158,962 m².

Example 3 Find the area of a circle whose diameter is 20.0 mm.

Step 1 You know the formula for the area of a circle is the square of the radius times π, and that the radius is half of the diameter.
$A = \pi\left(\dfrac{20.0}{2}\right)^2$

Step 2 Find the radius.
$A = \pi(10.0)^2$

Step 3 Find the square of the radius.
$A = 100\pi$

Step 4 Multiply the square of the radius by π.
$A = 314\,\text{mm}^2$

The area is 314 mm².

Practice Problem Find the area of a circle with a radius of 16 m.

Volume The measure of space occupied by a solid is the **volume** (V). To find the volume of a rectangular solid multiply the length times width times height, or $V = l \times w \times h$. It is measured in cubic units, such as cubic centimeters (cm^3).

Example Find the volume of a rectangular solid with a length of 2.0 m, a width of 4.0 m, and a height of 3.0 m.

Step 1 You know the formula for volume is the length times the width times the height.
$$V = 2.0 \text{ m} \times 4.0 \text{ m} \times 3.0 \text{ m}$$

Step 2 Multiply the length times the width times the height.
$$V = 24 \text{ m}^3$$

The volume is 24 m³.

Practice Problem Find the volume of a rectangular solid that 8 m long, 4 m wide, and 4 m high.

To find the volume of other solids, multiply the area of the base times the height.

Example 1 Find the volume of a solid that has a triangular base with a length of 8.0 m and a height of 7.0 m. The height of the entire solid is 15.0 m.

Step 1 You know that the base is a triangle, and the area of a triangle is $\frac{1}{2}$ the base times the height, and the volume is the area of the base times the height.
$$V = \left[\frac{1}{2}(b \times h)\right] \times 15$$

Step 2 Find the area of the base.
$$V = \left[\frac{1}{2}(8 \times 7)\right] \times 15$$
$$V = \left(\frac{1}{2} \times 56\right) \times 15$$

Step 3 Multiply the area of the base by the height of the solid.
$$V = 28 \times 15$$
$$V = 420 \text{ m}^3$$

The volume is 420 m³.

Example 2 Find the volume of a cylinder that has a base with a radius of 12.0 cm, and a height of 21.0 cm.

Step 1 You know that the base is a circle, and the area of a circle is the square of the radius times π, and the volume is the area of the base times the height.
$$V = (\pi r^2) \times 21$$
$$V = (\pi 12^2) \times 21$$

Step 2 Find the area of the base.
$$V = 144\pi \times 21$$
$$V = 452 \times 21$$

Step 3 Multiply the area of the base by the height of the solid.
$$V = 9490 \text{ cm}^3$$

The volume is 9490 cm³.

Example 3 Find the volume of a cylinder that has a diameter of 15 mm and a height of 4.8 mm.

Step 1 You know that the base is a circle with an area equal to the square of the radius times π. The radius is one-half the diameter. The volume is the area of the base times the height.
$$V = (\pi r^2) \times 4.8$$
$$V = \left[\pi\left(\frac{1}{2} \times 15\right)^2\right] \times 4.8$$
$$V = (\pi 7.5^2) \times 4.8$$

Step 2 Find the area of the base.
$$V = 56.25\pi \times 4.8$$
$$V = 176.63 \times 4.8$$

Step 3 Multiply the area of the base by the height of the solid.
$$V = 847.8$$

The volume is 847.8 mm³.

Practice Problem Find the volume of a cylinder with a diameter of 7 cm in the base and a height of 16 cm.

Volume

Problem 1
$$V = 8 \text{ m} \times 4 \text{ m} \times 4 \text{ m}$$
$$V = 128 \text{ m}^3$$

Problem 2
$$V = \pi r^2 \times \text{height}$$
$$V = \left[\pi\left(\frac{1}{2} \times 7\right)^2\right] \times 16$$
$$V = [\pi(3.5)^2] \times 16$$
$$V = [\pi(12.25)] \times 16$$
$$V = 38.46 \times 16$$
$$V = 615.36$$

Math Skill Handbook

Measure in SI

smaller; 1000; one thousandth

Dimensional Analysis

$x \text{ mg} = 1\,\cancel{kg} \times \dfrac{1000\,\cancel{g}}{1\,\cancel{kg}} \times \dfrac{1000\,\text{mg}}{1\,\cancel{g}} =$

1,000,000 mg

1,000,000 mg = 1 kg

Science Applications

Measure in SI

The metric system of measurement was developed in 1795. A modern form of the metric system, called the International System (SI), was adopted in 1960 and provides the standard measurements that all scientists around the world can understand.

The SI system is convenient because unit sizes vary by powers of 10. Prefixes are used to name units. Look at **Table 3** for some common SI prefixes and their meanings.

Table 3 Common SI Prefixes			
Prefix	**Symbol**	**Meaning**	
kilo-	k	1,000	thousand
hecto-	h	100	hundred
deka-	da	10	ten
deci-	d	0.1	tenth
centi-	c	0.01	hundredth
milli-	m	0.001	thousandth

Example How many grams equal one kilogram?

Step 1 Find the prefix *kilo* in **Table 3**.

Step 2 Using **Table 3,** determine the meaning of *kilo*. According to the table, it means 1,000. When the prefix *kilo* is added to a unit, it means that there are 1,000 of the units in a "*kilo*unit."

Step 3 Apply the prefix to the units in the question. The units in the question are grams. There are 1,000 grams in a kilogram.

Practice Problem Is a milligram larger or smaller than a gram? How many of the smaller units equal one larger unit? What fraction of the larger unit does one smaller unit represent?

Dimensional Analysis

Convert SI Units In science, quantities such as length, mass, and time sometimes are measured using different units. A process called dimensional analysis can be used to change one unit of measure to another. This process involves multiplying your starting quantity and units by one or more conversion factors. A conversion factor is a ratio equal to one and can be made from any two equal quantities with different units. If 1,000 mL equal 1 L then two ratios can be made.

$$\frac{1{,}000 \text{ mL}}{1 \text{ L}} = \frac{1 \text{ L}}{1{,}000 \text{ mL}} = 1$$

One can covert between units in the SI system by using the equivalents in **Table 3** to make conversion factors.

Example 1 How many cm are in 4 m?

Step 1 Write conversion factors for the units given. From **Table 3,** you know that 100 cm = 1 m. The conversion factors are

$$\frac{100 \text{ cm}}{1 \text{ m}} \quad and \quad \frac{1 \text{ m}}{100 \text{ cm}}$$

Step 2 Decide which conversion factor to use. Select the factor that has the units you are converting from (m) in the denominator and the units you are converting to (cm) in the numerator.

$$\frac{100 \text{ cm}}{1 \text{ m}}$$

Step 3 Multiply the starting quantity and units by the conversion factor. Cancel the starting units with the units in the denominator. There are 400 cm in 4 m.

$$4\,\cancel{m} \times \frac{100 \text{ cm}}{1\,\cancel{m}} = 400 \text{ cm}$$

Practice Problem How many milligrams are in one kilogram? (Hint: You will need to use two conversion factors from **Table 3**.)

Table 4 Unit System Equivalents

Type of Measurement	Equivalent
Length	1 in = 2.54 cm
	1 yd = 0.91 m
	1 mi = 1.61 km
Mass and Weight*	1 oz = 28.35 g
	1 lb = 0.45 kg
	1 ton (short) = 0.91 tonnes (metric tons)
	1 lb = 4.45 N
Volume	$1\ in^3 = 16.39\ cm^3$
	1 qt = 0.95 L
	1 gal = 3.78 L
Area	$1\ in^2 = 6.45\ cm^2$
	$1\ yd^2 = 0.83\ m^2$
	$1\ mi^2 = 2.59\ km^2$
	1 acre = 0.40 hectares
Temperature	$°C = \dfrac{(°F - 32)}{1.8}$
	$K = °C + 273$

*Weight is measured in standard Earth gravity.

Convert Between Unit Systems Table 4 gives a list of equivalents that can be used to convert between English and SI units.

Example If a meterstick has a length of 100 cm, how long is the meterstick in inches?

Step 1 Write the conversion factors for the units given. From **Table 4,** 1 in = 2.54 cm.

$$\frac{1\ in}{2.54\ cm}\quad and \quad \frac{2.54\ cm}{1\ in}$$

Step 2 Determine which conversion factor to use. You are converting from cm to in. Use the conversion factor with cm on the bottom.

$$\frac{1\ in}{2.54\ cm}$$

Step 3 Multiply the starting quantity and units by the conversion factor. Cancel the starting units with the units in the denominator. Round your answer based on the number of significant figures in the conversion factor.

$$100\ \cancel{cm} \times \frac{1\ in}{2.54\ \cancel{cm}} = 39.37\ in$$

The meterstick is 39.4 in long.

Practice Problem A book has a mass of 5 lbs. What is the mass of the book in kg?

Practice Problem Use the equivalent for in and cm (1 in = 2.54 cm) to show how $1\ in^3 = 16.39\ cm^3$.

Convert Between Unit Systems

$$\frac{(1\ in)^3}{(2.54\ cm)^3}$$

$$= \frac{1\ in \times 1\ in \times 1\ in}{2.54\ cm \times 2.54\ cm \times 2.54\ cm}$$

$$= \frac{1\ in^3}{16.39\ cm^3}$$

Math Skill Handbook

Math Skill Handbook

Precision and Significant Digits

Problem 1
7; 4

Problem 2
$5.28 \times 5.2 = 27.456$

5.28 has 3 significant digits.

5.2 has 2 significant digits.

When multiplying and dividing, the answer is rounded to the smallest number of significant digits of the numbers being multiplied or divided—in this case, 2.

27.456 is rounded to 27.

Scientific Notation

Problem 1
4; 4

Problem 2
0.000007

Problem 3
5.39×10^2

Precision and Significant Digits

When you make a measurement, the value you record depends on the precision of the measuring instrument. This precision is represented by the number of significant digits recorded in the measurement. When counting the number of significant digits, all digits are counted except zeros at the end of a number with no decimal point such as 2,050, and zeros at the beginning of a decimal such as 0.03020. When adding or subtracting numbers with different precision, round the answer to the smallest number of decimal places of any number in the sum or difference. When multiplying or dividing, the answer is rounded to the smallest number of significant digits of any number being multiplied or divided.

Example The lengths 5.28 and 5.2 are measured in meters. Find the sum of these lengths and record your answer using the correct number of significant digits.

Step 1 Find the sum.

5.28 m	2 digits after the decimal
+ 5.2 m	1 digit after the decimal
10.48 m	

Step 2 Round to one digit after the decimal because the least number of digits after the decimal of the numbers being added is 1.

The sum is 10.5 m.

Practice Problem How many significant digits are in the measurement 7,071,301 m? How many significant digits are in the measurement 0.003010 g?

Practice Problem Multiply 5.28 and 5.2 using the rule for multiplying and dividing. Record the answer using the correct number of significant digits.

Scientific Notation

Many times numbers used in science are very small or very large. Because these numbers are difficult to work with scientists use scientific notation. To write numbers in scientific notation, move the decimal point until only one non-zero digit remains on the left. Then count the number of places you moved the decimal point and use that number as a power of ten. For example, the average distance from the Sun to Mars is 227,800,000,000 m. In scientific notation, this distance is 2.278×10^{11} m. Because you moved the decimal point to the left, the number is a positive power of ten.

The mass of an electron is about 0.000 000 000 000 000 000 000 000 000 000 911 kg. Expressed in scientific notation, this mass is 9.11×10^{-31} kg. Because the decimal point was moved to the right, the number is a negative power of ten.

Example Earth is 149,600,000 km from the Sun. Express this in scientific notation.

Step 1 Move the decimal point until one non-zero digit remains on the left.
1.496 000 00

Step 2 Count the number of decimal places you have moved. In this case, eight.

Step 3 Show that number as a power of ten, 10^8.

The Earth is 1.496×10^8 km from the Sun.

Practice Problem How many significant digits are in 149,600,000 km? How many significant digits are in 1.496×10^8 km?

Practice Problem Parts used in a high performance car must be measured to 7×10^{-6} m. Express this number as a decimal.

Practice Problem A CD is spinning at 539 revolutions per minute. Express this number in scientific notation.

Make and Use Graphs

Data in tables can be displayed in a graph—a visual representation of data. Common graph types include line graphs, bar graphs, and circle graphs.

Line Graph A line graph shows a relationship between two variables that change continuously. The independent variable is changed and is plotted on the *x*-axis. The dependent variable is observed, and is plotted on the *y*-axis.

Example Draw a line graph of the data below from a cyclist in a long-distance race.

Table 5 Bicycle Race Data	
Time (h)	Distance (km)
0	0
1	8
2	16
3	24
4	32
5	40

Step 1 Determine the *x*-axis and *y*-axis variables. Time varies independently of distance and is plotted on the *x*-axis. Distance is dependent on time and is plotted on the *y*-axis.

Step 2 Determine the scale of each axis. The *x*-axis data ranges from 0 to 5. The *y*-axis data ranges from 0 to 40.

Step 3 Using graph paper, draw and label the axes. Include units in the labels.

Step 4 Draw a point at the intersection of the time value on the *x*-axis and corresponding distance value on the *y*-axis. Connect the points and label the graph with a title, as shown in **Figure 20**.

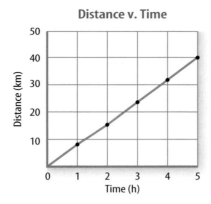

Distance v. Time

Figure 20 This line graph shows the relationship between distance and time during a bicycle ride.

Practice Problem A puppy's shoulder height is measured during the first year of her life. The following measurements were collected: (3 mo, 52 cm), (6 mo, 72 cm), (9 mo, 83 cm), (12 mo, 86). Graph this data.

Find a Slope The slope of a straight line is the ratio of the vertical change, rise, to the horizontal change, run.

$$\text{Slope} = \frac{\text{vertical change (rise)}}{\text{horizontal change (run)}} = \frac{\text{change in } y}{\text{change in } x}$$

Example Find the slope of the graph in **Figure 20**.

Step 1 You know that the slope is the change in *y* divided by the change in *x*.

$$\text{Slope} = \frac{\text{change in } y}{\text{change in } x}$$

Step 2 Determine the data points you will be using. For a straight line, choose the two sets of points that are the farthest apart.

$$\text{Slope} = \frac{(40-0)\ \text{km}}{(5-0)\ \text{hr}}$$

Step 3 Find the change in *y* and *x*.

$$\text{Slope} = \frac{40\ \text{km}}{5\ \text{h}}$$

Step 4 Divide the change in *y* by the change in *x*.

$$\text{Slope} = \frac{8\ \text{km}}{\text{h}}$$

The slope of the graph is 8 km/h.

Line Graph

x	y
3	52
6	72
9	83
12	86

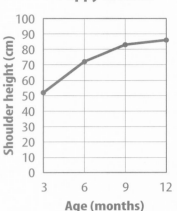

Puppy Growth

Bar Graph

Composition of Air

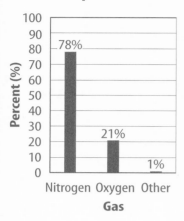

Circle Graph

The total amount of aluminum collected is:

$4.0\ kg + 1.0\ kg + 2.0\ kg = 7.0\ kg$

$\frac{4.0\ kg}{7.0\ kg} = \frac{x}{360°}; \ x = 206°$

$\frac{1.0\ kg}{7.0\ kg} = \frac{x}{360°}; \ x = 51°$

$\frac{2.0\ kg}{7.0\ kg} = \frac{x}{360°}; \ x = 103°$

Bar Graph To compare data that does not change continuously you might choose a bar graph. A bar graph uses bars to show the relationships between variables. The x-axis variable is divided into parts. The parts can be numbers such as years, or a category such as a type of animal. The y-axis is a number and increases continuously along the axis.

Example A recycling center collects 4.0 kg of aluminum on Monday, 1.0 kg on Wednesday, and 2.0 kg on Friday. Create a bar graph of this data.

Step 1 Select the x-axis and y-axis variables. The measured numbers (the masses of aluminum) should be placed on the y-axis. The variable divided into parts (collection days) is placed on the x-axis.

Step 2 Create a graph grid like you would for a line graph. Include labels and units.

Step 3 For each measured number, draw a vertical bar above the x-axis value up to the y-axis value. For the first data point, draw a vertical bar above Monday up to 4.0 kg.

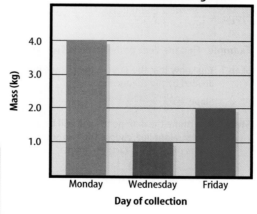

Practice Problem Draw a bar graph of the gases in air: 78% nitrogen, 21% oxygen, 1% other gases.

Circle Graph To display data as parts of a whole, you might use a circle graph. A circle graph is a circle divided into sections that represent the relative size of each piece of data. The entire circle represents 100%, half represents 50%, and so on.

Example Air is made up of 78% nitrogen, 21% oxygen, and 1% other gases. Display the composition of air in a circle graph.

Step 1 Multiply each percent by 360° and divide by 100 to find the angle of each section in the circle.

$78\% \times \frac{360°}{100} = 280.8°$

$21\% \times \frac{360°}{100} = 75.6°$

$1\% \times \frac{360°}{100} = 3.6°$

Step 2 Use a compass to draw a circle and to mark the center of the circle. Draw a straight line from the center to the edge of the circle.

Step 3 Use a protractor and the angles you calculated to divide the circle into parts. Place the center of the protractor over the center of the circle and line the base of the protractor over the straight line.

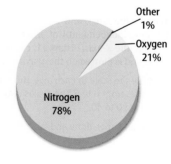

Practice Problem Draw a circle graph to represent the amount of aluminum collected during the week shown in the bar graph to the left.

Physical Science Reference Tables

Standard Units

Symbol	Name	Quantity
m	meter	length
kg	kilogram	mass
Pa	pascal	pressure
K	kelvin	temperature
mol	mole	amount of a substance
J	joule	energy, work, quantity of heat
s	second	time
C	coulomb	electric charge
V	volt	electric potential
A	ampere	electric current
Ω	ohm	resistance

Physical Constants and Conversion Factors

Acceleration due to gravity	g	9.8 m/s/s or m/s^2
Avogadro's Number	N_A	6.02×10^{23} particles per mole
Electron charge	e	1.6×10^{-19} C
Electron rest mass	m_e	9.11×10^{-31} kg
Gravitation constant	G	6.67×10^{-11} N $\times$ m^2/kg^2
Mass-energy relationship		1 u (amu) $= 9.3 \times 10^2$ MeV
Speed of light in a vacuum	c	3.00×10^8 m/s
Speed of sound at STP		331 m/s
Standard Pressure		1 atmosphere
		101.3 kPa
		760 Torr or mmHg
		14.7 lb/in.^{2}

Wavelengths of Light in a Vacuum

Violet	$4.0 - 4.2 \times 10^{-7}$ m
Blue	$4.2 - 4.9 \times 10^{-7}$ m
Green	$4.9 - 5.7 \times 10^{-7}$ m
Yellow	$5.7 - 5.9 \times 10^{-7}$ m
Orange	$5.9 - 6.5 \times 10^{-7}$ m
Red	$6.5 - 7.0 \times 10^{-7}$ m

The Index of Refraction for Common Substances

($\lambda = 5.9 \times 10^{-7}$ m)

Air	1.00
Alcohol	1.36
Canada Balsam	1.53
Corn Oil	1.47
Diamond	2.42
Glass, Crown	1.52
Glass, Flint	1.61
Glycerol	1.47
Lucite	1.50
Quartz, Fused	1.46
Water	1.33

Heat Constants

	Specific Heat (average) (kJ/kg $\times$ °C) (J/g $\times$ °C)	Melting Point (°C)	Boiling Point (°C)	Heat of Fusion (kJ/kg) (J/g)	Heat of Vaporization (kJ/kg) (J/g)
Alcohol (ethyl)	2.43 (liq.)	−117	79	109	855
Aluminum	0.90 (sol.)	660	2467	396	10500
Ammonia	4.71 (liq.)	−78	−33	332	1370
Copper	0.39 (sol.)	1083	2567	205	4790
Iron	0.45 (sol.)	1535	2750	267	6290
Lead	0.13 (sol.)	328	1740	25	866
Mercury	0.14 (liq.)	−39	357	11	295
Platinum	0.13 (sol.)	1772	3827	101	229
Silver	0.24 (sol.)	962	2212	105	2370
Tungsten	0.13 (sol.)	3410	5660	192	4350
Water (solid)	2.05 (sol.)	0	–	334	–
Water (liquid)	4.18 (liq.)	–	100	–	–
Water (vapor)	2.01 (gas)	–	–	–	2260
Zinc	0.39 (sol.)	420	907	113	1770

PERIODIC TABLE OF THE ELEMENTS

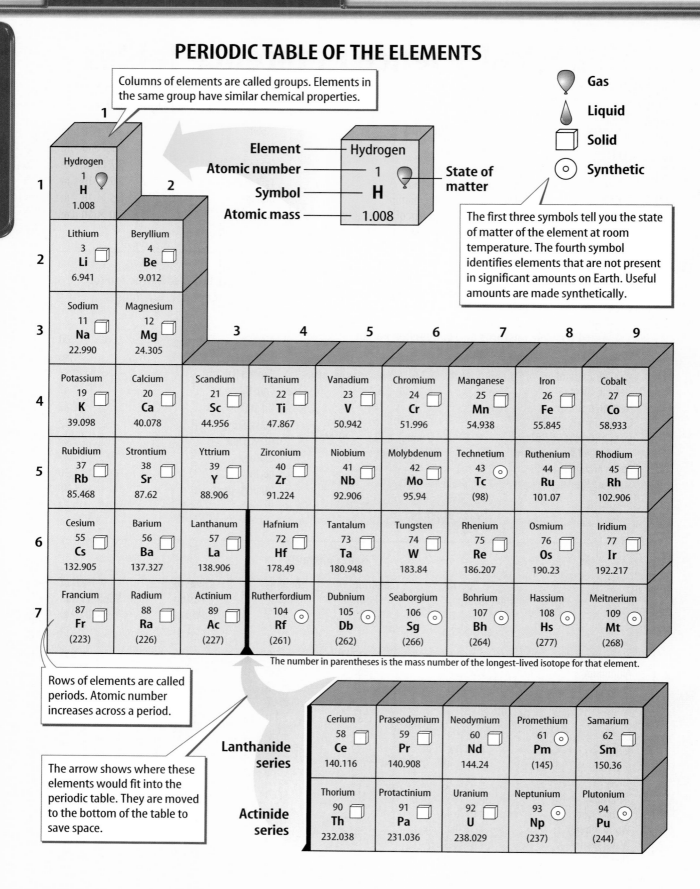

Columns of elements are called groups. Elements in the same group have similar chemical properties.

Element —— Hydrogen
Atomic number —— 1
Symbol —— H
Atomic mass —— 1.008

State of matter

Gas

Liquid

Solid

Synthetic

The first three symbols tell you the state of matter of the element at room temperature. The fourth symbol identifies elements that are not present in significant amounts on Earth. Useful amounts are made synthetically.

The number in parentheses is the mass number of the longest-lived isotope for that element.

Rows of elements are called periods. Atomic number increases across a period.

The arrow shows where these elements would fit into the periodic table. They are moved to the bottom of the table to save space.

Group	1	2	3	4	5	6	7	8	9
1	Hydrogen 1 H 1.008								
2	Lithium 3 Li 6.941	Beryllium 4 Be 9.012							
3	Sodium 11 Na 22.990	Magnesium 12 Mg 24.305							
4	Potassium 19 K 39.098	Calcium 20 Ca 40.078	Scandium 21 Sc 44.956	Titanium 22 Ti 47.867	Vanadium 23 V 50.942	Chromium 24 Cr 51.996	Manganese 25 Mn 54.938	Iron 26 Fe 55.845	Cobalt 27 Co 58.933
5	Rubidium 37 Rb 85.468	Strontium 38 Sr 87.62	Yttrium 39 Y 88.906	Zirconium 40 Zr 91.224	Niobium 41 Nb 92.906	Molybdenum 42 Mo 95.94	Technetium 43 Tc (98)	Ruthenium 44 Ru 101.07	Rhodium 45 Rh 102.906
6	Cesium 55 Cs 132.905	Barium 56 Ba 137.327	Lanthanum 57 La 138.906	Hafnium 72 Hf 178.49	Tantalum 73 Ta 180.948	Tungsten 74 W 183.84	Rhenium 75 Re 186.207	Osmium 76 Os 190.23	Iridium 77 Ir 192.217
7	Francium 87 Fr (223)	Radium 88 Ra (226)	Actinium 89 Ac (227)	Rutherfordium 104 Rf (261)	Dubnium 105 Db (262)	Seaborgium 106 Sg (266)	Bohrium 107 Bh (264)	Hassium 108 Hs (277)	Meitnerium 109 Mt (268)

Lanthanide series

Cerium 58 Ce 140.116	Praseodymium 59 Pr 140.908	Neodymium 60 Nd 144.24	Promethium 61 Pm (145)	Samarium 62 Sm 150.36

Actinide series

Thorium 90 Th 232.038	Protactinium 91 Pa 231.036	Uranium 92 U 238.029	Neptunium 93 Np (237)	Plutonium 94 Pu (244)

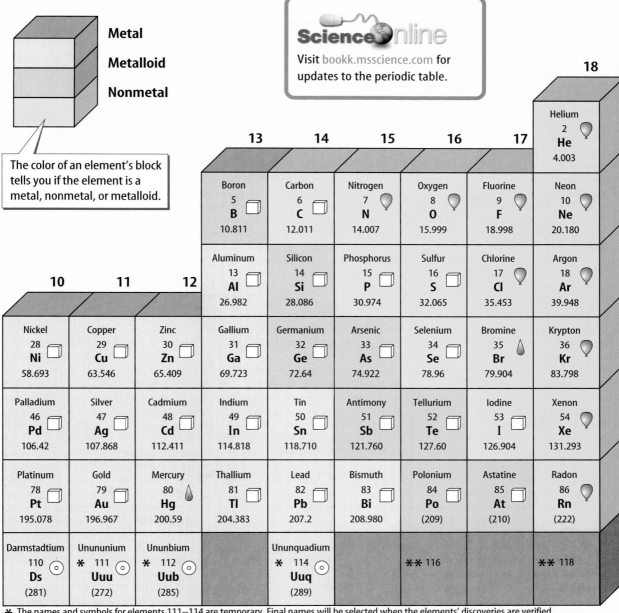

Metal

Metalloid

Nonmetal

Science online

Visit bookk.msscience.com for updates to the periodic table.

The color of an element's block tells you if the element is a metal, nonmetal, or metalloid.

18

Helium
2
He
4.003

13	14	15	16	17

Boron	Carbon	Nitrogen	Oxygen	Fluorine	Neon
5	6	7	8	9	10
B	**C**	**N**	**O**	**F**	**Ne**
10.811	12.011	14.007	15.999	18.998	20.180

Aluminum	Silicon	Phosphorus	Sulfur	Chlorine	Argon
13	14	15	16	17	18
Al	**Si**	**P**	**S**	**Cl**	**Ar**
26.982	28.086	30.974	32.065	35.453	39.948

10	11	12

Nickel	Copper	Zinc	Gallium	Germanium	Arsenic	Selenium	Bromine	Krypton
28	29	30	31	32	33	34	35	36
Ni	**Cu**	**Zn**	**Ga**	**Ge**	**As**	**Se**	**Br**	**Kr**
58.693	63.546	65.409	69.723	72.64	74.922	78.96	79.904	83.798

Palladium	Silver	Cadmium	Indium	Tin	Antimony	Tellurium	Iodine	Xenon
46	47	48	49	50	51	52	53	54
Pd	**Ag**	**Cd**	**In**	**Sn**	**Sb**	**Te**	**I**	**Xe**
106.42	107.868	112.411	114.818	118.710	121.760	127.60	126.904	131.293

Platinum	Gold	Mercury	Thallium	Lead	Bismuth	Polonium	Astatine	Radon
78	79	80	81	82	83	84	85	86
Pt	**Au**	**Hg**	**Tl**	**Pb**	**Bi**	**Po**	**At**	**Rn**
195.078	196.967	200.59	204.383	207.2	208.980	(209)	(210)	(222)

Darmstadtium	Unununium	Ununbium		Ununquadium			
110	* 111	* 112		* 114		** 116	** 118
Ds	**Uuu**	**Uub**		**Uuq**			
(281)	(272)	(285)		(289)			

* The names and symbols for elements 111–114 are temporary. Final names will be selected when the elements' discoveries are verified.

** Elements 116 and 118 were thought to have been created. The claim was retracted because the experimental results could not be repeated.

Europium	Gadolinium	Terbium	Dysprosium	Holmium	Erbium	Thulium	Ytterbium	Lutetium
63	64	65	66	67	68	69	70	71
Eu	**Gd**	**Tb**	**Dy**	**Ho**	**Er**	**Tm**	**Yb**	**Lu**
151.964	157.25	158.925	162.500	164.930	167.259	168.934	173.04	174.967

Americium	Curium	Berkelium	Californium	Einsteinium	Fermium	Mendelevium	Nobelium	Lawrencium
95	96	97	98	99	100	101	102	103
Am	**Cm**	**Bk**	**Cf**	**Es**	**Fm**	**Md**	**No**	**Lr**
(243)	(247)	(247)	(251)	(252)	(257)	(258)	(259)	(262)

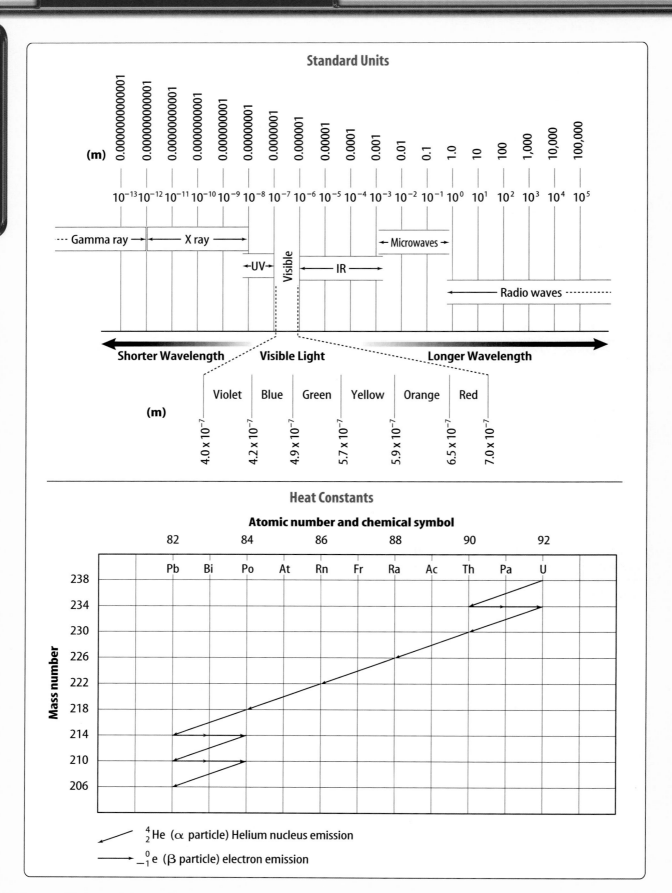

Standard Units

(m)

0.0000000000001
0.000000000001
0.00000000001
0.0000000001
0.000000001
0.00000001
0.0000001
0.000001
0.00001
0.0001
0.001
0.01
0.1
1.0
10
100
1,000
10,000
100,000

10^{-13} 10^{-12} 10^{-11} 10^{-10} 10^{-9} 10^{-8} 10^{-7} 10^{-6} 10^{-5} 10^{-4} 10^{-3} 10^{-2} 10^{-1} 10^{0} 10^{1} 10^{2} 10^{3} 10^{4} 10^{5}

Gamma ray → ← X ray → ← Microwaves →

←UV→ Visible ← IR →

← Radio waves ⋯⋯⋯

← Shorter Wavelength ⋯⋯ Visible Light ⋯⋯ Longer Wavelength →

Violet | Blue | Green | Yellow | Orange | Red

(m)

4.0×10^{-7}
4.2×10^{-7}
4.9×10^{-7}
5.7×10^{-7}
5.9×10^{-7}
6.5×10^{-7}
7.0×10^{-7}

Heat Constants

Atomic number and chemical symbol

82   84   86   88   90   92

Pb Bi Po At Rn Fr Ra Ac Th Pa U

Mass number

238
234
230
226
222
218
214
210
206

$^{4}_{2}$He (α particle) Helium nucleus emission

$^{0}_{-1}$e (β particle) electron emission

Cómo usar el glosario en español:
1. Busca el término en inglés que desees encontrar.
2. El término en español, junto con la definición, se encuentran en la columna de la derecha.

Pronunciation Key

Use the following key to help you sound out words in the glossary.

a.............back (BAK)		ew...........food (FEWD)	
ay............day (DAY)		yoo..........pure (PYOOR)	
ah............father (FAH thur)		yew..........few (FYEW)	
ow...........flower (FLOW ur)		uh............comma (CAH muh)	
ar............car (CAR)		u (+ con)......rub (RUB)	
e.............less (LES)		sh............shelf (SHELF)	
ee............leaf (LEEF)		ch............nature (NAY chur)	
ih............trip (TRIHP)		g.............gift (GIHFT)	
i (i + con + e)..idea (i DEE uh)		j.............gem (JEM)	
oh............go (GOH)		ing...........sing (SING)	
aw............soft (SAWFT)		zh............vision (VIH zhun)	
or............orbit (OR buht)		k.............cake (KAYK)	
oy............coin (COYN)		s.............seed, cent (SEED, SENT)	
oo............foot (FOOT)		z.............zone, raise (ZOHN, RAYZ)	

English ——— A ——— Español

actinide: the second series of inner transition elements which goes from thorium to lawrencium. (p. 114)

alkali metals: elements in group 1 of the periodic table. (p. 105)

alkaline earth metals: elements in group 2 of the periodic table. (p. 106)

Archimedes' (ar kuh MEE deez) principle: states that the buoyant force on an object is equal to the weight of the fluid displaced by the object. (p. 59)

atomic mass: average mass of an atom of an element; its unit of measure is the atomic mass unit (u), which is 1/12 the mass of a carbon-12 atom. (p. 22)

atomic number: number of protons in the nucleus of each atom of a given element; is the top number in the periodic table. (p. 21)

actínido: la segunda serie de los elementos de transición interna que abarca desde el torio hasta el laurencio. (p. 114)

metales alcalinos: elementos en el grupo 1 de la tabla periódica. (p. 105)

metales alcalinotérreos: elementos en el grupo 2 de la tabla periódica. (p. 106)

principio de Arquímedes: establece que la fuerza de empuje ejercida sobre un objeto es igual al peso del fluido desplazado por dicho objeto. (p. 59)

masa atómica: masa promedio de un átomo de un elemento; su unidad de medida es la unidad de masa atómica (u), la cual es 1/12 de la masa de un átomo de carbono 12. (p. 22)

número atómico: número de protones en el núcleo de cada átomo de un determinado elemento; es el número que se encuentra en la parte superior en la tabla periódica. (p. 21)

B

buoyant force: upward force exerted on an object immersed in a fluid. (p. 58)

fuerza de empuje: fuerza ascendente ejercida sobre un objeto inmerso en un fluido. (p. 58)

Glossary/Glosario

C

catalyst: substance that can make something happen faster but is not changed itself. (p. 113)

chemical change: change in which the composition of a substance changes. (p. 80)

chemical property: characteristic that cannot be observed without altering the sample. (p. 76)

compound: a substance produced when elements combine and whose properties are different from each of the elements in it. (p. 25)

condensation: the process of changing from a gas to a liquid. (pp. 51, 79)

catalizador: sustancia que puede hacer que algo suceda más rápidamente sin cambiar ella misma. (p. 113)

cambio químico: cambio en el cual la composición de una sustancia es modificada. (p. 80)

propiedad química: característica que no puede ser observada sin alterar la muestra. (p. 76)

compuesto: sustancia producida por la combinación de elementos y cuyas propiedades son diferentes de las de cada uno de los elementos. (p. 25)

condensación: el proceso de cambio de gas a líquido. (pp. 51, 79)

D

density: mass of an object divided by its volume. (p. 59)

deposition: the process by which a gas changes into a solid. (p. 79)

densidad: masa de un objeto dividida por su volumen. (p. 59)

deposición: el proceso mediante el cual un gas pasa a ser sólido. (p. 79)

E

electron: negatively-charged particle that exists in an electron cloud formation around an atom's nucleus. (p. 11)

electron cloud: region surrounding the nucleus of an atom, where electrons are most likely to be found. (p. 17)

element: substance that cannot be broken down into simpler substances. (p. 9)

electrón: partícula con carga negativa que existe en una nube de electrones alrededor del núcleo del átomo. (p. 11)

nube de electrones: región que rodea el núcleo de un átomo, en donde los electrones se encuentran con mayor probabilidad. (p. 17)

elemento: sustancia que no se puede descomponer en sustancias más simples. (p. 9)

F

freezing: change of matter from a liquid state to a solid state. (p. 49)

congelación: cambio de la materia de estado líquido a sólido. (p. 49)

G

gas: matter that does not have a definite shape or volume; has particles that move at high speeds in all directions. (p. 44)

group: family of elements in the periodic table that have similar physical or chemical properties. (p. 99)

gas: materia que no tiene ni forma ni volumen definidos; tiene partículas que se mueven a altas velocidades y en todas las direcciones. (p. 44)

grupo: familia de elementos en la tabla periódica que tienen propiedades físicas o químicas similares. (p. 99)

H

halogen: elements in group 17 of the periodic table. (p. 110)

heat: movement of thermal energy from a substance at a higher temperature to a substance at a lower temperature. (p. 46)

halógenos: elementos en el grupo 17 de la tabla periódica. (p. 110)

calor: movimiento de energía térmica de una sustancia que se encuentra a una alta temperatura hacia una sustancia a una baja temperatura. (p. 46)

I

isotopes (I suh tohps): two or more atoms of the same element that have different numbers of neutrons in their nuclei. (p. 21)

isótopos: dos o más átomos del mismo elemento que tienen diferente número de neutrones en sus núcleos. (p. 21)

L

lanthanide: the first series of inner transition elements which goes from cerium to lutetium. (p. 114)

law of conservation of mass: states that mass is neither created nor destroyed—and as a result the mass of the substances before a physical or chemical change is equal to the mass of the substances present after the change. (p. 87)

liquid: matter with a definite volume but no definite shape that can flow from one place to another. (p. 42)

lantánidos: la primera serie de los elementos de transición interna que va desde el cerio hasta el lutecio. (p. 114)

ley de la conservación de masas: establece que la masa no puede ser creada ni destruida; como resultado, la masa de una sustancia antes de un cambio físico o químico es igual a la masa presente de la sustancia después del cambio. (p. 87)

líquido: materia con volumen definido pero no con forma definida que puede fluir de un sitio a otro. (p. 42)

M

mass number: sum of the number of protons and neutrons in the nucleus of an atom. (p. 21)

matter: anything that takes up space and has mass. (p. 40)

melting: change of matter from a solid state to a liquid state. (p. 47)

metal: element that is malleable, ductile, a good conductor of electricity, and generally has a shiny or metallic luster. (pp. 22, 102)

metalloid (MEH tuh loyd): element that shares some properties with both metals and nonmetals. (pp. 23, 102)

mixture: a combination of compounds and elements that has not formed a new substance and whose proportions can be changed without changing the mixture's identity. (p. 27)

número de masa: suma del número de protones y neutrones en el núcleo de un átomo. (p. 21)

materia: cualquier cosa que ocupe espacio y tenga masa. (p. 40)

fusión: cambio de la materia de estado sólido a líquido. (p. 47)

metal: elemento maleable, dúctil, buen conductor de electricidad y generalmente con un lustre brillante o metálico. (pp. 22, 102)

metaloide: elemento que comparte algunas propiedades de los metales y de los no metales. (pp. 23, 102)

mezcla: combinación de compuestos y elementos sin llegar a formar una nueva sustancia y cuyas proporciones pueden cambiar sin que se modifique la identidad de la mezcla. (p. 27)

Glossary/Glosario

Glossary/Glosario

N

neutron (NEW trahn): electrically-neutral particle that has the same mass as a proton and is found in an atom's nucleus. (p. 15)

noble gases: elements in group 18 of the periodic table. (p. 110)

nonmetal: element that is usually a gas or brittle solid at room temperature and is a poor conductor of heat and electricity. (pp. 23, 102)

neutrón: partícula eléctricamente neutra que tiene la misma masa que un protón y se encuentra en el núcleo de un átomo. (p. 15)

gases inertes: elementos en el grupo 18 de la tabla periódica. (p. 110)

no metal: elemento que por lo general es un gas o un sólido frágil a temperatura ambiente y mal conductor de calor y electricidad. (pp. 23, 102)

P

Pascal's principle: states that when a force is applied to a confined fluid, an increase in pressure is transmitted equally to all parts of the fluid. (p. 60)

period: horizontal row of elements in the periodic table whose properties change gradually and predictably. (p. 99)

physical change: change in which the form or appearance of matter changes, but not its composition. (p. 78)

physical property: characteristic that can be observed, using the five senses, without changing or trying to change the composition of a substance. (p. 72)

pressure: force exerted on a surface divided by the total area over which the force is exerted. (p. 54)

proton: positively-charged particle in the nucleus of an atom. (p. 14)

principio de Pascal: establece que cuando se ejerce una fuerza sobre un fluido encerrado, se transmite un incremento de presión uniforme a todas las partes del fluido. (p. 60)

período: fila horizontal de elementos en la tabla periódica cuyas propiedades cambian gradualmente y en forma predecible. (p. 99)

cambio físico: cambio en el cual varía la forma o apariencia de la materia pero no su composición. (p. 78)

propiedad física: característica que puede ser observada usando los cinco sentidos sin cambiar o tratar de cambiar la composición de una sustancia. (p. 72)

presión: fuerza ejercida sobre una superficie dividida por el área total sobre la cual se ejerce dicha fuerza. (p. 54)

protón: partícula con carga positiva en el núcleo de un átomo. (p. 14)

R

representative elements: elements in groups 1 and 2 and 13–18 in the periodic table that include metals, metalloids, and nonmetals. (p. 99)

elementos representativos: elementos en los grupos 1 y 2 y 13-18 en la tabla periódica; incluyen metales, metaloides y no metales. (p. 99)

S

semiconductor: element that does not conduct electricity as well as a metal but conducts it better than a nonmetal. (p. 107)

solid: matter with a definite shape and volume; has tightly packed particles that move mainly by vibrating. (p. 41)

sublimation: the process by which a solid changes directly into a gas. (p. 79)

semiconductor: elemento que no conduce electricidad tan bien como un metal pero que la conduce mejor que un no metal. (p. 107)

sólido: materia con forma y volumen definidos; tiene partículas fuertemente compactadas que se mueven principalmente por vibración. (p. 41)

sublimación: proceso mediante el cual un sólido se convierte directamente en gas. (p. 79)

substance/viscosity

substance: matter that has the same composition and properties throughout. (p. 25)

surface tension: the uneven forces acting on the particles on the surface of a liquid. (p. 43)

sustancia: materia que tiene la misma composición y propiedades en cada una de sus partes. (p. 25)

tensión superficial: fuerzas desiguales que actúan sobre las partículas que se encuentran en la superficie de un líquido. (p. 43)

---

temperature: measure of the average kinetic energy of the individual particles of a substance. (p. 46)

transition elements: elements in groups 3–12 in the periodic table, all of which are metals. (p. 99)

temperatura: medida de la energía cinética prome dio de las partículas individuales de una sustancia. (p. 46)

elementos de transición: elementos en los grupos 3-12 en la tabla periódica, todos los cuales son metales. (p. 99)

---

vaporization: the process by which a liquid changes into a gas. (pp. 50, 79)

viscosity: a liquid's resistance to flow. (p. 43)

vaporización: proceso mediante el cual un líquido se convierte en gas. (pp. 50, 79)

viscosidad: resistencia de un líquido al flujo. (p. 43)

Italic numbers = illustration/photo **Bold numbers = vocabulary term**
lab = a page on which the entry is used in a lab
act = a page on which the entry is used in an activity

A

Actinides, 114, *115*
Activities, Applying Math, 59, 84;
  Applying Science, 27, 49, 103;
  Integrate Astronomy, 83;
  Integrate Earth Science, 29, 42;
  Integrate Health, 116; Integrate
  Life Science, 28, 81, 109;
  Integrate Physics, 16, 46, 114;
  Science Online, 19, 28, 43, 49,
  51, 61, 81, 102, 116;
  Standardized Test Practice,
  36–37, 68–69, 94–95, 124–125
Alkali metals, 105, *105*
Alkaline earth metals, 106, *106*
Alpha particles, 12, 13, *13,* 14, 16
Aluminum, *106*
Amalgam, 116
Americium, 114
Ammonia, 75, 108, *108*
Amorphous solids, 42, 47, *47*
Applying Math, Calculating
  Density, 59; Chapter Review, 35,
  67, 93, 123; Converting
  Temperatures, 84; Section
  Review, 23, 29, 76, 87, 104
Applying Science, How can ice
  save oranges?, 49; What does
  periodic mean in the periodic
  table?, 103; What's the best way
  to desalt ocean water?, 27
Applying Skills, 44, 111, 116
Archimedes' principle, 59, *59,*
  62–63 lab
Area, and pressure, 55, *55*
Argon, 111, *111*
Arsenic, 109
Astatine, 110
Atmospheric pressure, 55, *55–57, 56*
Atom(s), 8–17; history of, 8–17;
  mass number of, 21; model of,
  9, 9–17, *12, 14, 15,* 15 *lab;*
  nucleus of, *14,* 14–16, *15, 16*

Atomic mass, 22, *22*
Atomic number, 21

B

Balanced pressure, 56, *56*
Batteries, lithium, 105
Behavior, as physical property, 75,
  75
Beryllium, *106*
Blood, as mixture, 27, *27,* 28
Blood pressure, 61 *act*
Bohr, Niels, 16, 17
Boiling point, 50, *50;* as physical
  property, 74, 75
Boron, 106
Boron family, 106, *106*
Bromine, 75, 110
Buoyant force, *58,* **58**–59, *59,*
  62–63 lab
Burning, 84, *84*

C

Calcium carbonate, 75
Californium-252, 114
Carbon, 107, *107*
Carbon dioxide, 25
Carbon group, 107, *107*
Carbon monoxide, 25
Catalysts, 113, *113*
Cathode-ray tube (CRT), 10, *10,*
  11, *11*
Cerium, 114, *114*
Chemical changes, *80,* **80**–85;
  color, 81, *81;* comparing to
  physical changes, 81 *lab,* 85, *85;*
  and energy, 82, *82;* recognizing,
  81 *act;* reversing, 84, *84;* signs
  of, *81,* 81–84, *82, 83, 84*
Chemical formulas, 26
Chemical properties, 76, *76,* 77 *lab*
Chemistry, 8
Chlorine, 22, *22,* 110, *110*

Chlorophyll, 81
Chromium, 113
Classification, of elements, 19, *20,*
  22–23
Cobalt, 112
Communicating Your Data, 24,
  31, 53, 63, 77, 89, 119
Compound(s), *25,* **25**–26, *26;*
  comparing, 26 *lab;* formulas for,
  26, *26*
Computers, and semiconductors,
  107, *107*
Condensation, *48,* **51,** *51,* 51 *act,*
  79, *79*
Conservation, of mass, 87, *87*
Crookes, William, 9, 10
Crystal, 41, *41*
Crystalline solids, 41, *41,* 47
Cycles, water, 53 *lab*

D

Dalton, John, 9, 20
Data Source, 118
Density, 59, 59 *act*
Dentistry, elements used in, 116
Deposition, 79
Desalination, 27 *act*
Design Your Own, Battle of the
  Toothpastes, 88–89; Design
  Your Own Ship, 62–63
Diamond, 107
Dissolving, as physical change, 79,
  79
Dry ice, 52, *52*
Ductility, 22

E

Electron(s), 11, 16–17, *17*
Electron cloud, 17, *17*
Element(s), 9, 18–23, 102 *act;*
  atomic mass of, 22, *22;* atomic
  number of, 21;

boron family of, 106, *106;* carbon group of, 107, *107;* classification of, 19, *20,* 22–23; halogens, 110, *110;* identifying characteristics of, 21–22; isotopes of, 21, *21;* metalloids, 23, 102, *102,* 106, 107, *107,* 109, 110; metals, 22, *22,* 102, *102, 105,* 105–106, *106,* 107, *107,* 112–116; new, 19 *act;* nitrogen group of, 108, *108;* noble gases, *110,* 110–111, *111;* nonmetals, 23, *23,* 102, *102,* 107, *107,* 108, *108,* 109, 110, *110;* oxygen family of, 109, *109;* periodic table of, 19, *20, 21,* 24 *lab. See* Periodic table; radioactive, 114, *115;* representative, **99;** symbols for, 19, *20,* 104; synthetic, 18, **114,** *115;* transition, **99,** *112,* 112–116, *113, 114, 115*
Element keys, 103, *103*
Energy, and chemical changes, 82, *82;* thermal, *45,* **45**–46; types of, 46
Eruptions, volcanic, 70, *70–71*
Europium oxide, 114
Evaporation, *48, 50,* 50 *lab,* 50–51

Fertilizer, 108, *108*
Firefighting, foam for, 109, *109*
Fireworks, 80, *80*
Flint, 114, *114*
Fluids, 54–61. *See* Liquid(s). *See also* Gas(es); and Archimedes' principle, 59, *59,* 62–63 *lab;* and buoyant force, *58,* 58–59, *59,* 62–63 *lab;* and density, 59, 59 *act;* and Pascal's principle, *60,* 60–61, *61;* and pressure, 54–58
Fluoride, 116
Fluorine, 110
Foam, for firefighting, 109, *109*
Foldables, 7, 39, 71, 97
Force(s), 54; and area, 55, *55;* buoyant, *58,* **58**–59, *59,* 62–63 *lab;* measurement of, 54; and pressure, 54–58
Force pumps, 61, *61*
Formulas, chemical, 26; for compounds, 26, *26*

Freezing, 39 *lab, 48,* **49,** 79, *79*
Freezing point, 49, 49 *act,* 75
Fusion, 115

Gallium, 106
Gas(es), 44, *44. See also* Fluids; and chemical changes, 83, *83;* condensation of, *48,* 51, *51,* 51 *act;* pressure of, *57,* 57–58, *58*
Germanium, 107
Glass, 47, *47,* 107
Graphite, 107
Group, 19, **99**

Halogens, 110, *110*
Health, and heavy metals, 118–119 *lab;* and mercury, 116 *act*
Heart, 61, *61*
Heat, 46; specific, 47, *47;* and temperature, 46–47
Heavy metals, 107, *107,* 113, 118–119 *lab*
Helium, 110, 111, *111*
Hemoglobin, 112
Heterogeneous mixtures, 29
Homogeneous mixtures, 29
Hydraulic systems, 60, *60*
Hydrogen peroxide, 26, *26*
Hydrogen v. helium, 110

Ice, dry, 52, *52*
Inner transition elements, 114, *114, 115*
Integrate Astronomy, meteoroid, 83
Integrate Earth Science, freshwater, 42; rocks and minerals, 29
Integrate Health, dentistry and dental materials, 116
Integrate Life Science, blood as a mixture, 28; poison buildup, 109; signs of chemical changes, 81
Integrate Physics, bright lights, 114; quantum theory, 16; types of energy, 46

International Union of Pure and Applied Chemistry (IUPAC), 104
Iodine, 75, 110
Iridium, 113
Iron, 112, 114
Iron triad, 112, *112*
Isotopes, 21, *21*

Journal, 6, 38, 70, 96

Kilopascal (kPa), 54
Krypton, 111

Lab(s), Design Your Own, 62–63, 88–89; Elements and the Periodic Table, 24; Finding the Difference, 77; Launch Labs, 7, 39, 71, 97; Mini Labs, 26, 50, 74, 75, 99; Mystery Mixture, 30–31; Try at Home Mini Labs, 15, 57, 81; Use the Internet, 118–119; Water Cycle, 53
Lanthanides, 114, *114*
Lanthanum, 114, *114*
Launch Labs, Changing Face of a Volcano, 71; Experiment with a Freezing Liquid, 39; Make a Model of a Periodic Pattern, 97; Model the Unseen, 7
Lava, 71 *lab*
Lavoisier, Antoine, *20,* 87
Lawrencium, 114
Law(s), of conservation of mass, **87,** *87*
Lead, 107, *107,* 114
Leaves, changing colors of, 81, *81*
Lightbulb, 113, *113*
Liquid(s), *42,* **42**–43, *43. See also* Fluids; freezing, 39 *lab, 48,* 49; and surface tension, 43, *43;* vaporization of, *48,* 50 *lab, 50,* 50–51; viscosity of, 43
Lithium, 105
Lodestone, 75, *75*
Luster, 22
Lutetium, 114

M

Magnesium, *106*
Magnetic properties, 75, *75*, 112
Malleability, 20, *20*
Mass, conservation of, 87, *87*
Mass number, 21
Materials, semiconductors, 107, *107*
Matter, 40. *See also* States of matter; ancient views of, 8, 32; appearance of, 73, *73*; compounds, *25*, 25–26, *26*; describing, 72–77, 77 *lab*; elements in, 18–23, 24 *lab*
Measurement, of force, 54; of properties, 74 *lab*; of weight, 74
Meitner, Lise, 104
Melting, 47, *47*, *48*, 79, *79*
Melting point, 47, 74, 75
Mendeleev, Dmitri, 20, 98, *98*, 99
Mercury, 113, 116, 116 *act*
Metal(s), 22, *22*, **102;** alkali, **105,** *105;* alkaline earth, **106,** *106;* as catalysts, 113, *113;* heavy, 107, *107*, 113, 118–119 *lab;* iron triad, 112, *112;* misch, 114, *114;* on periodic table, 102, *102*, *105*, 105–106, *106*, 107, *107*, 112–116; transition, *112*, 112–116, *113, 114, 115*
Metalloids, 23, 102, *102*, 106, 107, *107*, 109, 110
Meteoroid, 83
Mineral(s), 29
Mini Labs, Comparing Compounds, 26; Designing a Periodic Table, 99; Identifying an Unknown Substance, 75; Measuring Properties, 74; Observing Vaporization, 50
Misch metal, 114, *114*
Mixtures, 27–31, 28 *act;* blood as, 27, *27*, 28; heterogeneous, 29; homogeneous, 29; identifying, 30–31 *lab;* separating, 28, *28*
Model(s), of atom, *9*, 9–17, *12, 14, 15*, 15 *lab;* of unseen, 7 *lab*
Moseley, Henry, 99

N

National Geographic Visualizing, The Periodic Table, 20; Recycling, 86; States of Matter, *48;* Synthetic Elements, *115*
Neodymium, 114, *114*
Neon, *73*, 111, *111*
Neutron(s), 15
Newton (unit of force), 54
Nickel, 112
Nitrogen, 108, *108*
Nitrogen group, 108, *108*
Noble gases, *110,* **110**–111, *111*
Nonmetals, 23, *23*, **102,** *102*, 107, *107*, 108, *108*, 109, 110, *110*
Nucleus, *14*, 14–16, *15, 16*

O

Ocean water, desalination of, 27 *act;* salt in, 27 *act*
Odor, and chemical changes, 83
Oil (petroleum), *73*
Oops! Accidents in Science, Incredible Stretching Goo, 64
Osmium, 113
Oxygen, on periodic table, 109, *109*
Oxygen family, 109, *109*
Ozone, 109

P

Palladium, 113
Particle(s), alpha, 12–13, *13*, 14, 16; charged, 11–13
Particle accelerator, 115, *115*
Pascal (Pa), 54
Pascal's principle, *60,* **60**–61, *61*
Period, 19, **99**
Periodic pattern, making models of, 97 *lab*
Periodic table, 19, *20, 21,* 24 *lab,* 96–117, *100–101;* boron family on, 106, *106;* carbon group on, 107, *107;* designing, 99 *lab;* development of, *98,* 98–99; element keys on, 103, *103;* halogens on, 110, *110;* metalloids on, 102, *102*, 106, 107, *107*, 109, 110;

metals on, 102, *102,* 105, 105–106, *106, 107,* 112–116; nitrogen group on, 108, *108;* noble gases on, *110,* 110–111, *111;* nonmetals on, 102, *102*, 107, *107*, 108, *108*, 109, 110, *110;* oxygen family on, 109, *109;* symbols for elements on, 104; zones on, 99, *99, 102,* 102–104, *103*
Phosphorus, 108, *108*
Physical changes, *78,* **78**–79, *79;* comparing to chemical changes, 81 *lab*, 85, *85;* reversing, 84
Physical properties, *72,* **72**–75, *74,* 77 *lab;* appearance, 73, *73;* behavior, 75, *75;* boiling point, 74, 75; magnetic, 75, *75*, 112; measuring, 74 *lab;* melting point, 74, 75; state, 73, *73*
Pigment, 81
Pistons, 60, *60*
Plant(s), chlorophyll in, 81; leaves of, 81, *81*
Plasma, 43 *act*
Platinum, 113
Platinum group, 113
Plutonium, 114
Poisons, 99
Polonium, 109
Potassium, 105
Potassium hydroxide, 75
Pressure, *54,* **54**–58; and area, 55, *55;* atmospheric, *55,* 55–57, *56;* balanced, 56, *56;* and force, 54–58; of gas, *57,* 57–58, *58;* and temperature, 58, *58;* and volume, 57, *57*
Properties, chemical, **76,** *76*, 77 *lab;* comparing, 71 *lab;* magnetic, 75, *75*, 112; physical. *See* Physical properties
Protactinium, 114
Proton(s), 14

Q

Quantum theory, 16
Quartz, 107

R

Radioactive elements, 114, *115*

Radon, 111
Reading Check, 10, 12, 14, 15, 21, 26, 27, 40, 41, 42, 44, 46, 51, 55, 58, 72, 75, 80, 84, 102, 106, 108, 110, 111, 112, 114, 116
Real-World Questions, 24, 30, 53, 62, 77, 88, 118
Recycling, 86, 90, *90*
Representative elements, 99
Rhodium, 113
Rock(s), 29
Rust, 80, *80*
Ruthenium, 113
Rutherford, Ernest, 12–13, 14

Salt(s), 105, 110, *110;* and chemical changes, 82, *82;* crystal structure of, 41, *41;* physical properties of, 75
Sand, 107
Science and History, Ancient Views of Matter, 32
Science and Language Arts, "Anansi Tries to Steal All the Wisdom in the World," 120
Science Online, blood pressure, 61; condensation, 51; elements, 102; freezing point study, 49; health risks, 116; mixtures, 28; new elements, 19; plasma, 43; recognizing chemical changes, 81
Science Stats, Strange Changes, 90
Scientific Methods, 24, 30–31, 53, 62–63, 77, 88–89, 117, 118–119; Analyze Your Data, 31, 63, 89, 119; Conclude and Apply, 24, 31, 53, 63, 77, 89, 119; Follow Your Plan, 63, 119; Form a Hypothesis, 62, 88; Make a Plan, 63, 119; Test Your Hypothesis, 63, 89
Selenium, 109, *109*
Semiconductors, 107, *107*
Shape, changes of, 78, *78*
Ship, designing, 62–63
Silicon, 107, *107*
Silver tarnish, 80, *80*
Smell, and chemical changes, 83
Sodium chloride, 41, *41,* 75, 105, 110, *110. See also* Salt(s)

Solid(s), *41,* **41**–42; amorphous, 42, 47, *47;* and chemical changes, 83, *83;* crystalline, 41, *41,* 47; melting, 47, *47, 48;* sublimation of, 52, *52*
Space shuttle, *25*
Specific heat, 47, *47*
Spring scale, *74*
Standardized Test Practice, 36–37, 68–69, 94–95, 124–125
States of matter, 38–63, *40;* changes of, 45–53, 53 *lab;* and condensation, 48, 51, *51,* 51 *lab;* and evaporation, 48, 50, 50 *lab,* 50–51; fluids, 54–61, 58, 59, 59 *act,* 60, 61, 62–63 *lab;* and freezing, 39 *lab, 48,* 49; gases, 44, *44;* liquids, *42,* 42–43, *43;* and melting, 47, *47, 48;* as physical change, 79, *79;* as physical property, 73, *73;* and pressure, 54–58; solids, *41,* 41–42; and sublimation, 52, *52;* and vaporization, 48, 50, 50 *lab,* 50–51
Steel, 112, *112*
Study Guide, 33, 65, 91, 121
Sublimation, 52, *52,* **79**
Substance, 25
Sugars, dissolving, 79, *79*
Sulfur, 109
Sulfuric acid, 109
Surface tension, 43, *43*
Symbols, for elements, 19, *20,* 104
Synthetic elements, 18, **114,** *115*

Tarnish, 80, *80*
Technology, cathode-ray tube (CRT), 10, *10,* 11, *11;* computers, 107, *107;* in dentistry, 116; fireworks, 80, *80;* lightbulb, 113, *113;* particle accelerator, 115, *115;* semiconductors, 107, *107;* space shuttle, *25;* spring scale, *74;* synthetic elements, 114, *115;* Tevatron, *18*
Teeth, 88–89 *lab. See also* Dentistry
Tellurium, 109
Temperature, 46, *46;* and heat, 46–47; and pressure, 58, *58*
Tevatron, *18*

Thermal energy, 45, **45**–46
Thomson, J. J., 11–12, 14
Thorium, 114
TIME, Science and History, 32
Tin, 107
Toothpastes, comparing, 88–89 *lab*
Transition elements, **99,** *112,* 112–116, *113;* in dentistry, 116; inner, 114, *114, 115*
Try at Home MiniLabs, Comparing Changes, 81; Modeling the Nuclear Atom, 15; Predicting a Waterfall, 57
Tungsten, 113, *113*

Unknown, finding, 59 *act,* 84 *act*
Uranium, 114, 115
Use the Internet, Health Risks from Heavy Metals, 118–119

Vapor, 44
Vaporization, 48, 50, 50 *lab,* 50–51, **79,** *79*
Viscosity, **43**
Volcanoes, changing face of, 71 *lab;* eruptions of, 70, *70–71*
Volume, and pressure, 57, *57*

Water, boiling point of, 50, *50;* changes of state of, 79, *79;* freshwater, 42; melting point of, 47; physical properties of, 75
Water cycle, 53 *lab*
Waterfalls, 57 *lab*
Wave(s), electron as, 17
Weight, measuring, *74*

Xenon, 111

Yttrium oxide, 114

Index

Credits

Magnification Key: Magnifications listed are the magnifications at which images were originally photographed.
LM–Light Microscope
SEM–Scanning Electron Microscope
TEM–Transmission Electron Microscope

Acknowledgments: Glencoe would like to acknowledge the artists and agencies who participated in illustrating this program: Absolute Science Illustration; Andrew Evansen; Argosy; Articulate Graphics; Craig Attebery represented by Frank & Jeff Lavaty; CHK America; John Edwards and Associates; Gagliano Graphics; Pedro Julio Gonzalez represented by Melissa Turk & The Artist Network; Robert Hynes represented by Mendola Ltd.; Morgan Cain & Associates; JTH Illustration; Laurie O'Keefe; Matthew Pippin represented by Beranbaum Artist's Representative; Precision Graphics; Publisher's Art; Rolin Graphics, Inc.; Wendy Smith represented by Melissa Turk & The Artist Network; Kevin Torline represented by Berendsen and Associates, Inc.; WILDlife ART; Phil Wilson represented by Cliff Knecht Artist Representative; Zoo Botanica.

Photo Credits

PERIODIC TABLE OF THE ELEMENTS

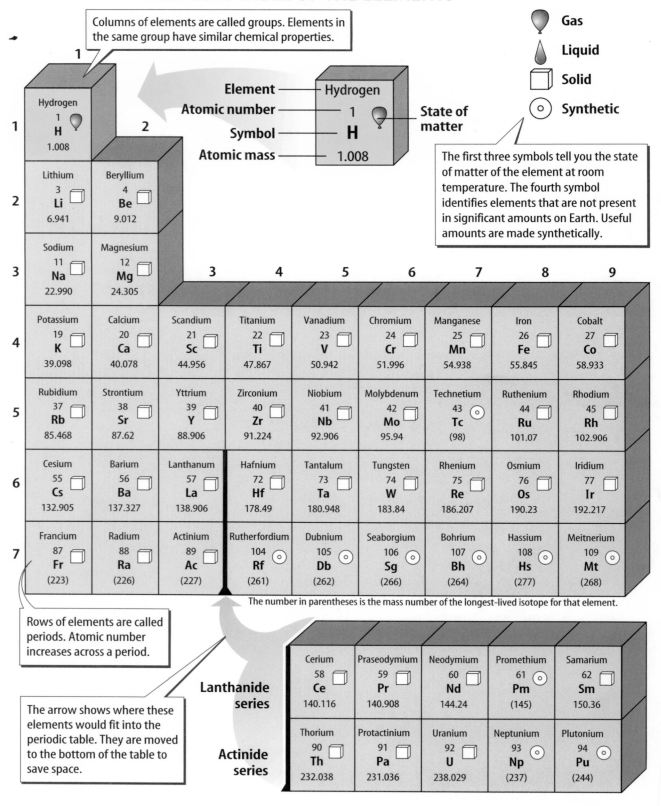

Columns of elements are called groups. Elements in the same group have similar chemical properties.

Gas
Liquid
Solid
Synthetic

Element — Hydrogen
Atomic number — 1
Symbol — H
Atomic mass — 1.008
State of matter

The first three symbols tell you the state of matter of the element at room temperature. The fourth symbol identifies elements that are not present in significant amounts on Earth. Useful amounts are made synthetically.

Rows of elements are called periods. Atomic number increases across a period.

The arrow shows where these elements would fit into the periodic table. They are moved to the bottom of the table to save space.

The number in parentheses is the mass number of the longest-lived isotope for that element.

Lanthanide series
Actinide series